Laboratory Administration
for Pathologists

Laboratory Administration
for Pathologists

Elizabeth A. Wagar, MD
Richard E. Horowitz, MD
Gene P. Siegal, MD, PhD

cap
PRESS
Northfield, Illinois

Library of Congress Control Number: 2011931808
ISBN: 978-0-9837068-0-9

Printed in the USA

College of American Pathologists
325 Waukegan Road
Northfield, Illinois 60093
800-323-4040
www.cap.org

Contents

6 Management of Pathology Information Systems 87

James H. Harrison Jr.

7 Quality Management in Laboratory Medicine 119

David S. Wilkinson, Elizabeth A. Wagar

13 Legal Affairs for Pathologists **235**

Elizabeth A. Wagar

14 Ethics for Pathology and Laboratory Medicine **249**

Elizabeth A. Wagar

Foreword

During our lifetimes, we have all witnessed major industries transform, reinvent themselves, and consolidate to remain competitive. Beginning with Orville Wright's diary entry dated October 9, 1903—"We began assembly today"—the airline industry has dramatically changed: from the past, where many companies using propeller-driven, short-haul planes transported at high prices the relatively few; to now, where several major behemoths carry large numbers of passengers inexpensively in wide-body jumbo jets capable of flying halfway around the world. The nascent telephone industry, which required hands-on operators to connect the few users who had stationary sets, progressed to the situation today, in which most everyone has a phone, if not two or three: stationary in the home, office, or car; and mobile for use anywhere.

Change with increasing complexity is inevitable. Medicine in general and pathology specifically are no different. The days of Bunsen burners and data written by hand into the medical record have changed. Now, systems consisting of highly complex and automated machinery can take a small aliquot of blood and automatically accession it, split it into multiple parts, perform even more tests, and electronically enter the tens if not hundreds of data items into the laboratory information system, which itself electronically speaks with the institution's information system. And, of course, the data feed the individual patient's electronic medical record, which may reside in the cloud.

At the heart of all systems are people. To function, manage, or lead, the engaged person must master the system. The leader, to use Peter Drucker's words, must "do the right thing." He must be highly proficient in the field and have the vision to plan and lead change, ie, transformation.

The manager must "do things right." He must stress quality and manage it. At the other end of the spectrum are the trainee and the pathologist new to the job. They are concerned with what is needed to show competence and what will be expected to show success. In the middle is the engaged pathologist, who lives and functions within the system. In addition, all are constantly reminded that their work and behavior must be ethical, legal, and conform to and satisfy the many regulations and laws that touch every aspect of daily life within the world of pathology and laboratory medicine.

Laboratory Administration for Pathologists is an outgrowth of the many lectures the widely respected authors have given over the past decades, heard by so many students of pathology, whether at the level of resident, new in practice, or senior pathologist. In 14 concise, highly readable chapters, any reader, regardless of level of sophistication, will find a comprehensive story about what is needed to manage and perform well in today's laboratory setting. In particular, those areas of endeavor, such as laboratory computing, that have grown so substantially during the past few decades and are now by necessity inordinately complex, are presented in such an easy-to-follow yet detailed manner that what might be incomprehensible without study becomes quite approachable.

To the reader who wishes to understand what constitutes the world of laboratory medicine, enjoy! This is your guide.

Stanley J. Robboy, MD, FCAP
Duke University Medical Center
Department of Pathology
Durham, North Carolina

Preface

Major imperatives for pathologists include keeping abreast of a myriad of scientific advances and managing the daunting problems of pathology practice. Diagnostic technology is proliferating explosively; the therapeutic armamentarium is expanding and the economics of medicine are being continually overhauled. The anatomic pathologist is enhancing pattern and image recognition with molecular and genetic analysis utilizing digital and computer science to provide more precise and relevant patient information; the clinical pathologist is utilizing emerging technologies and informatics to create and integrate meaningful, clinically useful information for patient care. At the same time, the comprehensive guiding role of the pathologist in the laboratory is coming into question and is being challenged.

The American Society for Clinical Pathology assessed Pathology's Future in a stakeholder discussion in June 2010. It was concluded that pathology and laboratory medicine must serve as the resource for test appropriateness, for result interpretation, for ensuring cost and value, and ultimately for ensuring patient safety and protecting public health. The key element necessary to enable the establishment of this new paradigm of pathology practice, one that will ensure that pathology and laboratory medicine remain relevant in the practice of medicine, is leadership. Developing future leaders was deemed the most important and most immediate course of action necessary to exact the needed changes for the profession to survive. The initiative for transforming pathologists is the College of American Pathologists' response to the challenges and opportunities facing the specialty. This will be a multiyear campaign to foster new and enhanced roles for the pathologist and greater recognition of the pathologist as a physician and a critical member of the patient care team.

In September 2007, the Centers for Disease Control and Prevention hosted an Institute addressing the critical issues in laboratory medicine.

The Institute agreed that the essence of pathology and laboratory medicine is the generation of data from multiple scientific and technologic sources and the analysis and integration of that data into clinically useful information for patient care. Among the "quality gaps" identified was lack of proactive pathology leadership and inadequate communication. Proposed action plans to bridge the gaps included educational initiatives on leadership and communication skills. The leadership gap has resulted in the loss of directorial control, loss of autonomy, and marginalization of pathologists. Hospital and commercial laboratories are now being directed by medical technologists or MBAs, with pathologists serving as "piece-workers," not as leaders or directors. Only by re-establishing the pathologist as the Director of the Laboratory, not merely the "Medical Director," will the gap be closed. But this requires pathologists who are interested in and understand management, and are skilled and are willing to devote the time needed to truly "run the lab." Validating the need for management training, both the Program Directors Section of the Association of Pathology Chairs and the Academy of Clinical Laboratory Physicians and Scientists have recently issued model curricula and suggested competencies in laboratory management.

The purpose of this text is to provide pathologists in training, young pathologists beginning their careers, and practicing pathologists with an overview of the fundamentals of management and leadership. The book evolved from, and is an expansion of the management seminars which two of us (Horowitz and Wagar), together with Wesley Y. Naritoku, MD, PhD, developed for the residency training programs in Los Angeles[1] and encompasses the recently proposed curricula. The book addresses all aspects of laboratory management but emphasizes the specific role and responsibility of the pathologist in directing the laboratory. It is not intended to make pathologists into accountants, attorneys, human resource specialists, purchasing agents, or health care administrators. But because pathologists have to deal with a variety of administrators, it is essential to become familiar with their unique areas of expertise and nomenclature. Our intent is that this text be used by pathology residents as a primer and also by practicing pathologists as a manual or "how-to" guide to the fundamentals of laboratory administration.

Reference

1. Horowitz RE, Naritoku W, Wagar EA. Management training for pathology residents: a regional approach. *Arch Pathol Lab Med.* 2004;128:59-63.

Acknowledgements and Contributors

The editors would like to thank Mrs. Judith Johnson, executive assistant, Department of Laboratory Medicine, University of Texas MD Anderson Cancer Center, for her gracious and excellent administrative assistance. Also, they wish to thank Mr. Joseph Munch, associate scientific editor, Department of Scientific Publications, University of Texas MD Anderson Cancer Center, for his careful and helpful editorial review.

Dr. Elizabeth A. Wagar acknowledges the support of the Trujillo family in memory of Dr. Jose M. Trujillo, a pioneer of laboratory medicine who served the University of Texas MD Anderson Cancer Center for almost 20 years. Additionally, Dr. Wagar would like to thank her daughter and husband, Sarah Gerson and Michael Gerson, for their patience during the writing of this manuscript.

Dr. Gene P. Siegal acknowledges the mentorship of Jay M. McDonald, MD, at the University of Alabama at Birmingham, who taught him how to successfully administer clinical laboratories; the hospital administrators, managers, and supervisors at UAB, who provided continuous and critical feedback; and his parents, Evelyne and Murray Siegal, who taught him how to interact with people and the importance of our legal and regulatory systems.

Dr. Richard E. Horowitz acknowledges William D. Evans, MD, chief of staff, and Art Stein and Al Cavalier, administrators at Los Angeles County General Hospital (1963 to 1968); and Sister Georgette Jean, Raymond Crerand, and Robert Schaffer of Providence Saint Joseph Medical Center (1968 to 1995), for providing models of ideal administrators.

Editors

Elizabeth A. Wagar, MD
Professor and Chair
Department of Laboratory Medicine
University of Texas MD Anderson Cancer Center
Houston, Texas

Richard E. Horowitz, MD
Clinical Professor of Pathology
University of Southern California
Los Angeles, California

Gene P. Siegal, MD, PhD
R.W. Mowry Endowed Professor of Pathology
Director, Division of Anatomic Pathology
Executive Vice-Chair–Pathology, UAB Health System
University of Alabama at Birmingham
Birmingham, Alabama

Contributing Authors

C. Bruce Alexander, MD
Vice-Chair and Professor of Pathology
University of Alabama at Birmingham
School of Medicine
Birmingham, Alabama

Isam-eldin A. Eltoum, MD, MBA
Professor of Pathology
Section Head, Cytopathology
University of Alabama at Birmingham
Birmingham, Alabama

James H. Harrison Jr, MD, PhD
Associate Professor and Director, Division of Biomedical Informatics
Departments of Public Health Sciences and Pathology
University of Virginia
Charlottesville, Virginia

Michael O. Idowu, MD, MPH
Associate Professor
Director of Breast Pathology and Anatomic Pathology
  Quality Management
VCU Medical Center / MCV Campus
Richmond, Virginia

Raouf E. Nakhleh, MD
Professor of Pathology
Mayo Clinic Florida
Jacksonville, Florida

David S. Wilkinson, MD, PhD
Professor and Chair, Department of Pathology
Virginia Commonwealth University
Richmond, Virginia

Ronald L. Weiss, MD
Professor, Department of Pathology / ARUP Laboratories
University of Utah
Salt Lake City, Utah

CHAPTER 1

Management Principles

Richard E. Horowitz, MD

Elizabeth A. Wagar, MD

Isam-eldin A. Eltoum, MD, MBA

Contents

History of Management

Although viewed as a "modern" phenomenon, complex work activities occurred in antiquity. The Egyptians were noted for planning, organizing, and controlling the activities of many workers. The role of work as described in biblical texts became inculcated into Judeo-Christian belief systems through the stories of Joseph in Genesis and Moses in Exodus. Similarly, ancient Chinese society established numerous control systems and worker descriptions as early as 1100 BCE. During Greek and Roman times, however, work was still performed by the lower classes to support the elite. During the Roman Empire, work became well organized, allowing the spread of Roman culture across Europe. In the 1400s, the Arsenal of Venice, which employed more than 1000 people, created personnel management, practiced inventory control, established accounting systems, and built assembly lines that had interchangeable parts.

Probably the greatest philosophical shift regarding the role of work occurred during the Christian Reformation. John Calvin (1509–1564) was most influential in establishing work as part of a value system. He believed that work was the will of God. This philosophy was transported to the New World during colonization.

Modern management and leadership may have started with Robert Owen in Scotland in the 1820s. Owen identified productivity and motivation as key components of a successful work environment; he also noted the importance of the relationship of the worker to work in establishing a successful enterprise. Joseph Wharton established a course of study for business at the University of Pennsylvania in 1881, and MBA programs such as that pioneered by Harvard University legitimized the study of business and management as academic endeavors and career goals.

A robust approach to management theory began in the twentieth century. Before then, the organization of work and the development of complex work environments were not specifically addressed as rigorous topics within the social sciences. A review of the written works of Peter F. Drucker, one of the founders of management theory, provides many concepts that can be applied even in today's complex business environment. It was Drucker who described the difference between management and leadership: "Management is doing things right; leadership is doing the right things."[1] In the second half of the twentieth century, management and leadership theory flourished. Peter Drucker, based at Claremont College, posited four essential features of management: (1) provision of a product/service, (2) assurance of productive work and worker achievement, (3) cognizance of community and societal responsibilities, and (4) making a profit. These four principles still apply to most business endeavors despite the sometimes confusing and diluting effects of complex consulting and self-help programs.

Table 1-1. Historical Perspectives of Management Theories

Dates	Theory	Guru/Theorists
Pre-20th century	No formal theory	—
1911	Scientific management	Fredrick Taylor
1916	Management function (the 14 points)	Henri Fayol
1922	Bureaucracy	Max Weber
1926	Participative management	Mary P. Follett
1932	The Hawthorne Experiments	Elton Mayo
1937	Manager activity (POSDCORB)	Luther Gulick
1941	Decision making and information	Herbert Simon
1951	Degree of social and technical fit between organization and employee	K.W. Bamforth
1960	Management attitudes toward employee (Theory X, Theory Y)	Douglas McGregor
1962	Strategic management and design	Alfred Chandler
1970	Maslow's laws (human needs)	Abraham Maslow
1977	Dissociation of satisfaction from dissatisfaction (the hygiene factors)	Frederick Herzberg
1978	Living systems	James G. Miller
1980–1990	Quality management era	W. Edwards Deming Philip B. Crosby
1970–2005	Decentralization; customer- rather than profit-focus; respect for workers; other concepts	Peter F. Drucker
1990–21st century	Re-emergence of strategic management	—

Various key management theories have been proposed throughout the last century (Table 1-1). Most of the details of these theories are best covered in formal studies of management. Realistically, an organization's management will be modeled on the organization's mission, its leader's vision, and its formal and informal structure. Various theories or certain elements of a specific theory may be applied at different levels of the organization and at different times. For example, current laboratory quality issues are rooted in the scientific management theories, while current staffing and organizing schemas borrow from various theories, including Maslow's hierarchy of needs, Theory X and Theory Y, and Fredrick Herzberg's theory, which states that the factors that lead to employee satisfaction must be differentiated from those that lead to employee dissatisfaction (Appendix 1-6).

Pathologists may find systems theory in particular to be an attractive proposition that explains many of the aspects of an organization, including structure (anatomy), function, culture (physiology and chemistry), and malfunction (pathology). Any system, including living systems, is a whole comprising interdependent, interrelated parts that maintain the integrity of the whole to achieve a specific goal. Consistently, any system exhibits features that are not present in its individual components. An important element in any system is the transformation process, by which material, energy, or information is processed and transformed into a new product that is exchanged within the internal or external environments. To maintain its functional and structural integrity and achieve its goal, the system must have a series of positive and negative feedback signals that regulate its inputs, outputs, and internal and external environments. Like cells and organisms, an organization is a living thing with a template that governs its development, progression, behavior, growth, and reproduction.[2]

Therefore, leaders and managers should understand the anatomy, physiology, and pathology of their organizations. With that concept in mind, they should be able to diagnose, or invite someone to diagnose, the organization's illness and prescribe appropriate treatment. According to systems theory, an organization is living and learning. Peter Senge articulated this concept in his famous book, *The Fifth Discipline*.[3] He proposed system thinking as a tool to develop an ideal organization; according to his thesis, system thinking is part of a set of disciplines, including personal mastery, mental models, shared vision, and team learning, that help an organization adapt, survive, and thrive in an ever-changing environment.

Management principles, theories, and ideas provide a framework of thinking that may enable leaders to understand their organization and its context and thus make appropriate management decisions. No one theory is superior to another in organization management; indeed, some theories become fads and fashions that are later discarded. Accordingly, the demand for data-driven, evidence-based management is increasing.[4-6] In response, management science has begun to borrow from biomedical science and from the evidence-based medicine movement in particular. The proponents of the evidence-based movement see that the ills that plague decision-making in medicine—the gap between knowledge and practice; the overuse, misuse, and underuse of evidence; and the difficulty in keeping up with information and innovations—are present in management as well. Information systems create an opportunity for obtaining evidence and disseminating it among and within organizations. However, managers may make decisions in span, context, and degrees of uncertainty that differ from those of physicians. In part, managers may make differing decisions due to the fact that decision support is not readily available, leading managers to make decisions based on their personal beliefs and "gut feeling" rather than facts.

In evidence-based management, as in evidence-based medicine, managers formulate problems as questions, review the literature, conduct original research, appraise the evidence, present results, and make decisions. Evidence-based management is currently practiced in total quality management. However, the search for evidence extends beyond the business operations to include strategy, marketing, finance, human resources, and administration. The evidence-based approach represents a new culture. Important concepts in this way of

doing business are to maintain the organization as an "unfinished prototype"—to "act on what you know," as Pfeffer and Sutton[6] explain—and change the way of doing things with constant experimentation. Mistakes are considered learning opportunities. This concept is similar to what medical educators call practice-based learning.

Still in its infancy, evidence-based management faces the same criticism that once faced evidence-based medicine, including questions about the meaning, context, generalizability, and ranking of evidence. The success of evidence-based practice in medicine attests to the likelihood of its success in at least some areas of management, especially in making short-term decisions that have a direct causal relation to their outcomes. Unlike previous management fads and fashions, evidence-based management should easily translate into the clinical laboratory because pathologists, as physicians, are becoming increasingly aware of the need for evidence-based practice. A current trend is to incorporate management models from industry into the laboratory; this includes Motorola's Six Sigma model, which aims to establish high efficiency without errors, and Toyota's Lean management model, which advocates no waste, more value, and less cost.

Principles of Management

At the beginning of the twentieth century, Luther Halsey Gulick described administrative management as a service function that handles a variety of organizational needs including planning, organizing, staffing, directing, and controlling activities (the POSDCORB model).[7] Management represents an institution or organization and enables it to accomplish specific objectives. According to Drucker, management is the means by which an organization defines its specific purpose and mission and manages its social impact and responsibility, as well as the mechanism by which work becomes productive and workers achieve institutional or organizational goals. Management in the marketplace, of course, must put economic performance first. But managing is not a passive activity in all aspects. It encompasses responses to and carries out changes in the economic environment. Work is also defined by management and people, as important resources should be provided with the capacity to grow and contribute. In addition, management assesses an organization's impact on physical, human, and social environments and its responsibility to adjust such impact, if necessary. For example, the Green movement is an ex-

Table I-2. Pathology Practice Survey (2007)

Type of Pathology Service	Average Weekly Hours
Surgical Pathology	26.6
Cytopathology	7.3
Clinical Pathology Consultation	4.5
Clinical Pathology Administration	10.2
Teaching / Research	6.3
Autopsy	2.6
Other	9.0

Source: College of American Pathologists. *Trends in Pathologist Workforce. Results from the 2007 Practice Characteristics Survey.* Available at: http://www.cap.org/apps/docs/advocacy/workforce_survey_07.pdf. Accessed Nov 12, 2010.

tension of management by multiple private and government organizations to better manage the environmental impact of the organizations' actions. In some cases, environmental protections are legislated. In other cases, industries recognize their negative impact and adapt to the use of cleaner fuels or processes.

Pathologists should be trained in management. The Joint Commission and other accrediting organizations expect the director of a laboratory to "assume the professional, scientific, consultative, and organizational responsibility for the facility." Pathologists are responsible for virtually all aspects of the clinical laboratory. The pathologist establishes the laboratory's goals and objectives and determines its organizational framework. The pathologist is involved in the day-to-day operations of the laboratory as well as short- and long-term planning decisions about personnel, equipment, and supplies. Quality assurance, safety, and quality management planning are all the responsibility of the pathologist. The medical-legal interests of laboratory operations are integral to all aspects of health care and are largely represented by pathologists. The overall performance and fiscal integrity of the laboratory are a function of good management by the pathologist. Ultimately, the pathologist is responsible for the success or failure of the laboratory.

In 2007, the College of American Pathologists *Practice Characteristics Survey* revealed that pathologists spend a significant proportion of their work time on management activities (Table 1-2). Clinical pathology activities—regarded as mostly managerial activities—represented nearly 30% of weekly activities. Assuming that the survey's "Other" category accounted for management activities related to anatomic pathology, hospital/institutional interactions, and/or social intercourse with the community and other physicians, nearly a third of a pathologist's weekly work involves management.

A recent white paper from the College of American Pathologists identified the managerial training of pathology residents as a gap in knowledge and skills requiring immediate attention. Residents were found to be least prepared to address regulatory and compliance issues, manage the clinical laboratory, and understand issues related to staffing and human resources as well as billing and reimbursement.[8]

Laboratories, which represent 5% to 10% of total health care expenditures, are big business in the health care industry and thus must be run in a businesslike manner. Despite the conversion of Medicare reimbursement to diagnosis-related groups (DRGs), clinical laboratories provide a significant source of revenue for health care facilities. Significant resources are also spent on laboratories; for example, the clinical laboratories of a moderately-sized, 300-bed hospital may employ more than 100 people and have a $30 million budget for which the pathologist is responsible. Therefore, it is not only a good idea for every pathologist to be fluent in management, it is a necessity.

In summary, the elements of effective management include a comprehensive knowledge of work and the resources (including people) required to accomplish an institution's goals and objectives. Evidence-based management additionally includes the use of data or facts to generate best work practices.

Specific models can be applied to management. One model is the plan, lead, organize, and control (PLOC) model, which was articulated many years ago by Louis Allen Associates.[9] The PLOC model establishes four functional areas in which one or more people, or a team of people, exercise management to achieve intended outcomes. Planning requires forming a concept, performing analyses, setting objectives, aligning resources, assessing strengths and weakness, and identifying opportunities and threats to create an operational program and a budget by extension. Leading, which is based on communication and understanding, is concerned with aligning the organization with the stated objectives and motivating and challenging staff to achieve their goals to ensure the continued effectiveness of the program. Organizing is concerned with constructing the means necessary to achieve organizational objectives by establishing procedures, policies, teams, operating units, and other systems. Controlling establishes standards and monitors and audits performance. The amount of time a manager spends performing these various activities depends on the management level. For example, lower level managers such as immediate supervisors will spend more time leading and organizing, whereas high-level managers such as executive vice presidents will spend more time planning.

The Primary Leadership in the Laboratory: The Pathologist

The first step in learning the leadership responsibilities of the laboratory director is to review the requirements for laboratory directors as defined by the federal government and described in Clinical Laboratory Improvement Amendments (CLIA) regulations. An excellent online resource is the Centers for Medicare and Medicaid Services brochure that provides an overview of the regulations.[10]

A laboratory director must have the necessary experience, education, and training. The mandatory minimum requirements for becoming a laboratory director at an acute care hospital are an MD or a DO with board certification. The directors of specialty laboratories (eg, clinical microbiology laboratories) may have a PhD with the appropriate training and board certification. In some states, the regulations may be stricter; for example, California requires that the director of an acute care hospital laboratory must be specifically trained in pathology and be board-certified by the American Board of Pathology.

The laboratory director responsibilities specified by CLIA are daunting. A laboratory director is responsible for the overall operation and administration of the laboratory, including the employment of competent qualified personnel. Although the laboratory director may delegate some responsibilities, the laboratory director ultimately must ensure that all duties are properly performed and that applicable CLIA regulations are met. The laboratory director must also ensure that a quality system approach that provides accurate and reliable test results is in place. However, there are some responsibilities that a laboratory director cannot delegate (Table 1-3). Chief among these nondelegable tasks are controlling test performance, maintaining the testing environment, and mandating the skills, training, and supervision of the technicians who perform the tests.

Table I-3. Laboratory Director Responsibilities That Cannot Be Delegated[10]

Testing systems provide quality services in all three aspects of test performance, preanalytic, analytic, postanalytic phases of testing, and are appropriate for your patient population.
Physical and environmental conditions of the laboratory are adequate and appropriate for the testing performed.
A general supervisor (high complexity testing) is available to provide day-to-day supervision of all testing personnel and reporting of test results and provide on-site supervision for specific minimally qualified testing personnel when they are performing high complexity testing.
The environment for employees is safe from physical, chemical, and biological hazards, and safety and biohazard requirements are followed.
Sufficient numbers of appropriately educated, experienced, and/or trained personnel are available to provide consultation, properly supervise, and accurately perform tests and report test results in accordance with the written duties and responsibilities specified by you, are employed by the laboratory.
New test procedures are reviewed, included in the procedure manual, and followed by personnel.
Each employee's responsibilities and duties are specified in writing.

The more complex features of a laboratory director's responsibilities are detailed in Chapter 12, "Laboratory Laws and Regulations." However, the list of responsibilities (Table 1-3) is impressive in its breadth, covering testing and quality assurance, environment and physical plant safety, and personnel competency and training. These responsibilities require the laboratory director and/or any section heads to whom the laboratory director has delegated responsibility to perform activities that bridge internal laboratory operations and external hospital or laboratory administration.

The laboratory director must have credibility, flexibility, emotional intelligence, positive self-esteem, vision, integrity, humility, self-awareness, and a sense of humor. Flexibility implies the use of a collection of leadership styles, each in the right measure and at just the right time. Different situations call for different ways of leading. As a laboratory director, the pathologist needs technical and human skills and may have to delegate and exert forceful authority. A pathologist chairing a hospital tissue committee must show professional knowledge and emotional intelligence and combine decisiveness with empathy, whereas a pathologist in charge of merging two groups needs to be a sensitive negotiator and a skilled motivator.

Daniel Goleman contends that intelligence and technical knowledge are important, but emotional intelligence is the *sine qua non* of leadership; he studied nearly 200 large companies and found that while effective leaders have a high degree of emotional intelligence, individuals without emotional intelligence cannot be effective leaders, despite their first-class education, exceptional training, and good ideas.[11]

The five components of emotional intelligence are self-awareness, self-regulation, motivation, empathy, and social skill. Self-awareness means having a deep understanding of one's own emotions, strengths, weaknesses, needs, and motivation. People with high self-awareness are neither overly critical nor unrealistically hopeful; rather, they are honest with themselves and others. Goleman defines self-awareness as a person's ability to recognize and understand his or her moods, emotions, and drives. A person with strong self-awareness is self-confident and realistic.

Self-regulation, the second component of emotional intelligence, is having the ability to control or redirect disruptive impulses or moods and the good sense to temporarily suspend judgment—to think before acting. Trustworthiness and integrity are the hallmarks of the self-regulated individual. A comfort with ambiguity and an openness to change are characteristics important to self-regulation.

Motivation is the third element of emotional intelligence. Motivation is an inner desire that enables a person to produce a work product not related to personal status or monetary rewards. Motivation includes other personal attributes such as perseverance and commitment. A motivated individual within the work environment will express optimism and the desire to achieve beyond expectations.

Empathy is a critical component of emotional intelligence; it means thoughtfully considering the feelings of one's associates and employees, along with other factors, in making intelligent decisions. Empathy requires one to understand and care about the emotional make-up of others and thus treat people with consideration for their emotional needs. The first three components of emotional intelligence—self-awareness, self-regulation, and motivation—concern the management of one's self. The last two components—empathy and social skill—concern one's ability to manage his or her relationships with others. Social skill is not simple; it is more than friendliness. (Although people with high social skill are rarely mean-spirited.) Social skill means being able to proficiently manage relationships and build networks, that is, an ability to find common ground and build rapport. Social skill is characterized by effectively leading to bring about change and externalizing one's motivation and infecting others with it.

Can the skills of self-awareness, self-regulation, motivation, empathy and social skill be learned, or are they in fact innate? According to Goleman, these skills can be both innate and learned. All people have varying baseline levels of self-awareness, self-regulation, motivation, empathy, and social skill, but additional competence can be learned. Almost everyone increases his or her emotional intelligence with age—it is a process we call maturity. If pathologists are to retain or regain their leadership role in the laboratory and in medicine, they must become more effective leaders. Developing emotional intelligence is essential to becoming an effective leader.

Leadership prerequisites must be accompanied by additional competencies, including scientific, technical, and professional expertise (Appendix 1-1). One cannot lead a microbiology laboratory if one does not know the difference between chocolate agar and standard blood agar plates. The leader must have the respect of his or her colleagues and subordinates. Communication skills such as listening and sending clear and convincing messages are essential. The results of a national survey of laboratory directors by the American Society for Clinical Pathology ranked "effective communication skills" at the top of the list of preferred skills for potential employees. Two additional competencies are the ability to motivate and the ability to make decisions (appendices 2 and 3).

A final competency is the ability to delegate. Delegation is the ability to assign or designate assignments to other employees. It requires an understanding of an employee's skills. Delegation is not easy; most leaders do not do it well. It requires the delegator to give specific instructions, define the expected results, set time lines, establish limits of authority, and describe how the expected results will be evaluated. Delegation also requires the leader to provide the necessary resources to accomplish the task.

Management styles can vary.[12] Various theories describe the balance of task-oriented and people-oriented management styles. Blake and Mouton described a managerial spectrum ranging from the concern for productivity to the concern for people; high productivity and high concern for people results in a "team" approach, which minimizes conflict between keeping people happy and getting the job done. Another model that examines task-oriented versus people-oriented manager functions is the Lorenzi-Riley model. This model focuses on change management, including the leadership qualities that allow for the organization of a heterogeneous group of employees in order to effect change.[13] McGregor developed Theory X, in which managers assume a large input for employees' attitudes and ability, and Theory Y, in which managers have an optimistic set of expectations for workers.[14] The more recently developed Theory Z model suggests that the highly motivated and self-disciplined employee described in Theory Y is cultural and may vary depending on country of origin. However, given the expansion of work to service-oriented, knowledge-based tasks, more employees are effectively independent, interchangeable, and more likely to be Theory-Y based on their unique skills. Radiation technologists and laboratory technologists are prime examples of knowledge-based workers.

Several authors have attempted to generalize leadership styles and behaviors and determine how different types of leaders respond to specific situations.[14] In one analysis, the three main categories of leadership style are authoritative, democratic, and laissez-faire. Authoritative behavior is a "telling" approach to leadership. Authoritative leaders tell others what to do after a problem has been assessed. Although the authoritative style is effective when time is limited and employees have limited skills and rarely work as a group, the style does not work when the employees are knowledgeable and work as a team. The democratic style is a "consulting" approach. The leader gives people a chance to influence a decision from the start, and the leader selects a solution that is likely to be successful. This style of leadership works well when plenty of time is available and people have some group skills and are motivated, but it does not work when the group is unmotivated or conflicted. The laissez-faire leader is a "joining" leader and basically works as another team member. This style of leadership works when the group is highly motivated and is familiar with each other—that is,

working well as a team. However, laissez-faire leadership does not work if a team is not present or the group expects to be told what to do.

Finally, competent leadership requires actual work—and hard work at that. Leaders set goals, priorities, and standards for an institution. A leader motivates (motivation strategies are provided in appendices 1-1 and 1-2). A leader also incorporates an institution's mission into his or her decisions by cross-checking the decision with the institutional mission, and helps employees internalize high standards and aspire to perform above these standards. Workers should feel as if they become better people by adopting the leadership's expressed goals, priorities, and standards. A truly effective leader also regards the leadership role as a responsibility rather than an honor granted by a position of rank and privilege.

The Primary Planning Procedure: The Strategic Plan

The essence of planning is the strategic plan: an ongoing management activity designed to provide the data, analytical components, and decision elements required to continuously manage an organization. The strategic plan is a fluid plan with multiple built-in feedback loops that allow or demand that everything from the organization's budget and projects to its goals and purpose be continuously updated. A strategic plan is also essential when implementing a major new or modified business activity, such as developing an outreach program for anatomic pathology, bringing in a new array of tests or instruments, or planning a separate off-site laboratory for outpatient services. The strategic planning template is shown in Figure 1-1.

The defining documents of a strategic plan are the mission statement and the vision statement. The mission statement clearly declares to the public: "This is who we are. This is our business. These are our customers, and this is what we will do to meet their needs." Before the mission statement can be used to formulate goals and directions, the critical exercise of prioritization of business activities is necessary. Laboratories do not have one or two types of customers, but many types, including doctors, nurses, patients, health insurance providers, hospital administrators, hospital employees, and pathology residents. Similarly, there are many aspects to consider when assessing the needs of laboratory customers. Doctors want immediate results, nurses want easy-to-read reports, insurance providers want inexpensive services,

"The fish stinks from the head" is an ancient saying found in many cultures that is applicable to leadership today. It simply means that leaders are responsible for everything and anything in their organizations. That includes everything that goes right and anything that goes wrong. When a laboratory is run well, don't expect any kudos—we are expected to do things well. But when things go wrong, the pathologist/director ("the head") will be found to be the source of the "unpleasant odor" and will be held responsible.

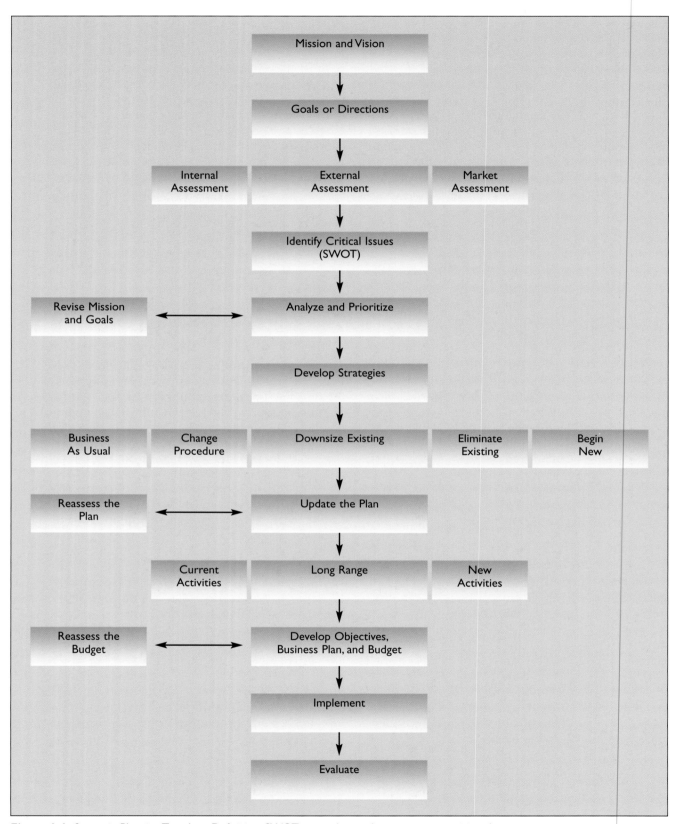

Figure 1-1. Strategic Planning Template. Definition: SWOT, strengths, weaknesses, opportunities, threats.

hospital administrators want a positive bottom line, and pathology residents want to perform as many tests as they can to gain experience. Owing to such conflicting needs, the first task in implementing the strategic plan is setting priorities by identifying the most important customers and which of their demands can—or cannot—be met.

The second defining document of a strategic plan, the vision statement, is an internal organizational statement regarding the organization's goals for the future, for example: "To be the dominant, most comprehensive, and most highly respected testing service in the region." Both the mission statement and the vision statement are vital to the development of the organization's directions and goals. However, before implementing those directions and goals, it is essential to perform some assessments and analyses.

The three initial assessments that are required in any strategic plan are the assessment of the internal environment, the assessment of the external environment, and the assessment of the "market." An assessment of the internal environment should include a review of the available personnel, including their talent profile and current productivity. Also important is an assessment of facilities space and equipment. Financial resources should also be evaluated. If the laboratory is hospital-owned but managed by an independent pathology group, input from financial and administrative leaders should be obtained. The organizational structure and current testing capacity should also be part of an assessment of the internal environment.

The assessment of the external environment may include aspects outside of the laboratory but within the institution. However, any strategic plan should also consider the environment beyond the hospital or free-standing laboratory. Regardless of the scope of the external assessment, the political structure, the socioeconomic environment, and the technological and scientific advances that affect the clinical laboratory should be considered. The scope of the assessment may, for example, consider changes in Medicare at the federal level, the use of automation in the clinical laboratory, and/or scientific advancements in biomarker development.

The third assessment is the market assessment. In large-scale outreach planning, this activity may need to be more comprehensive and might require professional or consultative assistance. Marketing elements, including any changes in customers' needs, should be thoroughly reviewed; for example, whether new distant clinics require specimen management should be determined. Good market research regarding the anticipated billable procedures and market share is also required. The competition should also be assessed. Other key aspects of the market assessment include product planning, pricing strategy (third-party billing), and the management of sales and service, along with a needs assessment for key operations such as informatics/computer support (bidirectional) and courier services.

Once these assessments are complete, the pathologist or laboratory director should have a fairly good idea of the viable approaches to an initiative. However, before going further, it may be prudent to re-examine the goals of the strategic plan to ensure that they are consonant with reality. For example, although one goal may be to increase expertise in the laboratory by hiring a urologic pathologist, the market assessment may reveal that the predominant managed care organization in the community has a contract with a national commercial laboratory to process prostate biopsy specimens, likely leading to diminished volume in the laboratory, in which case it would not be prudent to hire an additional pathologist.

After evaluating the assessments and validating the goals and directions, but before implementing any changes, the pros and cons of a proposal need to be evaluated. One model that can be used to evaluate such issues is the strengths, weaknesses, opportunities, and threats (SWOT) analysis (Appendix 1-4). Laboratory leaders should consider the strengths and weaknesses of the institution as well as external opportunities and threats and the ways in which they influence the laboratory's ability to respond to the issues identified in the internal, external, and market assessments. More importantly, laboratory leaders should consider what must be done to implement existing and/or new goals. For example, if one goal is to establish a virus laboratory, and the SWOT analysis shows that no technologist has the necessary expertise, it becomes clear that additional personnel are needed.

An alternative to the SWOT analysis is the five forces analysis (Figure 1-2).[15] Michael Porter developed this model for the detailed analysis of the external opportunities and threats in areas where these forces are more complicated. The five forces are the bargaining power of suppliers, the bargaining power of buyers, the threat of new entrants, the threat of substitute products, and the rivalry among existing entities. For example, a particular market might include four hospitals with clinical

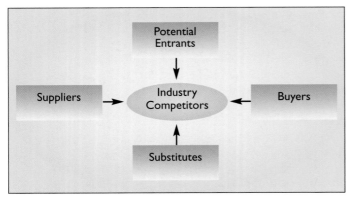

Figure 1-2. Michael Porter's Five Forces Model.

laboratories, two of which have laboratories with outreach testing services. The ability of an additional outreach program to survive may be impacted by the number of rivals already in the market.

Once these analyses of internal factors, external factors, and the market have been completed, one can re-examine the feasibility of previously articulated goals and determine whether the goals need to be deleted or changed. It may also be necessary to prioritize competing or conflicting goals and directions before proceeding to the next step in the planning process, which is to define what needs to be done. A laboratory may choose to continue business as usual or alter their menu and procedures. Likewise, a laboratory may review activities that can be downsized or eliminated. These decisions constitute the revised plan, which can then be separated into current and new activities that need immediate funding, and long-range activities that might require a business plan before funding is provided (see Chapter 9, "Financial Management of the Laboratory").

The implementation of the strategic plan is essentially the operation of the laboratory (see Chapter 3, "Laboratory Operations"). The evaluation of the strategic plan is an ongoing process. An important part of this evaluation is the variance analysis that is performed on a monthly basis as part of the budgeting process (see Chapter 9, "Financial Management of the Laboratory").

References

1. Drucker PF. *Management*. Revised ed. New York, NY: Harper Collins; 2008.
2. Miller JL, Miller JG. Greater than the sum of its parts, II: matter-energy processing subsystems. *Behav Sci*. 1993;38:1-73.
3. Senge PM, Kleiner A, Roberts C, Ross R, Smith B. *The Fifth Discipline Fieldbook. Strategies and Tools for Building a Learning Organization*. New York, NY: Doubleday/Currency; 1994.

Case Example: How to Lead

Read the following scenario and answers to the questions below.

Dr. Quiet is the Chief of Pathology at a 250-bed hospital. He primarily performs surgical pathology but is also the director of the hospital laboratory, which has 80 employees. The hospital would like to reorganize the laboratory as a Core Laboratory so hematology and chemistry instrumentation can be managed in the same space. Dr. Quiet discusses this possibility with the two supervisors of the existing hematology and chemistry laboratories and asks them for their ideas. The two supervisors do not often work together and cannot come to a consensus They also distrust each other, each thinking that her job is in jeopardy.

1. What type of leadership style best applies to Dr. Quiet? *Democratic.*
2. Why is this style ineffective in this scenario? *Members of the team are not accustomed to working with each other and are distrustful of the outcome.*
3. What recommendations would you make to Dr. Quiet regarding how to lead this restructuring project? *This may be a longer project than anticipated. Restructuring one job may affect a score of other jobs. Because you are dealing with knowledgeable supervisors who have never worked as a team, it may be best to build a team approach from the beginning by bringing in other representatives from hematology and chemistry. This would work with Dr. Quiet's democratic style of leadership. However, such a major operational change requires strategic planning, including assessments, SWOT analysis, the development of specific strategies, a business plan, and a budget prior to implementation.*

4. Walshe K, Rundall TG. Evidence-based management: from theory to practice in health care. *Milbank Q*. 2001;79:429-57.
5. Arndt M, Bigelow B. Evidence-based management in health care organizations: a cautionary note. *Health Care Manage Rev*. 2009;34:206-213. Review.
6. Pfeffer J, Sutton RI. Profiting from evidence-based management. *Strategy & Leadership*. 2006;34:35-42.
7. infed (the informal education homepage and encyclopaedia of informal education). Luther Halsey Gulick. Available at: http://www.infed.org/thinkers/gulick.htm. Accessed Nov 10, 2010.
8. Talbert ML, Ashwood ER, Brownlee NA, et al. Resident preparation for practice: a white paper

Challenge Questions

How does SWOT analysis contribute to the development of a strategic plan?
A. It identifies internal weaknesses in the institution.
B. It provides cash flow analysis for business planning.
C. It identifies the key personnel required for a new initiative.
D. It identifies assets and liabilities.
E. None of the above.
Answer: A; see pages 9 and 13.

Which of the following laboratory director responsibilities cannot be delegated according to CLIA?
A. Signing annual reviews of chemistry procedures.
B. Maintaining a quality management plan.
C. Approving a new hemoglobin A1C test validation.
D. Performing annual competencies on laboratory technologists.
E. None of the above.
Answer: B; see page 5.

What is the difference between an organization's mission and vision?
Answer: See page 7.

Appendix 1-1.
Leadership Competencies

Leaders are made, not born. Effective leadership is based on a number of prerequisites and requires a great deal of practice.

- A leader must have professional and technical expertise. A leader must be trustworthy, consistent, and have unquestioned integrity and the respect of colleagues and subordinates.
- A leader must demonstrate emotional intelligence with accurate self-assessment, self-confidence, and persuasiveness.
- A leader must be able to conceptualize and be visionary.
- A leader must have communication skills in listening and sending clear, convincing messages.
- The most difficult thing a leader must do is to motivate.
- A leader must be decisive, but not impetuous.
- The ability to delegate is one of the things most leaders do not do well. It requires that the delegator gives specific instructions, provide the necessary resources, give the needed authority, define the expected results, establish a time line, and detail how the results will be evaluated.
- A leader must show appropriate humility.

from the College of American Pathologists and Association of Pathology Chairs. *Arch Pathol Lab Med*. 2009;133:1139-1147.

9. Louis Allen Worldwide, Inc. Legacy of Louis Allen. Foster City, CA: Louis Allen Worldwide; 2010. Available at: http://www.louisallenworldwide.com. Accessed Nov 10, 2010.
10. US Department of Health and Human Services. Centers for Medicaid and Medicare Services. Clinical Laboratory Improvement Amendments (CLIA). Laboratory Director Responsibilities. What Are My Responsibilities as a Laboratory Director. Brochure 7. 2006. Available at: http://www.cms.hhs.gov/CLIA/downloads/brochure7.pdf. Accessed Nov 10, 2010.
11. Goleman D. *Working with Emotional Intelligence*. New York, NY: Bantam Books; 1998.
12. Travers EM. *Clinical Laboratory Management*. Baltimore, MD: Williams & Wilkins; 1997.
13. Lorenzi NM, Riley RT. Managing change: an overview. *J Am Med Inform Assoc*. 2000;7:116-124.
14. McGregor D. *Leadership and Motivation*. Cambridge, MA: MIT Press; 1966.
15. Porter M. *Competitive Strategy. Techniques for Analyzing Industries and Competitors*. New York, NY: The Free Press; 1980.

Appendix 1-2.
Motivation Strategies

A critical function of leadership and management is motivating employees. The success of an enterprise depends on its workers, and they must be continually inspired and encouraged to achieve goals within the scope of the organization's mission and vision. What must a leader do to motivate employees?

- Forget money, fringe benefits, parking, and a good cafeteria; these are not motivators. They are expected and are only important if they are not available.

- Employees are often unhappy about low salaries, annoying bosses, stupid rules, or poor working conditions, but changing these things does not satisfy or motivate employees.

- Employees are motivated by interesting work, challenges, and increasing responsibility.

- Employees must have a sense that their job is meaningful and relevant and that their work has a purpose. Tell employees that they are important! Tell them again and again!

- A leader must have high expectations. By way of analogy: If a teacher thinks the students are bright, the students will rise to meet the teacher's expectations. If a teacher thinks the students are slow, the students will learn slowly.

Appendix 1-3.
How to Make a Decision

A leader must be able to make decisions in a timely, coherent fashion. One of the keys to effective decision making is to take your time. Other keys to effective decision making include:

- Identifying and articulating the problem
- Verifying that the problem exists
- Determining whether the problem needs to be solved
- Determining whether you want or need to address the problem
- Gathering all the facts and evaluating the information
- Considering alternative solutions
- Exploring the consequences of the various solutions
- Determining how these solutions fit within the strategic plan
- Selecting the best alternative
- Implementing the solution
- Following up and evaluating the outcome

Appendix 1-4.
Performing a SWOT Analysis

A critical component of the strategic planning process is the strengths, weaknesses, opportunities, and threats (SWOT) analysis. Consider the following example regarding the plans for a new, small, off-site laboratory that will serve four new hematology–oncology clinics. The specific areas requiring analysis are quickly identified.

Strengths

- Your institution specializes in hematology–oncology and has a hematopathology director and specialists.
- An automated line has been implemented in the main laboratory for a large volume of hematopathology and oncology services, and you have experience with most large-equipment vendors.
- New hematology–oncology clinicians are being hired by the primary existing practice in your hospital.

Weaknesses

- The new hematopathology business will require hiring additional technologists because the main laboratory has already met its capacity for testing.
- The clinics and new laboratory will be 15 miles from the hospital, and you do not have a courier system.
- You do not have a distant computer link to the new clinics and new laboratory site.

Opportunities

- The hematology–oncology service anticipates hiring 10 new clinicians, resulting in a 50% increase in hematology testing.
- The new laboratory site will be in an area with no other laboratory services, potentially bringing in work for other clinics in that region.
- Expansion of distant computer services may enable the development of an advanced electronic medical records system.

Threats

- A cross-town rival hospital has a strong hematology–oncology service that already attracts 35% of the market share.
- Decreasing revenue from the anticipated patient cohort (Medicare recipients) may not fully support an opportunities budget.
- Hiring laboratory technologists is difficult because of the aging laboratory technologist workforce and lack of young trainees.

Will a 50% increase in test volumes justify the anticipated expenses for personnel, information systems infrastructure, and a courier system? How will the anticipated decrease in Medicare revenue over the next 3 to 5 years impact this plan? What will be the start-up costs (variable and fixed) for a new operation? How will the limited pool of laboratory technologists affect a start date that aligns with the opening of the new clinics? What percentage of the cross-town rival's service is anticipated to cross over to the new clinics? Carefully analyzing each of these areas and assembling them into a strategic plan puts you in a stronger position in negotiating with hospital administration. The strategic planning process is an ongoing process that undergoes continual re-evaluation and re-assessment and should be regarded as a flexible instrument that is reformulated and remolded as conditions change.

Appendix 1-5.
Maslow's Needs Categories

This hierarchy of needs implies that the highest human needs involve self-esteem and self-actualization; these are the needs that leadership must address.

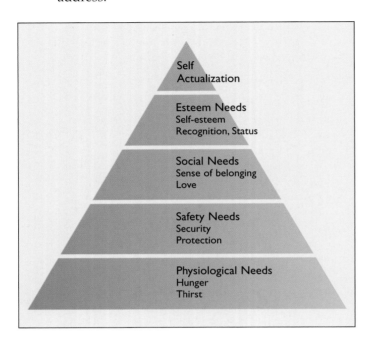

Source: Maslow AH. A theory of human motivation. *Psychol Rev.* 1943;50:370-396.

Appendix 1-6.
Herzberg's Satisfiers and Dissatisfiers

According Herzberg, although the absence of some factors can create job dissatisfaction, the presence of these factors does not motivate or create satisfaction. In contrast, the motivators (satisfiers)—the elements that enriched a person's job—were associated with long-term positive effects in job performance, while the dissatisfiers consistently produced only short-term changes in job attitudes and performance, which quickly fell back to its previous level.

Dissatisfiers (important only when absent)

- Competent management
- Competent technical supervision
- Good interpersonal relations with supervisors, peers, and subordinates
- Salary
- Job security
- Working conditions
- Status

Satisfiers (the real "motivators")

- Achievement
- Recognition
- Advancement
- Growth potential
- Responsibility

Source: Herzberg F, Mausner B, Snyderman BB. *The Motivation to Work.* 2nd ed. New York, NY: John Wiley & Sons; 1959.

- Determining the quality of medical care the hospital provides.
- Establishing a mechanism for reporting the quality of professional medical care to the administration.
- Making recommendations for enforcing professional standards and implementing corrective action when necessary.
- Making recommendations concerning the appointment and reappointment of physicians to the medical staff and the delineation of privileges for each appointee.
- Supervising and ensuring compliance with medical staff bylaws and regulations and hospital policies.
- Exercising necessary discipline within the authority of the medical staff organization.
- Providing input on the budget process.
- Assisting in planning hospital goals to meet community needs.
- Maintaining educational programs.
- Monitoring and supervising postgraduate trainees if the hospital has a medical training program.

The Joint Commission is the Centers for Medicare and Medicaid Services (CMS)–appointed accreditation agency for hospitals and other patient care facilities. The Joint Commission recognizes the medical staff organization as the means through which professional quality is managed and assessed. Therefore, it is important for pathology departments to have representation on the primary medical staff oversight committee. Pathologists are not only well versed and active in daily quality management activities, they also provide an important patient-care service; thus, their skills and leadership are often required to evaluate medical staff functions. It is essential for the laboratory director of anatomic pathology and/or the division director of laboratory medicine to be a standing or ex-officio member of the medical staff executive committee.

Pathologists can interact with medical staff in numerous informal ways. For example, pathologists can establish a presence as clinicians. Often, pathologists are out of sight, residing in their offices and interacting with others as infrequently as possible. However, to be truly effective managers and leaders, and to be acknowledged by clinicians as important assets, pathologists must interact daily with other health care professionals. Pathologists should also be available to provide clinical knowledge, sometimes in "curbside consultations." Although it may seem superficial, wearing scrubs may serve as an important visual cue for the pathology service. Above all, regularly interacting with clinicians teaches young pathologists the importance of being diplomatic and sensitive to clinicians' needs and helps all pathologists understand that everything they do is intimately tied to patient care.

Two special aspects of interacting with medical staff are complaint management and conflict resolution. When a clinician brings a complaint to the attention of the laboratory director, the complaint often reflects more than a single unwanted occurrence and deserves special attention. The laboratory director should respond promptly to all complaints. If the pathologist needs to understand the depth of the complaint and believes that further investigation is warranted, he or she should let the complainer know that more time is required by saying, for example, "I will get back to you shortly." However, if the problem could cause patient harm, the laboratory director should address the complaint immediately. (Transfusion medicine is one area in which an immediate response may be required.) If time is available to investigate such a complaint, the pathologist should use all available resources to determine the problem, what caused the problem, how to correct the problem, and how to prevent the problem in the future (ie, corrective actions). It is appropriate for the laboratory director to use all resources, including laboratory supervisors and managers, to solve a problem, but the laboratory director should never delegate the responsibility of responding to the complaining clinician to another employee. The saying "the customer is always right" plays an important role in addressing complaints from clinicians. When confronted with a complaint, pathologists should always say, "Thank you for bringing this to my attention."

One strategy pathologists can use to enhance their interface with the medical staff is to volunteer for medical staff committees and educational functions. Generally, pathologists are expected to chair the infection control, tissue, and transfusion committees, and serve on many other medical staff committees and/or subcommittees; therefore, pathologists must have proficiency in chairing committees (see Appendix 2-3). By chairing committees, less experienced pathologists will learn a great deal about their institutions' patient care operations. Pathologists should also be eager to organize meetings such as clinical-pathological correlation conferences, tumor boards, and morbidity and mortality reviews (see Appendix 2-4). Other strategies pathologists can use to enhance their interface with the medical staff include participating in medical staff oversight functions such as utilization review, peer review, and outcomes research. Volunteering to edit the medical staff newsletter (see Appendix 2-5) and participating in medical staff social events, eg, dances and golf tournaments, are other important activities. Pathologists and clinicians can build new bridges once the medical staff leadership understands that pathologists are both helpful and reliable.

Interfacing with Hospital or System Administration

Typically, a president or CEO leads the administration of a hospital or health care system. In some hospitals, the CEO is a physician; in other circumstances, the CEO is a nonphysician health care administrator. To designate specific high-level leadership and functions, the hospital or health care organization may use a series of chiefs, including the chief operating officer, who oversees all aspects of operations, often including the laboratory; the chief nursing officer, who oversees the nursing staff; the chief financial officer; the chief medical officer (CMO), who may be a hospital employee and/or a member of the medical staff; and the chief information officer, who usually oversees the institution's computer systems. (Other institutions use titles such as president, vice president, or executive vice president to describe similar positions.)

Pathologists may have significant interaction with each of these chiefs. The chief operating officer may be an important resource for understanding laboratory staffing requirements and laboratory budgets. The chief financial officer may interact with the pathology department to develop budgets and capital programs. The chief information officer may be a major player in assessing laboratory information systems and computer services. The CMO may be an important link to the medical staff or other clinicians; in some hospitals, hospital-based physicians in pathology, radiology, and/or emergency medicine may report to the administration through the CMO. The chief nursing officer may provide perspective on the quality of laboratory services and point-of-care testing.

To establish and maintain effective interfaces with administration, the pathology laboratory director must be aware of the critical economic and regulatory issues facing hospitals and must be knowledgeable in health care economics. The director should also know what the administration expects. For example, are administrators only interested in the bottom line? Are they influenced by clinician complaints? Do they value excellence and the science that pathology brings to the hospital?

The pathologist must, of course, be thoroughly conversant in the day-to-day business and economic operations of the laboratory (see Chapter 9, "Financial Management of the Laboratory"). The pathology laboratory director and the administrator to whom the laboratory reports should meet at least monthly to discuss the status and needs of the laboratory as well as current events in the hospital, new or emerging plans for the institution, and the hospital's expectations for the pathology group. The agenda for such meetings should include discussing workload and productivity statistics; budget and financial performance; human resource issues; professional accomplishments, such as publications and awards; the results of inspections, complaints, and other incidents; and information about hospital planning. In addition to these regular meetings, pathologists should conduct informal "administrative" rounds by visiting various administrators' offices to just say "hello" or to invite the administrators to a coffee break.

Nonmedical staff committees that demand pathologists' participation and input include committees on patient safety, bioethics, equipment, utilization review, performance measurement, and budget and finance. Pathologists who do not volunteer in the hospital budgeting process or in the hospital equipment decision-making process basically allow others to make decisions for the laboratory. If the hospital also has a local governing body or board, it behooves the pathology laboratory director to establish rapport with at least some of its members. Financial contributions by the laboratory director or pathology group to the hospital would definitely facilitate such an interface. Another strategy pathologists can use to facilitate hospital or administrative interface is preparing an annual report (see Appendix 2-6). Other hospital administration activities include contributing reports to or editing medical staff or hospital newsletters, participating in hospital social events, volunteering to be active in charitable activities, and contributing to the hospital's fundraising campaigns.

It is critical that pathologists interface with the nursing service. In the majority of community hospitals, the nursing service is the fulcrum upon which all patient care rests. A pathologist, usually with the chief technologist or laboratory manager,

At Parkland in Dallas they are called "Ambassadors"; in Burbank we called them "Liaisons." They are a critical adjunct to the interface between the laboratory and the nursing service. A supervising or higher level medical technologist, preferably one who had been working in the laboratory for some time, is assigned as the Ambassador or Liaison to a ward or nursing station. They are encouraged to have lunch with the nursing supervisor from that ward at least once a month, go up to the ward on occasion, and invite the nurse to come to the laboratory. Whenever there is a problem or complaint of any kind, they are the main contact between nursing and the laboratory. They are available to address the problem, fix it if possible, or see to it that it is triaged to the appropriate person so it can be fixed. The nursing service loves this arrangement; when they have a problem, they have a special number they can call, and there is someone there that they know who will know them—so much better than a faceless voice! And if the laboratory has a problem, the reciprocal situation applies.

should visit each nursing station in the hospital at least once a month to determine whether laboratory services are satisfactory, any questions can be answered, or any problems can be averted. Conducting these nursing rounds helps pathologists establish a relationship with the rest of the hospital; they provide pathologists with the opportunity to show the nurses and physicians on the wards who is in charge of the pathology laboratory and that the laboratory director cares about how inpatient services operate. Furthermore, pathologists should volunteer to participate in in-service educational programs for nurses and other hospital personnel, such as seminars aimed at educating chaplains about autopsies. Another critical interface is with the decedent affairs office, which is usually a function of the nursing service. A knowledgeable and sensitive decedent affairs office is essential for maintaining a useful autopsy function in the pathology department. Autopsy authorization obtained from the decedent's next-of-kin by an effective decedent affairs coordinator not only increases the autopsy rate, but also improves public relations, increases organ donations, and facilitates risk management.

In some hospitals, pathologists volunteer to be the medical information officer for the hospital's information system. No physicians are better suited than pathologists to fill this role, because pathologists tend to be experts in computers, automation, quality control, and quality assurance. Also, pathologists are conversant in disease presentation and practice management. The essence of the administrative interface is to maintain a high level of visibility; administrators should be continually reminded that pathologists are critical to the

operation of one of the hospital's largest departments. The pathologists' many roles beyond diagnostic pathology must be emphasized. Staff education, research support, utilization statistics, and revenue generation and/or savings are all important pathology contributions. Also, the pathologist's responsibilities in the clinical laboratory extend beyond clinical consultation and include test selection and validation, personnel selection and performance, quality assurance, accreditation, and compliance as well as medical-legal responsibility for the entire laboratory operation.

Interfacing with the Laboratory Staff

Perhaps the pathologist's most important interface is with the laboratory staff. No other medical specialty is so dependent upon its technical associates; in no other medical specialty is the physician legally and ethically responsible for the work of others without necessarily personally overseeing the performance of an individual procedure. The laboratory staff can make the pathologist look like a hero or a villain. To interface with the laboratory staff, pathologists must know who they are, their education and training, and their needs and agendas. Pathologists must also understand how the staff is organized within the laboratory.

A starting point for learning about personnel categories is to review the categories as described in the 1988 and 2003 CLIA regulations (Table 2-2).[4] (Categorical responsibilities are described in Chapter 4, "Personnel Management.") Somewhat confusingly, the titles used for these various personnel categories do not necessarily match the titles used in all clinical laboratories. In states that require individual licenses, the licensure requirements provide additional information about the requirements for certain positions (eg, testing personnel). In some circumstances, pathologists may find it helpful to supplement the organizational chart with a diagram that cross-references the titles used in their laboratories with the federal CLIA titles.[4]

Colloquial titles that may compare to different categories include clinical laboratory scientist, medical technologist, or laboratory technologist (usually testing personnel); laboratory technician or laboratory assistant (who may not be qualified to perform testing but are qualified for phlebotomy, specimen handling, and specimen processing); laboratory manager, chief tech, or even technical director (who is usually a qualified laboratory technologist with additional management training and/or

Table 2-2. Centers for Medicare and Medicaid Services CLIA Personnel Categories

Personnel Title	Training Requirements
Moderate Complexity Testing	
Laboratory Director	MD, DO, or PhD (specialties); state licensure and board certification
Technical Consultant	Laboratory Director can serve as Technical Consultant for Moderate Complexity; licensure and board certification as required by states MD, DO, or PhD (specialties); may have Masters/Bachelors with 2 years experience; licensure and board certification as required by states
Clinical Consultant	MD, DO, DPM, or Laboratory Director qualifications; licensure and board certification as required by states
Testing Personnel	MD, DO, PhD, Masters, or Bachelors; board certification if applicable; licensure if required by a given state; high school diploma plus experience acceptable in some states
High Complexity Testing	
Laboratory Director	MD, DO, or PhD (specialties); state licensure and board certification
Clinical Consultant	MD, DO, DPM, or Laboratory Director qualifications
Technical Supervisor	MD, DO or PhD (specialties); may have Masters/Bachelors with 2 years experience; licensure and board certification as required by states
General Supervisor	Laboratory Director or Technical Consultant qualifications or Masters/Bachelors; licensure if required by a given state
Testing Personnel	Laboratory Director or Technical Consultant qualifications or Masters/Bachelors; licensure if required by a given state

experience); laboratory supervisor or section supervisor (usually a qualified laboratory technologist); and specialist (who qualifies as a laboratory technologist but often has additional specialty training in hematology, chemistry, etc). As testing personnel, many laboratory technologists also acquire or may be required (depending on the state) to have American Society for Clinical Pathology or other CMS–approved board certification.

In addition to knowing who works in the laboratory, pathologists must know and influence the organizational structure of the laboratory staff itself. Organizational structure is commonly presented in an organizational chart, which diagrams how an organization divides and coordinates its tasks to achieve its goals. A sample hierarchal organizational chart is shown in Figure 2-1.

This hierarchal functional structure pressures the operations to become more rigid; however, it also conveys a clear understanding of responsibility and authority. Communication among the three laboratories shown in Figure 2-1 may be limited; for example, this type of structure may make it more difficult to cross-train technologists. Other types of organizational charts are also used occasionally. The self-contained unit structure (Figure 2-2) is organized around a common domain—a discipline (eg, microbiology), service type (eg, core laboratory), or location—and is less descriptive of authority and responsibilities.

A matrix organizational chart accounts for different lines of authority; for example, if an existing laboratory is restructured into a core laboratory, a stat laboratory, and a point-of-care testing facility, pathologists might account for technical direction from the various division directors with a matrix (Figure 2-3).

Most institutions' organizational structure has flattened over the past 20 years. Typically, large businesses have fewer than half the levels of management than they did two decades ago.[5] Some of these changes have been attributed to an increase in the use of so-called highly trained and educated knowledge workers, such as radiology and laboratory technologists, who resist command-and-control models. In addition, the economics of service industries that are populated by workers with a high degree of education and training and consequently higher salaries (eg, health care) also necessitates a more efficient management structure.

One unique issue in laboratory organization is the coexistence of two supervisory hierarchies: professional supervision via the pathologists and doctoral scientists, and technical or administrative supervision via the laboratory manager or chief technician. Regardless of the organization, and as stated by Peter Drucker, "the best structure will not guarantee results and performance, but the wrong structure is a guarantee of nonperformance."[5] Pathologists must know the categories of personnel in their institutions and understand the

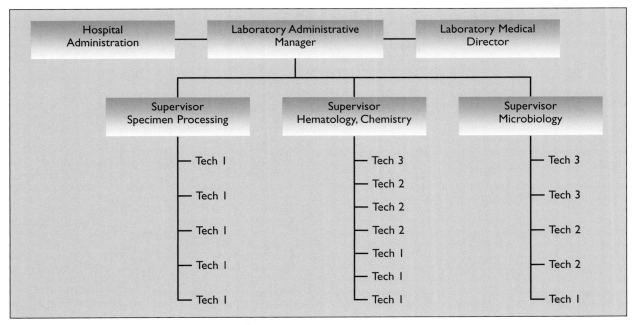

Figure 2-1. Sample Hierarchal or Multilayered Organization Chart.

working relationships of the various categories within and among the sections of the laboratory. division directors or section chiefs must meet regularly with the laboratory staff to discuss operational and technical issues. More frequent meetings are required to validate new tests, select instruments, restructure programs, and allocate space. The laboratory director must also meet regularly with laboratory managers or supervisors from all areas to review similar operational and technical projects.

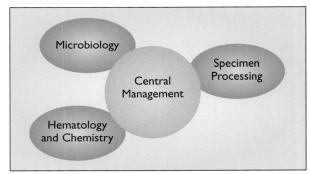

Figure 2-2. Self-Contained Organizational Chart with Overlapping Circles of Expertise.

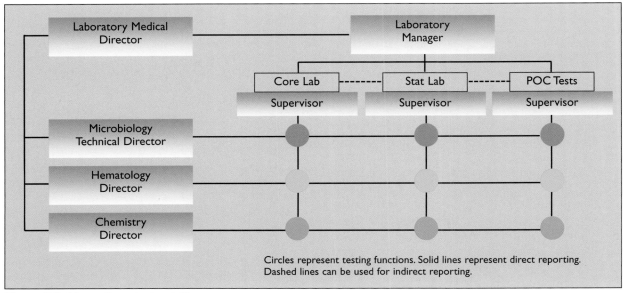

Figure 2-3. Matrix Organizational Chart.

The pathologist in charge of each laboratory section should make daily rounds to get a sense of any workload or staffing issues and discuss any problems or interesting cases. However, pathologists must have a purpose when walking through laboratories—a discussion about the hematology or chemistry instrumentation, perhaps. By having a purpose for walking through the laboratory, pathologists demonstrate that they are interested in and knowledgeable about the laboratory activities. If possible, pathologists should become familiar with the evening, graveyard, and weekend shifts. When appropriate, department resources can be used to provide treats; for example, the laboratory technologists can be surprised with pizzas from time to time.

One of the prime goals of interfacing with the laboratory staff is to constantly remind the staff of the importance of their work in patient care. Pathologists are responsible for emphasizing this linkage. Given the physical distance between the laboratory and patient care, it can be difficult to motivate the staff and emphasize the meaningfulness of their work. Most testing personnel are highly skilled and well-educated workers who can exchange their jobs and easily be recruited by neighboring institutions. The impression a pathologist leaves with laboratory staff also reflects on the staff's perception of his or her leadership qualities. Finally, pathologists' participation in staff social events facilitates communication and enhances leadership. Pathologists should not only attend, but should consider sponsoring events such as a party celebrating all birthdays in a month, an annual holiday party, or an annual softball game.

Interfacing with the Pathology Group

The professional practice group provides the framework for one's professional, financial, and emotional satisfaction or discontent. Group members are the pathology peers and doctoral scientists who work with pathologists, sharing cases, expertise, and administrative responsibilities. Pathologists spend more waking hours with their practice group than with their families. (The financial aspects of the professional practice group are discussed in detail in Chapter 10, "Financial Management of the Pathology Practice.") This section focuses on variations in practice group organization and interfaces within the practice group. The prime prerequisites for group success are that the group be composed of excellent pathologists;

the pathologists have respect for one another; the group includes leaders and followers who are comfortable in their respective roles; and that all members are good communicators. Other prerequisites include:

- A formal organization plan for the pathology group, describing domains, authority, and reporting relationships.
- A designated director with a written position charter or job description to which all members of the group agree, as well as a succession plan for the directorship.
- Written position charters or job descriptions for all group members, including partners, associates, employed pathologists, per diem employees, and postdoctoral scientists.
- A formal decision-making process that defines directorship, hierarchies, domain leadership, and empowerment and involvement in the development of policies and procedures.
- A formal, written, financial planning and control mechanism for preparing budgets, establishing a salary schedule, and monitoring contracts.
- A shared sense of participation in group decision making.
- Consensus on the group's as well as the laboratory's mission statements and strategic plans.
- Consistency and fairness in group operations.
- A "one for all and all for one" philosophy. A single pathologist who "keeps score" can destroy the group.

Every group needs structure. In academic medical centers and in large health care organizations such as Kaiser Permanente, the professional practice group may be centrally managed by a board, with representation from each specialty. In community hospitals, the more common format is for each specialty group to contract separately with the hospital and manage its own professional practice. Some hybrid forms exist, with centralized billing services and revenues and expenses managed by individual groups. In some cases, hospital administration performs both professional and technical billing for hospital-based services such as radiology, pathology, emergency medicine, and anesthesiology.

Depending on the nature of the contractual relation with the hospital, a community hospital pathology practice group may be a partnership of several pathologists, a partnership of professional corporations, a single professional corporation, or an entity wholly owned by one pathologist. In some places, several pathologists working in a

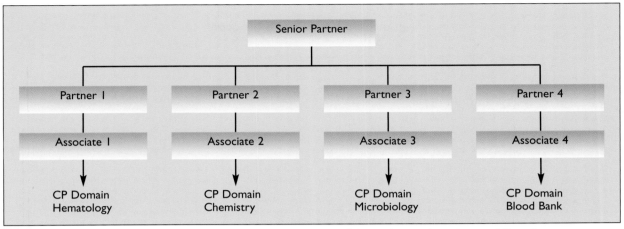

Figure 2-4. Pathology Group Organizational Chart Showing Partner Relationships to Associates and Domains.

hospital may each have separate contracts with the hospital. Regardless of the organization's structure, the structure must be clearly defined in writing in the form of a letter of agreement, a partnership agreement, or corporate bylaws. Such written agreements among pathologists practicing in an association are essential and must be prepared by a qualified attorney. They should also be reviewed and approved by all members of the group. An organizational chart distinct from the laboratory organizational chart that shows the structure, function, and reporting and professional relationships is also useful.

An organizational chart for a simplified partnership of five partner pathologists and four associate pathologists in a general hospital-based, surgical pathology practice is shown in Figure 2-4. The organizational chart may also designate laboratory domains for which individual partners have oversight. The partner-associate relationship also may indicate a mentoring component in which associate pathologists are considered for future partnership.

The head or the director of the pathology practice group may be designated in the hospital contract or elected by the group. In either case, there should be a written position charter or job description that formalizes the director's responsibilities and authority and is agreed to by all members of the group. There may also be an elected or designated secretary and/or treasurer, in which case formal documents should delineate these officers' responsibilities and authority. Although rare in community practice, a position charter or job description for each member of the professional practice group, whether partner, associate, perdiem employee, or postdoctoral scientist, is useful because it defines expectations and dictates performance evaluation (see Appendix 2-7).

Certain tasks also need to be accomplished within the group. These tasks include establishing a scheduling system and calendar that are used to assign on-call, autopsy rotation, frozen section, surgical center, teaching, and committee duties fairly. These calendars should be published monthly. A formal written vacation policy that defines priorities and privileges of rank and tenure should also be established. Domains should be assigned on the basis of competencies and experience. A system of peer review within the group also must be established. In addition, a culture of informal daily communication should be encouraged—if nothing else, one should say "Good morning" when one comes in to work and "Good bye" when one departs. Finally, there should be biweekly or monthly formal group meetings with set agendas that include recurrent items such as fiscal review, operations review, incident discussions, schedules, and peer review as well as open agendas that include topics that any member of the group can introduce. Such meetings should be mandatory for all group members. A dinner meeting with food and drink may make the process less painful.

Every group should obtain the services of two consultants, an attorney, and an accountant who can solve problems in their areas of expertise and periodically attend the weekly group meetings. Dysfunctional groups may consider periodically engaging an industrial psychologist to solve interpersonal or interface problems.

Interfaces Beyond the Hospital

Although not always evident, a professional life exists beyond the laboratory. Achieving excellence beyond the laboratory makes pathologists more valuable—even indispensable—in the professional hospital setting. The prerequisites for interfacing outside the hospital include an awareness of and a willingness to engage in communication. The first and possibly the easiest step to enter the external environment is to become involved in medical professional organizations, local and state medical associations, and the AMA. If the majority of clinicians in a community belong to the local medical association, it is important that the pathologist become a member as well; membership in such associations clearly demonstrates collegiality, mutual support, and respect. Similarly, membership in the local, state, and national pathology societies is essential, and active involvement in the committees and governance of such specialty societies carries an enormous reward of knowledge and prestige (see Appendix 2-8).

Pathologists should also have intellectual pursuits, including teaching and research. No specialist is better positioned to provide overviews and updates in the clinical sciences. If a medical school is nearby, the community pathologist may obtain a voluntary clinical faculty appointment, volunteer to teach medical students or residents, and/or volunteer to provide medical student or resident rotations through the laboratory. Several years ago, for example, both the University of Southern California (USC) and the University of California, Los Angeles (UCLA) provided their pathology residents with collaborative programs with community hospitals. The USC program was an elective three-month rotation in which fourth-year residents shadowed the director of a community hospital laboratory, sitting in his office, listening to his phone calls, attending meetings, making rounds, performing frozen sections, reviewing cases, and handling laboratory crises. The UCLA program, which had a similar format, collaborated with several community hospitals to provide fourth-year medical students with a one-month elective that concentrated on anatomic pathology. Both programs were very popular at one time but were eventually eliminated because the community pathologists were facing increasing work loads and decreasing reimbursement and found the programs to be very time-consuming. Also, residency program directors were adapting to changing rotation requirements from the Accreditation Council for Graduate Medical Education for residency rotations.

Research in the community hospital is possible. Pathologists can conduct clinical or translational research in collaboration with active clinicians; in some instances, such research may be supported by the community hospital's foundation. Because the community hospital is a rich source of study materials, it is not uncommon for community hospital pathologists to collaborate on university research projects. Obviously, interfaces in an academic position require a research interface that may range from clinical or translational research to basic research programs. However, familiarity with research is an important adjunct to routine laboratory activities such as validating tests and determining reference ranges. Basic research skills also apply to these important laboratory functions required of the community pathologist.

A pathologist should also have outside civic pursuits that include supporting local schools, community institutions, and events. Pathologists may serve on the school board, participate in the hospital's speaker's bureau, or support community-sponsored activities. Pathologists should also have a political agenda that supports the advancement of the profession of pathology. The AMA and the CAP provide training programs that teach pathologists how to speak to the press or converse with politicians comfortably. Finally, the pathologist must have a philanthropic agenda. Every hospital has a foundation or other fund-raising entity, and pathologists must be major and significant contributors to that entity. Hospital administrators are always members of their hospitals' foundation boards, and they know the financial status of their hospitals' pathologists. If a pathologist's contribution is minimal, the next contract negotiation might not be so easily accomplished. On the other hand, if the pathologist not only contributes generously but also becomes involved in the fund-raising activities and governance of the foundation, he or she will become truly indispensable to the institution.

Strategies for Improving Interfaces

Interfaces outside the laboratory can represent an obstacle for both the clinical laboratory and the pathologist. Pathology laboratories have become a "black box" from which clinicians expect certain services. The intensity of a medical education often leaves clinicians with relatively little training in pathology and laboratory medicine. Thus, their expectations may not be based on what can actually be performed in the laboratory. Also, the rapid rate of knowledge expansion means that many clinicians may not be aware or knowledgeable of emerging tests and technologies. There is a perception that pathologists are more introverted than clinicians. This may or may not be true. However, because of their physical location in the institution (frequently in the basement) and their somewhat isolated practice, pathologists may find it difficult to interface with hospital administration, medical staff, and other key members of the health care community.

Another way for pathologists to create better interfaces is to become more involved in clinical care. An example is laboratory consultative services for coagulation testing and clinical chemistry described by Laposata[3] and Lim.[6] Laposata noted that many clinicians were ordering coagulation tests without much knowledge regarding the proper sequence and interpretation of the test results. He implemented a system in which clinical laboratory data in coagulation are systematically interpreted by a physician-pathologist who writes a patient-specific narrative as a consultative note. However, the quality of the comments or interpretations is of utmost importance. Lim et al reviewed comments added by the Royal College of Pathologists of Australasia to clinical chemistry interpretations and found that the quality of the added comments varied considerably and in some cases were inappropriate and/or misleading.[6] They concluded that should such a system be put in place, the pathologists who provide comments should have clear expertise. With better interfaces, pathologists could conceivably provide similar support for the interpretation of complex diseases such as endocrine disorders and neurological disease.

One way that pathologists can increase their effectiveness in interfacing with patient care is to more directly identify with the patient. Twenty years ago, anesthesiologists did not typically see patients before entering into a procedure. Recognizing that their professional billing practice was plagued by patients' ignorance of their services, anesthesiologists started meeting with patients before the procedure to explain their role in the surgery. By clearly demonstrating that they are physicians and part of the surgical team, anesthesiologists have vastly improved their patients' satisfaction.[7] Similarly, pathologists can identify opportunities to interface with patients more directly. Fine-needle aspiration and bone marrow procedures provide excellent opportunities for pathologists to introduce themselves to patients. In addition, many hospitals provide educational programs for patients who undergo complex procedures or receive complicated services. Pathologists who become part of these educational programs can meet with patients and explain some of the aspects of tissue management as well as when the patients can expect their physicians to have pathology reports.

References

1. Keitges PW. The Involved Pathologist. Paper presented at: American Society of Clinical Pathologists/College of American Pathologists Spring Meeting, Chicago. April 8, 1997.
2. Catalano EW Jr, Ruby SG, Talbert ML, Knapman DG; for the Members of the Practice Management Committee, College of American Pathologists. College of American Pathologists consideration for the delineation of pathology clinical privileges. *Arch Pathol Lab Med.* 2009;133:613-618.
3. Laposata M. Patient-specific narrative interpretations of complex clinical laboratory evaluations: who is competent to provide them? *Clin Chem.* 2004; 50:471-472.
4. Department of Health and Human Services. Centers for Disease Control and Prevention. Current CLIA Regulations. Available at: http://www.cdc.gov/clia/regs/toc.aspx. Accessed Nov 12, 2010.
5. Drucker PF. *Management.* Revised ed. New York, NY: Harper Collins; 2008.
6. Lim EM, Sikaris KA, Gill J, et al. Quality assessment of interpretative commenting in clinical chemistry. *Clin Chem.* 2004;50:632-637.
7. Practice advisory for preanesthesia evaluation: a report by the American Society of Anesthesiologists Task Force on Preanesthesia Evaluation. *Anestheiology.* 2002;96(2):485-496.

Challenge Questions

How can a pathologists document their general competencies and their ongoing and focused professional practice evaluations?
Answer: See pages 15, 16, and 28.

Describe six strategies for interfacing with the medical staff.
Answer: See pages 18 to 20.

Describe a program for maintenance of esprit de corps in the laboratory.
Answer: See pages 21 to 24.

Appendix 2-1.
Options for Satisfying Pathologists' General Competencies and for Ongoing and Focused Professional Practice Evaluation (OPPE and FPPE)

Laboratory Accreditation
Proficiency testing
Laboratory inspection

Maintenance of Certification
Record of activities
Global ratings
Self-assessment
Certification and recertification

Continuing Education
35 category 1 Continuing Medical Education (CME) credits per 2-year period
State CME requirements

Quality Assurance and Improvement
Peer review and attestation
Volume and turnaround data
Discrepancy rates
Proficiency testing
Incident report response
Q-Probes, Q-Tracks, LMIP

Participation in the Profession
Governance of the practice
Medical staff functions
Medical and specialty society functions

Maintenance of Licensure

Satisfaction Surveys

Source: Catalano EW, Ruby SG, Talbert ML, Knapman DG; for the Members of the Practice Management Committee, College of American Pathologists. College of American Pathologists consideration for the delineation of pathology clinical privileges. *Arch Pathol Lab Med.* 2009;133:613-618.

Appendix 2-2.
Model Privilege Delineation Form

I. Documentation
A. Education and training
B. Licensure
C. Impairment
D. Specific training for requested privileges
E. Professional liability insurance

II. Certification
A. Primary AP and/or CP
B. Subspecialty
C. Recertification

III. Request for Privileges
A. Basic privileges
  1. Anatomic: list all sections requested
  2. Clinical: list all sections
B. Procedural privileges
  1. Bone marrow aspiration/biopsy
  2. Fine-needle aspiration/biopsy
  3. Phlebotomy
  4. Apheresis
  5. Isotope injection
  6. Other privileges
  7. Prescribing blood products

IV. General Competencies
A. Patient care
B. Medical knowledge
C. Practice-based learning and improvement
D. Interpersonal and communication skills
E. Professionalism
F. Systems-based practice

Source: Catalano EW, Ruby SG, Talbert ML, Knapman DG; for the Members of the Practice Management Committee, College of American Pathologists. College of American Pathologists consideration for the delineation of pathology clinical privileges. *Arch Pathol Lab Med.* 2009;133:613-618.

Appendix 2-3.
How to Conduct a Meeting

Among his many contributions to the science, art, and practice of pathology, Paul Bachner, MD, professor and chair of pathology at the University of Kentucky and former president of the College of American Pathologists, taught us how to conduct meetings, how to make them meaningful, how to use committee meetings to achieve consensus, how to use them to establish control, how to get things done, and, most important, how to make attendees feel that they have accomplished something.

Prerequisites

- Become familiar with parliamentary procedure—no one else will.*
- Define the committee's charge and objectives in writing.
- Define the committee's policies and procedures in writing.
- Develop position charters or job descriptions for the chairperson and members
- Determine the membership of the committee: regular, ex-officio, invited guests, and troublemakers (eg, a surgeon who consistently violates "sterile" procedures should be on the Infection Control Committee). When asking people to serve on a committee, show them the committee's charge, policy, procedures, and the members' job descriptions so they know what will be expected of them and of the committee.

Pre-Meeting

- First ask if you really need this meeting. Could email or a conference call do as well? What if the meeting were not held?
- Develop a preliminary agenda with the committee staff.
- Circulate the preliminary agenda to members, asking for input.
- Distribute the final agenda with necessary handouts or other documents at least 48 hours before the scheduled meeting time. Never distribute lengthy documents or handouts at the meeting—they will not be carefully read or considered and will be a distraction.
- Arrive early and check out the room: Are there enough chairs? Is the white board clean? Does the projector and other equipment work? Has the food arrived?

Meeting

- The location of a meeting is very important. It must be easily accessible to the attendees and must be in a pleasant place, preferably one with windows, nice décor, comfortable chairs, and modern audio and visual equipment.
- Seating assignment can be very important. For example, if you wish to have a sense of collegiality and collaboration, the committee chairperson should sit toward the middle of a rectangular table; on the other hand, if you want a more authoritarian format, the chairperson should sit at the end of the table. If there are windows, the chair should always sit with his or her back to the windows, especially if it is bright outside. Any troublemakers should be seated facing the window.
- Attendance can be assured if good food is present; however, if the meeting is a luncheon or dinner meeting, the food should be simple, not require a lot of table space or implements, and be fine even if not hot.
- Always begin the meeting on time. If there are not sufficient members to conduct the meeting, cancel it immediately. The next time people will be on time.
- Start by introducing yourself. If it is the committee's first meeting, ask people to introduce themselves and say where they are from, why they are on the committee, and what they hope to accomplish. Then introduce any guests or visitors and describe their role at the meeting.
- If it is a hospital or medical staff committee, begin the meeting by reviewing the hospital's mission and strategic plan. If it is a laboratory committee, review the laboratory's mission and vision.
- Review the committee's charge, policies, and procedures. This should be done every time the committee meets. Most institutions have many committees that are not well defined. By reviewing the committee's charge and policies, the committee members can focus on the job to be done, and extraneous comments or diatribes can be averted.
- Ask if there any changes or additions to the agenda, eg, "Does anyone have to leave early and wish to move some items up the agenda?"
- Review the minutes of the previous meeting; ask for changes and approval.
- Review the assignment list from the previous meeting.

- Conduct the business of the committee.
- Schedule the next meeting.
- It is most important to recap the discussion and the decisions made. The chair should make notes during the meeting of what transpired and what conclusions were reached and then present a verbal summary. However, the chair should also ask if anything was left out or if there are other interpretations of what happened.
- Finally, recapitulate the assignment or "to do" list and establish who will accomplish what, and when.
- It is imperative that you finish on time! Never go over the scheduled time—people will become annoyed, will not pay attention, and will not want to come to future meetings.

Post-Meeting

- Circulate the preliminary minutes and assignment list among the committee members. Although a knowledgeable committee staff person can take minutes, it is essential that the chair review the preliminary minutes before they are sent out. Ask for corrections from the members, and clarify that no response to their suggestions implies agreement.
- Correct the minutes on basis of input.
- Distribute the final minutes.
- Implement assignments.

* Source: Sturgis A. *Standard Code of Parliamentary Procedure.* 3rd ed. New York, NY: McGraw-Hill; 1988.

Appendix 2-4.
How to Give a Talk

An essential component of interfacing is giving a talk. It may be a formal lecture, the delivery of a paper, a presentation at grand rounds, or a short comment at tumor board. All talks require preparation and practice.

Before Preparing the Talk

- Why are you speaking? To inform, convince, provoke?
- Why you, and not someone else? Are you the expert?
- Know the subject.
- Know who else will be speaking.
- Know who the audience will be.
- Know the length of the talk.
- Prepare an outline, a slide list, and reminder notes.
- At the end of the talk, can anyone ask: "So what?"

Prepare the Talk to Match the Audience

- To scientists. Follow the format of a scientific paper: introduction, hypothesis, materials and methods, results, statistical analysis, discussion, and conclusion.
- To physicians. Follow the format of a patient encounter: history, physical exam, labs, images, diagnosis, treatment, course.
- To a tumor board. Follow the synoptic report format: operation, gross, microscopic description, special studies, stage, grade.
- To the nonmedical public. Know the level of knowledge. Emphasize signs and symptoms, give the disease incidence, know the audience's main concerns.

How to Talk

- Take a public-speaking course.
- Learn about your voice. Can it be heard? Practice projecting your voice to the back of the room. Keep your voice relaxed, calm, and composed. How is it perceived? Is it appropriate to the audience? Listen to an audio recording of your voice—how does it sound? Get critiques.
- Is the vocabulary of the talk geared to the audience?
- Speak slowly, simply, and clearly.
- Never read a text; do not memorize your talk—use reminder notes.

- Maintain eye contact with the audience, but look around the room. Don't fixate on one member of the audience exclusively.
- Don't look at the screen; look at the audience.
- Pretend that you are speaking to a friend.
- Don't freeze behind the podium; move around and gesture naturally.

Before the Talk

- Review the venue, audio/visual equipment, seating, temperature.
- Load your talk into the audio/visual equipment; make sure everything works.
- Are handouts available? Carry an extra copy of any handouts you distribute.
- Carry an extra copy of your presentation slides on a flash drive.
- Rehearse your talk, obtain critiques, rehearse your talk again, edit your talk, and rehearse your talk again.

The Introduction

- Who are you and what are your credentials?
- Why are you speaking to this group?
- What are you going to tell the group? Why should they care?
- What is in it for the audience if they listen to you?

Text Slides

- The audience is there to listen to you, not to look at slides.
- Slides should support the spoken presentation.
- PowerPoint makes slides, not presentations.
- PowerPoint should not distract, but enhance.
- Do not use fancy backgrounds, animation, or fly-ins; these are distractions that prevent the audience from concentrating on your talk.
- Keep text slides simple: Five lines per slide, five words per line, 40-point font for titles, 30-point font for text.
- Use few slides. A rate of 90 seconds per slide is fast (20 slides for 30-minute talk). Generally allow 2 minutes per slide.
- Edit slides ruthlessly, both in number and content.
- When using text slides, give audience time to read slide and then comment or expand on what is shown.
- Never read text slides; look at the audience.

Tables and Graphs

- Tables and graphs should illustrate your talk.
- Tables and graphs must be kept simple and made specifically for the talk.
- Never copy a table or graph from a publication.
- Do not make more than two or three points per slide.
- Never say: "I know you can't read this, but …."

Pathology Slides

- The slides should illustrate your talk. No one is interested in pictures of your children or your recent vacation.
- Never begin with a high-power IHC slide.
- Start with a gross photo, then low-power H&E, then intermediate-power H&E, and finally high-power H&E.
- Show special stains and IHC only after H&E.
- If showing a new technique, explain how it is done and what it means. Assume the audience does not know the technique.

Handouts

- Handouts can be distributed before or after the talk.
- Handouts should be a copy of the talk's slides, not a text version of the talk.
- Handouts should include your name and email address and a copyright symbol (©).

Concluding the Talk

- It is better to finish early than to go over time. Never go over time!
- Acknowledge those who helped without using long lists or pictures.
- Recapitulate why you gave the talk, what your main points were, and why the talk is significant for the specific audience.
- Thank the audience members for their attention and ask if they have any questions or comments.
- When responding to questions or comments, first restate the question.
- Answer questions by reiterating a point from your talk. Keep eye contact with the questioner. If you do not know the answer, say so. If a comment is nasty or provocative, don't respond in kind.

Appendix 2-5.
Assembling a Medical Staff Newsletter

Interfacing with the medical staff is essential for the involved pathologist and entails volunteering for a variety of committees and tasks. One "job" that often is hard to fill is editor of the professional staff newsletter. The job may seem daunting, but the editor is at the center of medical staff activities and knows everything that is going on in the institution. Remember, knowledge is power. But editing, like speaking, must be learned. Here are some tips for getting started:

- Take a course on newsletter editing or an online tutorial covering:
  - Soliciting, editing, and writing articles
  - Planning and scheduling the content
  - Design and layout
  - Distribution
- Monthly features
  - Lead article
  - Notes from the chief of staff
  - Notes from the administrator
  - Calendar of events
  - Nursing notes
  - Executive Committee actions
  - Library notes (eg, new books)
  - Pharmacy notes (eg, new drugs)
  - Laboratory notes (eg, new tests)
  - Case of the month
  - Scientific papers
  - New technology
  - Editorial
- Other recurring features
  - Letters to the editor
  - 25 and 50 years ago
  - Book reviews
  - Physician of the month
  - Hospital employee of the month
  - Doctor's office employee of the month
  - Spouse of the month
  - Managed care news
  - Talent on the staff
  - Abstracts of papers published by staff members
  - Biographies of new staff members
  - MediQuiz
  - Cartoon

Appendix 2-6.
Annual Report of a Pathology Department

A hospital's administration, governing body, and medical staff may not be aware of the pathologist's role in or the laboratory's contributions to high-quality patient care. An annual report can highlight the clinical and financial impact of the laboratory and the pathologist's various roles. The annual report is a powerful management tool that, in addition to reporting laboratory operations in relation to prior goals and objectives, describes achievements, laments failures, identifies needs, and delineates future goals and objectives. The distribution of the annual report should coincide with the budget approval process so that administrators have full knowledge of the laboratory's past performance and future needs. The report should be distributed to the hospital governing body, hospital administration, medical staff officers, committee chairs, nursing directors, and other hospital services. Most importantly, the report should be distributed to each laboratory employee to foster an esprit de corps.

The annual report should include the following categories:

- Workload and turnaround times, with comparisons of actual to budgeted performance and comparison to previous years' workload and turnaround times.
- Budget and financial performance, showing comparisons and trends over three to five years. Emphasize the laboratory's impact on the hospital's financial success.
- Operational metrics: Describe new tests and procedures and their impact on diagnosis, therapy, length of stay, facilitation of emergency department disposition, etc. Describe education provided for physicians and other health care workers.
- Personnel costs and performance, including productivity and efficiency metrics.
- Supply and expense costs, including the major expense categories such as equipment rental, maintenance, depreciation, reagent costs, reference laboratory send-out test costs, utilities, and allocated expenses.
- Any new equipment acquired, including a description of its function.

- New construction.
- Satisfaction surveys, including results from both patients and physicians.
- Achievement of prior goals and objectives; explain why certain prior goals and objectives, if any, were not achieved.
- Employee development, employee turnover, new personnel, retiring personnel, employee awards/recognition, employee participation in hospital and medical staff committees (eg, Infection Control Committee).
- Educational activities: school of medical technology, continuing medical education, seminar or course attendance.
- Professional activities: physicians' and doctoral researchers' academic appointments, participation in hospital and medical staff committees, participation in educational programs, published papers, awards, and activities in local and national medical organizations.
- Inspections and accreditations: results of the various inspections and proficiency testing programs.
- Incidents: accidents, injuries, patient errors, etc, with an emphasis on remediation and corrective actions. In particular, risk-avoidance activities such as efforts to reduce errors should be described.
- Required changes and enhancements: next years' goals and objectives, new tests or procedures, new equipment required to improve efficiency and decrease costs.

Source: Horowitz RE. Annual report of a pathology department. *Pathologists*. 1983;37:184-186.

Appendix 2-7. Pathologist Performance Evaluations

In this era of documentation and requirements for ongoing evaluation, a guide to the performance evaluation of pathologists might be useful, if only to establish uniformity and consistency within a pathology group.

Maintenance of Competence Elements

- Professional standing: Licensure, certification, recertification, hospital privileges
- Continuing medical education (CME) and periodic self-assessment
- Cognitive expertise (an examination)
- Performance in practice

General Competencies (see Appendix 2-1)

- Patient care
- Medical knowledge
- Practice-based learning and improvement
- Interpersonal and communication skills
- Professionalism
- Systems-based practice

Performance Elements

- Mastery of the fundamentals of anatomic and clinical pathology
- Appropriate use of special studies
- Work output and turnaround time
- Use of scientific literature and scientific accomplishments
- Innovation and creative ability
- Teaching ability
- Skill in chairing committees and presenting conferences
- Personal skills: ability to apply self, determine priorities, complete work in a timely fashion, work and remain calm under pressure, take failure or handle mistakes gracefully, demonstrate emotional maturity
- Interpersonal skills: integrity, reliability, honesty; ability to work harmoniously with peers, subordinates, and superiors; ability to accept others' points of view; willingness to volunteer assistance; ability to accept responsibility; ability to empathize with clinicians
- Decision skills: ability to reason well, capacity for logical thinking, ability to make good decisions
- Communication skills: clear, concise, convincing oral communication, sensitive listener, good written communication

Summary

- Performing at advanced level: ready for promotion, partnership, or bonus
- Performing satisfactorily in present assignment
- Needs additional training, development, or experience (specify any additional work or experience needed, how it will be assessed, and the time frame for completing the work or obtaining the experience)

Appendix 2-8.
Laboratory Specialty Societies

Presented in alphabetical order. Descriptions are derived from societies' websites.

AABB is an international association dedicated to the advancement of science and the practice of transfusion medicine and related biological therapies, whose membership consists of institutions and individuals, including physicians, administrators, medical technologists, nurses, researchers, and blood donor recruiters. (www.aabb.org)

American Association for Clinical Chemistry (AACC) is an association of professional laboratory scientists, including MDs and PhDs, whose members develop and perform tests conducted in hospital laboratories, clinics, medical centers, and other health care settings. (www.aacc.org)

American Association of Bioanalysts (AAB) is a professional association whose members are clinical laboratory directors, owners, supervisors, managers, medical technologists, medical laboratory technicians, physician office laboratory technicians, and phlebotomists. AAB also three specialized membership sections for laboratory professionals: the College of Reproductive Biology (CRB), the Environmental Biology and Public Health Section (EBPH), and the National Independent Laboratory Association (NILA). (www.aab.org)

American Clinical Laboratory Association (ACLA) is an organization that represents national, regional, and local independent clinical laboratories, providing its members representation with federal and state governments, private health plans, education, information, and research. (www.clinical-labs.org)

American Pathology Foundation (APF) is a non-profit professional society devoted to the business and management of pathology, providing quality educational programs and practice management resources for its members. (www.apfconnect.org)

American Society for Clinical Laboratory Science (ASCLS) is a nonregistry professional society, representing nonphysician clinical laboratory practitioners, whose members include clinical laboratory directors, managers, supervisors, hematologists, immunologists, educators, clinical chemists, microbiologists, phlebotomists, and other professionals. (www.ascls.org)

American Society for Clinical Pathology (ASCP) is a medical specialty society representing pathology and laboratory medicine, whose members are board certified pathologists, other physicians, clinical scientists (PhDs), medical technologists and technicians. (www.ascp.org)

American Society for Microbiology (ASM) is a life science society, comprising scientists and health professionals, whose mission is to advance the microbiological sciences and the profession of microbiology by disseminating information and stimulating research and education. (www.asm.org)

American Society of Hematology (ASH) is a professional society concerned with the causes and treatment of blood disorders, whose mission is to further the understanding, diagnosis, treatment, and prevention of disorders of the blood, bone marrow, and the immunologic, hemostatic, and vascular systems. (www.hematology.org)

Association for Molecular Pathology (AMP) promotes clinical practice, basic research, and education in molecular pathology, with a mission to represent and unify practitioners of molecular pathology. (www.amp.org)

Canadian Society for Medical Laboratory Science (CSMLS) is the national certifying body and professional society for medical laboratory professionals, whose members include medical laboratory technologists, medical laboratory assistants, educators, and scientists who work in public and private laboratories. (www.csmls.org)

Canadian Society of Clinical Chemists (CSCC) is a scientific and professional society representing clinical biochemists across Canada, providing leadership in the practice of clinical biochemistry and clinical laboratory medicine through service, education, and research. (www.cscc.ca)

Clinical and Laboratory Standards Institute (CLSI), formerly NCCLS, promotes quality health care through consensus standards, guidelines, and best practices. (www.clsi.org)

Clinical Laboratory Management Association (CLMA) is an international professional association of health care managers who are responsible for the operations of laboratories and clinical services provided by hospitals and other health care organizations. (www.clma.org)

College of American Pathologists (CAP) is an organization of board-certified pathologists, whose mission is to serve patients, pathologists, and the public by fostering and advocating excellence in the practice of pathology and laboratory medicine. (www.cap.org)

National Academy of Clinical Biochemistry (NACB) is the official Academy of the AACC, whose membership consists of doctorate level scientists involved in developing the scholarship and practice of laboratory medicine. (www.aacc.org/members/nacb)

United States and Canadian Academy of Pathology (USCAP) is a global leader in the transmission of knowledge in the field of pathology, providing pathology education and fostering ongoing innovation and scientific breakthroughs for the field of pathology. (www.uscap.org)

CHAPTER 3

Laboratory Operations

Elizabeth A. Wagar, MD
Richard E. Horowitz, MD

Contents

History

The history of laboratory operations parallels the development of science and technology. Well into the middle of the twentieth century, physicians were still performing their own "lab tests" on their patients. In hospitals, there was a "ward laboratory" where interns and medical students performed common tests. The "central laboratory" was mainly for more complicated chemistry and bacteriology procedures. Hematology and the blood bank were often part of the department of medicine, and surgical pathology was a section in the department of surgery. The only "pure" pathology operation was the autopsy department. While autopsy as a discipline is rapidly fading away owing to false medical-legal concerns, the mistaken belief that modern laboratory testing and radiological imaging can be used to identify all major pathologies, and some level of failure to embrace new technologies in the autopsy room, other sections of pathology and laboratory medicine have thrived and grown both in prestige and significance to patient care because they have used advanced technologies to bring basic science and the art of diagnostic pathology to the bedside. As diagnostic technologies became more complex, and because clinicians no longer desired or were incapable of running laboratories, the specialty of pathology, with its two main branches, anatomic pathology and laboratory medicine, was conceived.

In 1922, a group of physicians who focused on laboratory medicine came together to form the American Society of Clinical Pathologists (ASCP; now American Society for Clinical Pathology) with a goal of "achieving greater scientific proficiency... and maintaining the status of clinical pathologists on an equal plane with other specialists."[1] In 1946, the College of American Pathologists (CAP) was spun off of the ASCP to deal more directly with the socioeconomic, regulatory, and practice issues facing pathologists.

Until recently, laboratories were strictly organized according to subspecialty. In the clinical laboratory, these subspecialties consisted of chemistry, hematology, transfusion medicine, microbiology, and immunology. Anatomic pathology as a specialty was further subdivided into the areas of autopsy, surgical pathology, and cytopathology. New science and technology have blurred the borders between these subspecialties in the laboratory. For example, hematologists may use flow cytometry to analyze a population of lymphocytes, while surgical pathologists may use flow cytometry to perform a cell cycle analysis of a tumor. Today, laboratories are often organized and operated to meet the needs of their customers, so much so that the laboratory may include a stat subsection that performs tests for blood gases, Gram stains, complete blood counts, drug screens, and enzymes, as well as a "12-hour" laboratory that does all non-stat tests that require a 12-hour turnaround time. Other trends include the increasing use of point-of-care testing, waived testing, and self-testing. In-vivo testing, in which probes placed in or on a patient will constantly monitor a variety of analytes, is just on the horizon.

Within the laboratory, new instrumentation utilizing miniaturization, nanoscale technology, microfluidics, and biochips will generate huge amounts of data, requiring clinical pathologists to shift from merely overseeing data generation to creating meaningful, clinically useful information. Similarly, the introduction of new technologies, such as multi-spectral imaging, spatial imaging, partial wave backscattering microscopy, digital imaging, digital telepathology, microarrays, and molecular sensors for genetic analysis, will require anatomic pathologists to move beyond mastering pattern recognition and cytomorphology to providing consultation for molecular diagnoses. The potential impact of these new technologies on laboratory operations, regulations, and revenue and on the education of pathologists and laboratorians is enormous.

Organization

Efficiently and effectively accomplishing the mission and goals of the clinical laboratory requires the integration of personnel, equipment, supplies, and facilities, which in turn requires a structure or organization that identifies *who* is authorized and responsible for specific functions, *what* the specific goals and operations are, and *how* personnel, space, equipment, and supplies are deployed. The principal directives of an organization are its organizational chart, policies, and procedure manuals.

The Organizational Chart

The organizational chart defines positions of authority and responsibility, identifies hierarchies and relationships, spells out reporting lines, and clarifies expectations. (Different types of organizational charts are discussed in Chapter 2, "Competencies and Interfaces of the Involved Pathologist.") More important are the unique features of the laboratory's organizational chart. The

clinical laboratory has two types of hierarchies: a professional hierarchy and a technical or administrative hierarchy. Each hierarchy has important functions. The professional hierarchy addresses operational issues related to the scientific and clinical purposes of the laboratory. The technical or administrative hierarchy is responsible for organizing the work of the nonprofessional staff to ensure that the staff is productive and can meet administrative requirements and goals. For example, in the histology laboratory, a question regarding the correct molecular method to use to identify a specific tumor marker may arise. This "professional" question might follow a track from the laboratory director to the anatomic pathology director (both of whom are pathologists) to the technical supervisor and finally to the histology technologist who is actually performing the work. On the other hand, a problem regarding the assignment of an individual to perform the assay would be an "administrative" question that would follow the track from the laboratory administrator (chief technologist) to the technical supervisor and then to the technician. These parallel tracks are required to achieve the ideal outcome, ie, an appropriate and accurate biomarker result. The professional input provides the scientific reasoning, and the administrative input provides the technical support to identify who has the appropriate talent and skills to achieve the result.

Another organizational aspect of most laboratories is the educational mission of its pathology and laboratory medicine services. Pathology and laboratory medicine are by definition unique areas and serve in many educational capacities within an institution. For example, if the laboratory is located within a medical school, it may support multiple educational activities, ranging from training medical students to providing advanced postdoctoral fellowships. A pathology and laboratory medicine department may also be associated with an independent pathology residency program or a school of medical technology. Laboratories may agree to provide internships for outside medical technology schools or rotations for other specialties; for example, a clinical microbiology laboratory may provide rotations for postdoctoral fellows specializing in infectious disease. In the community hospital setting, pathologists often serve as "educators" for the medical staff and hospital employees by chairing critical committees, giving in-service conferences, and organizing and presenting grand rounds and tumor boards. Such activities have to be accommodated by work in the laboratory, and

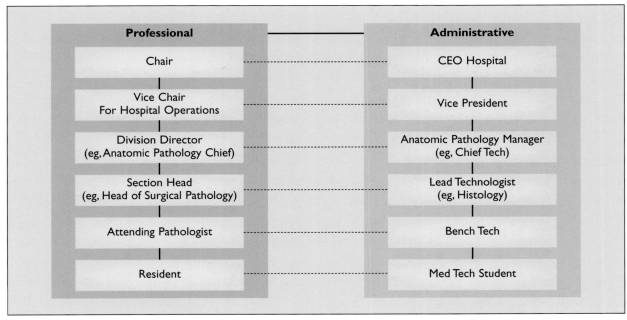

Figure 3-1. A Matrix Management Scheme for Incorporating Professional and Administrative Oversight.

the educational directors and students need to appear on the organizational chart with the appropriate lines of authority clearly defined.

The administrative line of authority is critical to laboratory operations. Many larger laboratories have both a medical director and an administrative director. In some instances, particularly in commercial laboratories and proprietary for-profit hospital laboratories, the administrative director reports to a corporate executive, not to the pathologist medical director. This line of authority may cause unexpected consequences for the pathologist, because he or she is ultimately responsible for all laboratory operations, including quality assurance, safety, regulatory compliance, and the medical-legal aspects of laboratory operations as defined by the 1988 Clinical Laboratory Improvement Amendments (CLIA). Furthermore, the Joint Commission and other accrediting organizations expect the laboratory director to "assume the professional, scientific, consultative and organizational responsibility for the facility." If the administrative director does not report to the pathologist director, that directorial expectation will not be met. A pathologist director may compromise by agreeing that the administrative director can report to both a hospital executive and the pathologist director. If such a compromise is created, it should include the pathologist director's appraisals of the administrative director's performance.

Another potentially successful strategy is to utilize a matrix management scheme in which clear lines of authority are defined for both the professional and administrative arms, and dotted lines of authority are defined between the professional and technical organizations, with an agreement to reach consensus or take unresolved issues to the immediate supervisor for "higher-level" resolution (Figure 3-1).

Several other types of organizational charts reflect the structure of the organization and define the division of its powers, degrees of delegation, divisions within an organization, departmentalization, and staff structure.

In addition to the formal organizational structure of the laboratory, management must recognize and utilize the informal organization of the laboratory. Informal organization consists of the actions and examples of various employees who, regardless of their official title or position, come to be accepted as leaders by their colleagues. If it is not recognized or appreciated, the informal organization can become a destructive force; however, if the informal organization is properly recognized and utilized, it can become a potent builder of morale and success.

One example of informal leadership is the presence of a recognized authority in a given specialty in a group of practicing pathologists. Although such an individual may not have an official title, the other pathologists in the group (and perhaps outside pathologists as well) tend to address their difficult diagnostic questions to this individual, perhaps even acknowledging that individual's review in the final pathology report. Administrative examples may include a technologist with special expertise in hematology or coagulation testing; other technologists will defer to this individual for advice and help with difficult cases. In some academic and large hospital settings, official titles exist for people who perform such activities in the form of "specialist" titles. In other settings, the recognition is less evident and more informal.

The "Test" as the Fundamental Unit of Operations

George D. Lundberg, MD, the long-time editor of the *Journal of the American Medical Association* and then Medscape, was an innovative pathologist who furthered several concepts in laboratory operations, including critical values and the expanded definition of the "test." According to Lundberg, it is essential to look at a test in the broadest of possible terms. A test involves more than just one step:

1. A physician has a diagnostic or therapeutic problem.

2. The physician thinks of ordering a test to help solve the problem.

3. A test is ordered verbally, electronically, or in writing.

4. The test requisition is entered into a hospital information system (HIS) or website.

5. The requisition is transferred to the laboratory information system (LIS).

6. The laboratory computer generates pick-up lists, work lists, and billing data and checks for duplicate test orders and appropriateness of order (admitting diagnosis, ICD-9 codes).

7. A phlebotomist or nurse obtains the specimen and sends it to the laboratory.

8. Specimen triage is performed in the laboratory's central receiving area.

9. The test is performed and verified (the original concept of a test).

10. The pathologist interprets test results if required.

11. The test results are transferred to the originating information system.

12. Test information is sent to the billing system(s).

13. Printed or electronic test results are available at the nursing station.

14. Test results are placed in the patient chart or electronically transferred to the electronic medical record and sent to the physician's office.

15. The ordering physician reads test results and takes appropriate action to solve his initial problem.

Most laboratories directly control and are generally concerned with items 6 through 10 only. However, a successful laboratory influences and controls the entire process. To manage this complex sequence, it is useful to break it down into a series of interrelated subsystems that address each component of the test. The central and critical role of the HIS and the LIS in each subsystem of laboratory operations cannot be overemphasized. The pathologist must have an intimate knowledge of both the HIS and the LIS and must actively participate as a member of the hospital's information technology committee or as the information specialist in the hospital or medical center.[2,3] (See also Chapter 6, "Management of Pathology Information Systems.")

Test Ordering Subsystem

The test ordering subsystem must have a customer education component to help ensure that physicians know which test(s) to order. The educational component should include formal conferences, clinical pathological correlation conferences, a laboratory newsletter, and seminars for nurses, ward clerks, and physician office personnel, as well as a laboratory user manual that lists the available tests, their indications, specimen collection requirements, turnaround times, reference ranges, sensitivities, specificities, predictive values, and diagnostic efficiencies. Laboratory personnel who respond to test orders should also be trained; receptionists, telephone operators, and phlebotomists should have a working knowledge of the laboratory user manual. This is a monumental task because these individuals are generally the lowest paid, least-educated laboratory employees with the highest turnover rate. Nevertheless, they are the "face of the lab," representing the laboratory to the outside world. Special education to acquaint them with laboratory operations is essential; further, they must be taught how to respond to inquiries and triage questions to which they have no answers.

The next component of the test ordering subsystem is the requisition. The design of the requisition, whether a paper or computerized version, is the responsibility of the laboratory and ultimately the responsibility of the pathologist. Designing the requisition should not be delegated to the marketing or information technology staff. Ideally, the requisition form is designed with input from the physicians, nurses, ward clerks, and others who will use it on a daily basis.[4-6] The format of the requisition can guide how tests will be ordered and guide laboratory personnel at order

Mamie B. was one of the most important people in the hospital laboratory. She started working in the hospital kitchen as a dishwasher many years ago. She then transferred to the laboratory as an aide, mainly glassware washing. In that capacity, she came to know most of the people in the laboratory and pretty soon had a fairly good idea of what they were doing. When an opening in the phlebotomy section came up, Mamie applied. We trained her and she became quite proficient and became known all over the hospital. She also got to know the nurses and the ward clerks and even the doctors, what their jobs were like, and what their needs were. A few years later, we needed a receptionist and Mamie applied. By this time she knew the laboratory, the technologists, and, most important, she knew the "customers"—the ward clerks, nurses, and doctors. When she answered the phone, more often than not she knew the caller, and they knew her. She knew enough about the laboratory to answer most questions or would know who could provide the answer. Mamie was the ideal interface between the laboratory and the "outside world"—every laboratory should have one like her.

entry. The requisition is the document that facilitates communication between clinical services and the laboratory by providing the name of the test requested, correct patient identifiers, and any special requests (timing of specimen collection, stat request, or other special instructions). The requisition can also be customized for specific services and research projects.

The final component of the test ordering subsystem is order entry into the LIS. The interface between the hospital's or physicians' office computers and the LIS must be able to transfer test orders as well as patients' identification, demographic data, current location, and insurance and billing data. It should also be able to transfer not only the name and contact information of the admitting physician, but also that of the ordering physician. The system must also let users check for duplicate orders, check the appropriateness of orders based on diagnosis and insurer, and issue Advance Beneficiary Notices, if needed, for tests that may not be reimbursed by the federal government.

Specimen Acquisition Subsystem

Once a test order arrives in the laboratory, the specimen acquisition subsystem activates. A critical prerequisite for this subsystem is flawless patient and specimen identification. In most inpatient facilities, barcoded wristbands or radiofrequency technologies are used to ensure accurate patient and specimen identification. When used in conjunction with additional identification technologies, radiofrequency technologies can significantly reduce the number of mislabeled specimens.[7-9] However, despite the most error-free identification

systems, patient identification mistakes will be made but can be minimized by training laboratory personnel as well as the nursing and physician office personnel who send many of the specimens. In many intensive care units and emergency rooms, the nurses obtain the specimens from the patients and therefore must be trained in and retain competencies for specimen acquisition (eg, how to flush IV lines, how much specimen is needed for a given test). Many specimens, such as urine and sputum specimens, may be collected by patient care assistants or clerical staff who have had little or no training in specimen collection. When the laboratory receives an inadequate specimen—eg, saliva rather than sputum—it may be due to miscommunication. Even though the physician ordered a sputum specimen, and even though the nurse told the ward clerk to collect a sputum specimen, the ward clerk may have given the patient a sputum cup and said, "Spit in this cup." Of course the specimen will be saliva.

The personnel in all the different venues from which specimens are received, including hospital wards, surgical centers, outpatient laboratories, outpatient clinics, and physicians' offices, need to be trained and periodically retrained in adequate specimen collection. Training may be a scheduled annual event that includes a luncheon for the staff of the physician offices and surgical centers (in accordance with the rules and regulations concerning gifts allowed in the course of doing business), or it can be performed as a component of nursing in-service education. Regardless of the approach, training and retraining require a close relationship between the laboratory and those who collect specimens.

The LIS electronically generates "pick-up" lists complete with barcode-readable labels for the phlebotomy teams' use. Phlebotomy services in inpatient settings are now frequently managed through dispatch centers to ensure that personnel are distributed appropriately to match draw requirement demands. There should also be "anticipation" lists for specimens that will be acquired by non-laboratory personnel. The LIS acknowledges the receipt of specimens, whether they are brought in by the phlebotomists or come directly from the wards or physicians' offices. The LIS then generates a "Not Received" list, which is different from an "Overdue" test list and can be used to compile a "Re-draw" list. Specimen triage, aliquotting, and distribution are generally done in a central receiving and processing section of the laboratory and may be manual or highly automated. The send-out test area is also located in this section. Processes and monitors for specimens sent to reference laboratories require additional management tools. For a myriad of reasons, anatomic pathology rules and regulations concerning specimen acquisition often developed independently of those of laboratory medicine. For example, while criteria for rejection and re-drawing may be clear for select laboratory medicine tests, in surgical pathology, owing to the nature of the specimens, no mislabeled or unidentified tissue is ever rejected and discarded before Herculean tasks are undertaken to link the specimen to the correct patient.

In addition to its reliance on the LIS, the specimen acquisition subsystem is dependent on electronic interfaces with the HIS and physicians' office computers. The specimen acquisition subsystem may also include other equipment, such as automobiles (if the laboratory has a major outreach program and its own couriers), a pneumatic tube system for specimen delivery, barcode printers, phlebotomy carts, and in-laboratory robots for specimen delivery. Even though these items may not be under the direct control of the laboratory or the pathologist, it will be viewed as a failure of the laboratory if they malfunction or break.

The supplies used in the specimen acquisition subsystem are of great importance not only in ensuring proper specimen acquisition, but also in overall laboratory operations. For example, the use of standard urine collection cups in one facility, which performed 250 urine drug screens a day, led to innumerable problems. The caps of the collection cups were not screwed on securely, and there were frequent spills, often within the pneumatic tube carriers. When the specimens arrived in the laboratory, the caps had to be removed and the aliquots manually transferred to tubes, which were then placed in racks for testing. The urine cups then had to be stored and refrigerated for repeat or confirmatory testing. When the laboratory switched to a new urine cup with an integrated transfer device, the specimen was transferred to tubes in the originating clinic or ward with no spillage, risk of leakage, or contamination. The transfer tube could be directly placed on the instrument racks for testing without pouring or exposing the specimen. In addition, the new tubes took up one fourth as much storage space as the original urine cups did. Investigating new supply options and evaluating them in real-world situations are important activities associated with this step.

Testing Subsystem

The testing subsystem covers what is commonly believed to be the essence of laboratory operations. The testing subsystem, which is also referred to as the analytic phase, involves much more than is readily apparent to the average laboratory customer. The testing subsystem includes selecting test methodology, equipment, and reagents; evaluating test performance; scheduling personnel; and performing quality assurance. The first prerequisite of the testing subsystem is space planning. The layout of a laboratory is much more than a floor plan; it reflects the organizational structure of the laboratory and is the culmination of operational goals that are integral to the mission of the laboratory and its leadership. Laboratories require unique facilities with special water, plumbing, and electrical resources; ventilation; and resources for the management of chemical, biological, and infectious materials and waste. The Clinical Laboratory Standards Institute provides valuable standards for addressing this feature of the testing subsystem.[10] The details of equipment and supply management are covered in Chapter 5, and the essentials of personnel and quality management are discussed in Chapter 4, "Personnel Management," and Chapter 7, "Quality Management in Laboratory Medicine."

Actual test performance is of course the key element of the testing subsystem. The evaluation of test performance is discussed in relation to test validation as required by CLIA. It should be adequately described and documented in the individual laboratory section procedure and standard operating procedures (SOPs) for each analyte. The testing subsystem must be able to recognize the completion and verification of a test, transmit that information to the billing and reporting subsystems, and then remove the test from the "to do" queue.

Billing Subsystem

Because the first laboratory and hospital information systems were designed by hospital finance officers, the laboratory's billing subsystem often operates in tandem with the hospital or institutional financial system and is usually quite sophisticated. Pathologists must be knowledgeable about the system, monitor the system, and change the system if necessary. The essential prerequisite to billing is the receipt of patient identification, insurance, and diagnostic information from the ordering entity. For hospital inpatients, this transfer is typically automatic by direct interfaces between the HIS and the LIS. The design of the requisition, which highlights the essential information fields, often facilitates the acquisition of such information. Problems arise when the necessary information must be obtained from physicians' offices, clinics, and various other outpatient venues. The most common problems include incomplete patient information, absent International Classification of Diseases (ICD) codes, absent Current Procedural Terminology (CPT) codes as required by the Centers for Medicare and Medicaid Services, expired insurance coverage, and absent Advance Beneficiary Notices. When a physician orders a test that is not covered by Medicare for a Medicare patient, he or she must provide the patient with an Advance Beneficiary Notice to inform the patient that they are responsible for payment. An essential component of the billing subsystem is the fee schedule, which is usually generated by an approved cost-accounting method and changed periodically. (See Chapter 9, "Financial Management of the Laboratory.")

An often-overlooked aspect of the billing system is its quality control mechanisms. Every laboratory needs to continually monitor and audit its billing system to make certain that all tests are paid for, that coding and billings are correct, and that a functioning compliance program is in place (see Chapter 10, "Financial Management of the Pathology Group"). Compliance with federal and state regulations is an increasingly prominent aspect of health care. Either the LIS or the HIS and the billing service should issue monthly reports on the total number of procedures and billings classified by payer type, ordering entity, patient days or admissions, and diagnostic-related groups. A variance analysis should be done monthly to compare that month's actual performance to its budgeted performance, the actual performance for the preceding month, and the actual performance for the preceding year. For example, in a certain month, the billing service may note a marked decline in Medicare billings but no change in Medicare patient admissions or Medicare patient days; investi-

gation may reveal a problem with the HIS to LIS electronic billing interface.

Reporting Subsystem

The reporting subsystem communicates the laboratory's work to its customers. Pathology and laboratory medicine are information specialties; their product is in the form of numbers, words, graphs, pictures, or descriptions and diagnoses.[4-6] The way in which this information is packaged and presented to the customer is critical. The format of the report, whether a paper report, a telephone report, or an electronic computer-based report, is the "gift wrap," and the data is the "gift." A visually appealing and easily readable laboratory report—one that has no unnecessary or redundant information, highlights abnormal findings, sequences information logically, is customized for specific individuals or groups, and enhances the recipient's ability to care for patients—will be well received. In contrast, a poorly formatted report that is illegible, contains unnecessary information, and/or obscures important data can be misinterpreted and may be the source of a "lab error." The laboratory is responsible for the design of the various report forms. Designing the report forms cannot be delegated to the information technology department or the local print shop; it must be done by those who know how clinicians think and what they need.[6,7]

Laboratory Medical DirecTIPs, a CAP publication, provides some good guidelines for formatting reports.[4] These guidelines include making the report legible; clearly, completely, and prominently identifying the patient; clearly identifying the laboratory; including a phone number for questions; using a "standardized" format so the same test results appear in the same location and in the same sequence consistently; emphasizing techniques used to highlight critical values, high results, low results, and deltas; and clearly relating comments about specific test results. For anatomic pathology reports, each pathologist in the group should use the same format and nomenclature, eg, the CAP cancer protocol synoptic report formats. A pathology group should annually audit a sample of test result forms, including computer screen images. One customer-friendly approach is to send out a packet of sample test-result forms to prime customers, including physicians, nurses, and clerical staff, and request comments and suggestions; this approach identifies customers' needs as well as complaints.

Every laboratory should establish a formal system of forms control. Forms control entails the pe-

> **The importance of the "gift wrap,"** or the format of a report, cannot be overemphasized. If I were to bring my wife an ounce of expensive perfume in a crystal flask, packaged in a fancy box from an elegant boutique, it would be joyfully received. If however, that exact same perfume were packaged in a plastic laboratory bottle without a fancy ribbon, just in a plain brown paper bag, the reception would certainly be less enthusiastic and would likely engender questions or confusion. The gift wrap (the report format) is critical in how a gift (the test result) will be received.

riodic collection of all the forms used by the laboratory, including paper report forms, computer-generated forms, and screen formats, as well as forms used for internal laboratory operations. The forms must be critically reviewed: Is the form essential, or can it be eliminated? Can several forms be consolidated into one form? If the form is needed, does it need to be revised? Has there been clinician input?

Two critical, often troublesome aspects of results reporting are (1) reporting stat or critical value results and (2) verbally reporting the results of intraoperative consultations and critical surgical pathology diagnoses. One of the most exasperating problems a laboratory faces is being unable to contact the ordering physician when a highly abnormal test result has been detected. This is particularly vexing when specimens arrive from a physician's office or from an outpatient facility. The physician who orders a stat test may not be the admitting physician, and the name of the ordering physician may not appear on the requisition. Any stat reporting system should require the name of the ordering physician and his or her contact number, if different from the admitting physician, to be included on the requisition. Clinicians should be involved in deciding which tests to include on the stat test list and determining reasonable turnaround times for such tests. In addition, some sophisticated computer programs can display previous test results when an abnormal result appears so that known or persistent abnormal results are not called in to the ordering physician unnecessarily.

Although the laboratory technologist is obligated to notify the ordering physician of potentially life-threatening findings, that obligation can be difficult to fulfill.[11] In the hospital, a page can go unanswered, or the office receptionist may fail to put a telephone call through. The ordering physician may be "off call"; the physician "covering" the ordering physician's practice may claim a lack of knowledge regarding the patient and reject responsibility. If the technologist calls the hospital ward after the ordering physician has completed rounds, the nurses or ward clerks, particularly on the short-staffed evening and graveyard shifts, may hesitate to take responsibility. The situation may not be much better in hospitals with residents; residents may be reluctant to accept a critical value result, especially if they are covering a service for a colleague or unknown attending physician.

Many hospitals have implemented a calling hierarchy (often automated), so if the intern cannot be found, the resident is called; if the resident does not respond, the chief resident is called; if the chief resident does not respond, the chief of service is notified. This is cumbersome and builds little in the way of collegial interactions. A more effective approach to reporting inpatient critical values is to give the report to the nurse who is caring for the patient. The nurse knows the patient and knows which physician ordered a specific test, and can relay the critical test result. Most importantly, the nurse can answer the ordering physician's questions about the patient's current condition and immediately implement any changes the physician orders in the patient's medication or procedure on the basis of the test results. However, each institution must decide how the reporting structure for critical values best serves their patients.

Pathologists' reports of diagnoses—not only official telephone reports of intraoperative consultations, but also personal phone calls about malignant, interesting, or problematic diagnoses—must be given special consideration. Pathologists should meet periodically with surgeons to get their input and determine if they are satisfied with the methodologies and formats used to report test results. For example, are the surgeons satisfied with the existing phone, intercom, or televised reporting system, and does the "repeat back" protocol work for them? Which kinds of cases would they like to be called about, and do they find the current reporting hierarchy useful? Similar input should be solicited from oncologists, gastroenterologists, and other major pathology service customer groups. Recently, pathologists have been grappling with the concept of critical test results in anatomic pathology. Silverman et al reported that critical result reporting practices vary among anatomic pathology and surgical pathology directors.[12] However, many institutions have declared that there are no "critical values" in anatomic pathology. Nevertheless, with the Joint Commission's emphasis on critical results, an increasing number of anatomic pathology services are building some type of reporting procedure into their quality-assurance programs.[13] It is useful from both a marketing and patient-care perspective to report important diagnoses not only to the surgeon, but also to the primary care physician who referred the patient to the surgeon.

Describing the "Work" of Laboratory Operations

Laboratory policies and procedures are two types of directives that guide laboratory organization. Policies, the laws and rules of the laboratory, are guides to thinking and decision making in the laboratory. They are the framework within which the strategic plan is implemented and address a variety of issues related to personnel, quality management, safety, education, finance, public relations, and compliance. Policies that apply to the laboratory may reside at the level of hospital administration and/or within the laboratory. In an academic setting, the institution's policies also apply to employees whose duties in the medical school overlap with their clinical care duties. Procedures, the instructions for performing specific tasks, generally reside in the individual sections of a laboratory. Most laboratories maintain procedures that are based on analyte type and instrumentation as well as procedures related to quality management and regulatory affairs. A standard operating procedure format that is used in widespread form in clinical laboratories is available from the Clinical and Laboratory Standards Institute.[14] An example of a procedure delineating the elements of an SOP is provided Appendix 3-1.

Recently, accreditation agencies, including the CAP, CLIA, and the Joint Commission, have emphasized overall document control. Document control is the overall management governing documents to assure that all documents are accurate, reviewed regularly and appropriately, and retired according to protocol. Document control is different from forms control, which refers to the specific development and review of forms. Document control includes four key guidelines to good document management: (1) all procedures, policies, plans, and other documents must be approved by authorized personnel prior to issue; (2) only currently authorized versions of documents are available for active use; (3) documents are periodically reviewed, revised if necessary, and re-approved by authorized personnel; and (4) retired documents and versions of documents are archived and quarantined.[15] Despite the ingrained and long-term use of procedures and document control in clinical laboratories, a survey of 120 laboratories revealed that many of the laboratories did not meet regulatory and accreditation requirements related to document control.[16] Procedures and document control remain very important issues for pathologists and laboratory administrators.

Organizational Charts, Policies, and Procedures

Examples of traditional organizational charts are provided in Chapter 2, "Competencies and Interfaces of the Involved Pathologist." Given the unique nature of the bidirectional professional and administrative hierarchies in the clinical laboratory, several variations on the standard hierarchy chart may apply. Other organizational charts have a more complex, two-dimensional "matrix" pattern that is based on laboratory organization and the input of professional and administrative supervisors.

Both the laboratory medical director and the laboratory manager oversee the core laboratory, the stat laboratory, and the point-of-care testing team. The microbiology, hematology, and chemistry directors may provide specific input depending on the type of test provided. The supervisors of each laboratory determine how personnel and workloads are distributed and the work performed. Thus, a clinical laboratory's approach to management may be more complex than that of many other industries.

An example of an SOP for formatting a procedure (a "procedure for writing procedures") is provided in Appendix 3-1. This example shows the basic elements of an SOP, which include:

- Purpose/Principle
- Scope
- Specimen
- Reagents and Equipment
- Calibration
- Quality Control
- Procedure
- Calculations
- Interpretation and Reporting Results
- Procedure Notes
- Related Procedures
- References
- Supplemental Materials/Addendum
- History Page

Especially important is the history page, which documents the posting of a new procedure before testing begins, the annual review of the procedure, any changes to the procedure, and the retirement of the procedure. The history page also provides a synopsis of document control for that particular procedure and provides a quick overview of its history.

Test Development

There are nine essential steps to test development:
1. Current or send-out test cost analysis
2. Present and future workload
3. Technology assessment
4. Test cost comparison
5. Technology management
6. Information technology management
7. Employee education
8. Test validation
9. "Going live"

Deciding whether to bring a test into a laboratory as compared to sending it out to a reference laboratory requires a full understanding of test development. The first step in test development is to analyze the cost of a billable test. A billable test is defined as a piece of medical information acquired as the result of a procedure (test). A review of Chapter 9, "Financial Management of the Laboratory," shows the details required to fully understand the indirect and direct costs. Typically, the higher the test complexity, the higher the cost per test and the higher the revenue required to recover individual test costs. Before considering bringing a new test into the laboratory, a preliminary test cost analysis should be performed for any current testing or send-out testing.

As a second step in test development, the present work volume and the anticipated workload in 3 to 5 years should be evaluated. As part of this step, any anticipated changes in the institution's capacity or facilities, or changes in specialty clinical services and patient mix should be part of the analysis. Are increased outpatient services anticipated? Will the medical staff profile change, altering test requirements? For example, if the laboratory chooses to enhance its oncology coverage, a unique set of laboratory services may be added to the test menu.

A third step in test development is technology assessment. Laboratories may be leading-edge or competitive-edge laboratories. A leading-edge laboratory has within its mission a goal to investigate and implement new technologies. Most laboratories will instead choose a mid-level competitive position in choosing technology as compared to the few leading-edge laboratories. In this position, resources are carefully evaluated, and proven effectiveness, increased quality, and improved throughput are the basis for the technology decision. A component of the technology assessment may also reflect historical experience. For example, so-called "wet" versus "dry" technology in clinical chemistry may be a historic feature of the

laboratory service. The required support for the selected technology has evolved over the years, making it easier to stay with one versus the other on a facilities basis.

Once several vendors have been selected through the RFI (request for information) and RFP (request for proposal) process described in Chapter 5, "Equipment, Supplies, and Space," a full test cost comparison should be performed. In addition, this step should include any facilities issues (instrument size, power requirements, cooling requirements, electrical needs, etc). All such requirements should be fully and impartially vetted to assure the best match of technology to space. In some circumstances, the institutional purchasing department may support this step and assist in providing a graded analysis of the vendors.

The next step is to fully review the test (technology) management. This includes any proposed maintenance contracts, emergency technical and maintenance service, and the cost of employee time in providing on-site maintenance checks. Also, the management review should determine whether duplicate instrumentation is required to support a high-volume or critical test. Duplicate instrumentation may considerably alter the test development analysis by increasing costs.

A critical test development step is the assessment of test and instrument interfaces with the existing LIS. This step is described in detail in Chapter 6, "Management of Pathology Information Systems." The contract should define who provides and pays for the interface and the information technology support.

In some circumstances, a trial instrument is provided by a vendor for comparison to current technology or for research purposes. This provides an excellent "hands-on" opportunity for the laboratory to evaluate the fit of the instrumentation into the laboratory workflow. Regardless, once a new test or instrument has been selected, the next very important step is to assess the vendor support for employee education and in-service. Most instrumentation vendors are familiar with the educational needs of a laboratory when new instrumentation is introduced. In some cases, on-site in-service is provided. Under other circumstances, off-site training will be offered. Sometimes a vendor will train a key or lead technologist, and that technologist will train others within the laboratory. This is often referred to as a "train-the-trainer" model.

In consultation with the clinical and technical consultant and technical supervisor, a validation plan will then be drafted to include all the elements of test validation as required by CLIA 2003 (see Chapter 12, "Laboratory Laws and Regulations"). The validation plan may include vendor input but should primarily originate with the clinical laboratory. Validation should additionally include validation of the information technology associated with the test and instrumentation. After final validation, a "go live" date should be selected. An institution or laboratory may choose, for example, a low-volume day or time interval as a best time to bring up a new test.

Point-of-Care and Ancillary Testing

Point-of-care testing is becoming increasingly widespread in both scope and volume and thus presents an ever-increasing administrative challenge to the central laboratory. Point-of-care testing can also create management issues in other sections of the hospital. For example: How does one bill for testing that was not done by laboratory personnel but was performed using laboratory equipment and with quality assurance provided by the clinical laboratory? Point-of-care testing has formally existed since CLIA '88 and began to expand exponentially on a global basis thereafter.

As stipulated by the US Food and Drug Administration, waived tests are tests requiring no additional expertise to perform. The number of waived tests by category has increased from 8 in 1988 to more than 80 today.[17] The Food and Drug Administration now lists more than 1600 individual waived tests, and it is estimated that waived tests are performed in physician offices more than 520 million times annually.[18] The worldwide incidence of waived testing is rapidly expanding, with a 12% to 15% annual growth rate.[17]

Guidelines for ancillary and point-of-care testing include the following[19-21]:

- There should be a medical, patient care, or turnaround time rationale that justifies performing the test outside the main laboratory.
- The test method must be simple enough that non-laboratory (ie, ward) personnel can perform the test consistently.
- The test methodology and instrumentation must be selected and approved by the laboratory.
- Laboratory personnel are responsible for training and certifying non-laboratory personnel.

- Only trained and certified non-laboratory personnel are to perform the testing.
- The laboratory is responsible for the preventive maintenance of instruments.
- Collecting quality control data and performing proficiency testing is the responsibility of the non-laboratory personnel performing the test.
- The laboratory is responsible for monitoring and reviewing quality control and proficiency test data and providing feedback to the non-laboratory personnel.

One example of effective point-of-care testing is glucose testing. In many inpatient settings, glucose testing is now widely available and managed through an electronic interface with the LIS. Glucose test results appear in the electronic laboratory record if the electronic laboratory record is properly interfaced with the HIS and electronic medical record. Glucose testing is a valuable test in the outpatient setting, allowing physicians to adjust drug therapy and consult effectively with their patients.[18] Other types of point-of-care testing support emergency room and operating room services. Some point-of-care testing instruments are multi-analyte models that use whole blood for electrolyte and glucose analysis or an even wider panel of tests. In addition, given the increasing number of patients on anticoagulant therapy, point-of-care PT/INR testing has gained traction in warfarin clinics.

In large institutions, point-of-care testing is commonly managed through a point-of-care testing committee that includes some of the personnel shown in Figure 3-2.

SOPs for point-of-care tests must be available to all users, including nurses at inpatient and outpatient locations. Laboratory representatives should include a laboratory supervisor and, if interfaced systems are involved, an information technology consultant. Clinical representatives should include physicians and nursing staff, especially from major users such as the diabetes service and intensive care units.[18]

The challenge in point-of-care testing is to provide good clinical outcomes at the bedside. The results of good clinical outcomes may seem obvious. In fact, actual value probably occurs when the physician can quickly interact with a patient in the clinic or at the bedside. Additional studies proving the clinical value of clinical outcomes for point-of-care testing must be performed to fully address whether good clinical outcomes can be demonstrated.

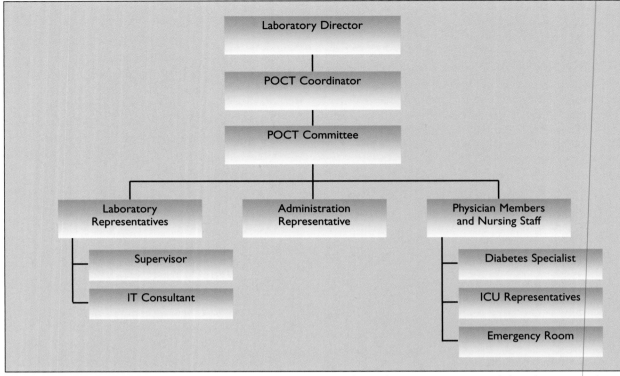

Figure 3-2. Point-of-Care Testing (POCT) Committee Organizational Chart. A generic organizational chart for a point-of-care testing committee showing important membership categories.

Signs and Symptoms of Poor Laboratory Operations

The operation of the laboratory needs to be assessed on an ongoing basis. Ongoing assessment, the *sine qua non* of operational success, needs to be incorporated into the monthly laboratory staff meeting and should include reviews of marketing, finance, space, equipment, human resources, productivity, and efficiency, as well as a nod toward the bottom line (ie, achievement of goals). Certain signs and symptoms that should alert laboratory management to operational problems may include the following[22]:

- Recurrent overload crises
- Prolonged turnaround times
- Supervisors unable to handle their sections
- Excess overtime
- Skilled workers doing menial tasks
- Supervisors doing bench work
- Recurrent scheduling or staffing problems
- Excess employee turnover
- Too many phone calls
- Too many stat test requests
- Complaints
- Too many forms
- Too many notices or rules posted in the laboratory
- Excess traffic, noise, or talking
- Poor lighting, ventilation, and temperature control
- Overcrowded laboratories
- Hallways crowded with instruments or supplies
- Dirty or messy labs, hallways, and staircases
- Frequent equipment failure
- Frequent supply problems
- Decreasing productivity
  - Total Tests/FTE or Billable Tests/FTE or WLU/FTE or Billable Tests/Total Labor Expenses
- Decreasing efficiency
  - Total Revenue/Test or /Admission or /Month
  - Total Expense/Test or/Admission or /Month
- Excessive or recurrent deficiencies on CAP inspections
- Recurrent failures in proficiency testing programs

	Information
4	The acceptable collection containers (eg, coagulant-containing containers, sterile containers).
5	The stability of the specimen and requirements for storage.
6	The criteria for an unacceptable specimen and the action to be taken by the laboratory. Identify physical characteristics of the specimen that may compromise the test results (eg, hemolysis, lipemia, presence of serum separator).
7	Identify drugs that may interfere with test results.

5.2 Handling Considerations. Handling conditions should be specified.
- List special timing considerations.
- List transport or storage conditions.
- List special precautions that should be taken with potentially infectious specimens.

6. Reagents and Equipment

6.1 Materials. List reagents, supplies, forms, records, and equipment, if applicable.

	Information
1	The name and chemical formula or active ingredients if possible.
2	The acceptable grade of reagent, if critical to the performance of the test.
3	A statement in **bold type** of any extraordinary health or safety information associated with the reagent, supplies, equipment, or material used in the procedure; the general category or class of hazard (eg, "toxic," "corrosive," "carcinogenic," "explosive," "biohazard," "radiation").
4	The usual source supply company for reagent kits, prepared reagents, and/or media.
5	The supplies and equipment used at a standard work station may be listed on one page in the procedure manual and referred to in each SOP, but reagents should be listed in each SOP.

6.2 Preparation. Include the following information, if applicable.

	Information
1	The directions for preparing each medium or reagent that is produced in the laboratory.
2	Any instructions for special cleaning or handling of glassware and volumetric or other equipment.
3	The degree of accuracy required for measuring reagents.
4	The quality of glassware and volumetric equipment required to meet performance requirements.

6.3 Performance Parameters
Parameters used to determine acceptable reagent performance should be defined.

6.4 Storage Requirements

Storage requirements, including the appropriate container, temperature, and stability (shelf life) of the specimen, should be defined.

6.5 Labeling. Specify the following information.

	Information
1	Substance (contents), including the concentration or titer if applicable.
2	Lot number, if required by the manufacturer to ensure the use of consistent lot numbers of reagents within the performance of a specific test.
3	Preparation date.
4	Expiration date.
5	Storage instructions.

7. Calibration

- Include preparation of standards and calibration for equipment in this section, if appropriate.
- Specify acceptable tolerances and what to do when tolerances are not met.

8. Quality Control. Describe the Quality Control system.

	Information
1	Identify the control materials to be used.
2	Give instructions for preparing and handling control materials.
3	State the frequency with which control materials are to be run.
4	Describe how tolerance limits for controls are to be established.
5	State the corrective actions to be taken when tolerance limits are exceeded.
6	If no controls are available, list alternatives.

9. Details of Procedure. Include the following information.

	Information
1	Detailed, step-by-step instructions for performing the procedure. • Include sufficient detail to make the procedure easy to follow.
2	Use the present imperative verb tense. Examples: • *Obtain* units for discard. • *Record* unit numbers on discard log. • *Ensure* all components are present.

Information	
3	Leave out explanations or rationale. • This information may be included in the Procedure Notes section.
4	Include specific requirements such as: • Labeling of tubes • Examples of report forms • Speed or centrifugal time • Description of work flow • Length of time for centrifugation • Labels • Temperature • Whether microscopic examination is required
5	If necessary, include computer screen printouts for clarity.

6	Include hazards and specify the course of action for handling and disposing of hazardous materials.
	• Specify protective clothing and safety equipment.
	• Include the type of spill kit or disposal method.
	• Reference the Department of Pathology and Laboratory Medicine safety manual for general procedures.
	• The author may set health and safety instructions in a boxed or underlined area. Example:
	
	    CAUTION: HAZARDOUS MATERIAL
	    Wear safety glasses when using this reagent.

10. Calculations

Step	Action
1	Include a brief description of any calculations applicable to the procedure.
2	Give step-by-step instructions.
3	Provide the equation in its basic form and show the steps involved in the equation so the process can be followed logically.
4	Provide an example.

11. Reporting and Interpreting Results

Step	Action
1	Include an explanation for procedures that require interpretation. (This section is not necessary for administrative procedures in which test results are not generated.)
2	Reference ranges should be stated, if applicable.
3	Identify procedures for reporting abnormal or unexpected results to the physician.
4	Provide guidelines for an acceptable reporting format, applicable units, and preferred terminology.
5	Clearly define the interpretation and acceptability of results.

12. Procedure Notes

Step	Action
1	Information concerning the procedure that is too voluminous to include in the Principle or other area of the procedure may be included in the Procedure Notes section.
2	Explain the reason for special precautions or the reason this additional information may be necessary.
3	List the possible sources of error in the performance of this procedure.
4	Include helpful hints as well as pitfalls or precautions.
5	Describe acceptable alternative procedures. List expected differences when an alternative procedure is used.
6	Include a statement describing the clinical situations that may influence the performance validity of the test results.
7	Elaborate on clinical applications; indicate how the test result relates to other tests performed on the sample.
8	State the known interfering substances. • Chemical interferences: substances that cause sources of error in the analytical system (ie, preservatives or drugs). • In vivo interferences: usually drugs that cause abnormally high or low results that do not reflect the true physiological state.

13. References

Step	Action
1	References are required for technical procedures but may not be relevant for administrative or clerical procedures.
2	Obtain the following from the manufacturer's product literature: • Manufacturer name/location • Title of literature • Publication code number or lot number • Revision date
3	Literature references. • Use a style acceptable for scientific publications.
4	Textbook references. List: • Author(s) • Title and edition number • Publisher and place of publication • Year • Page(s)

Step	Action
5	General publication reference information. List: • Author(s) • Title • Publication identification number • Year
6	Written personal communication.
7	Research, including validation methods.
8	Other works deemed to be authoritative.

14. Supplemental Materials/Addendum

Certain materials extracted from the procedure may be used at the technical workbench and may include flow diagrams and manufacturer's product literature. Supplemental materials are not a substitute for the procedure. Author-owned materials (eg, forms, flow diagrams) must reference the procedure by number and effective date.

14.1 Manufacturer Product Literature

Step	Action
1	Assure that literature is current and applicable to kits or reagents in use. • Lot numbers may be referenced in the literature when product changes result in a change in procedure.
2	Append the actual copy to be used in proper page sequence.
3	Mark clearly those parts that apply to the method followed by the laboratory.
4	Identify ancillary information.
5	Document any revisions (manufacturer) or modifications (laboratory). • If a manufacturer's protocol is modified, update as appropriate in the formal procedure. • If a modification is made by the laboratory apart from the manufacturer's directions, justification for this modification must be documented. • Validation must support this change and must be reviewed and approved by the compliance officer and medical director.

14.2 Flow Diagrams

Step	Action
1	Flow diagrams may be helpful in demonstrating work patterns. Computer screens could be used as illustrations in this section.
2	When possible, make flow diagrams with waterproof material, because these items are normally posted in open working areas of the laboratory.
3	If the flow diagram is an element of the procedure, it must be included as part of the procedure.

14.3 Forms

Step	Action
1	List any forms that are part of the procedure in the Supplemental Materials/Addendum.
2	All forms must be associated with a procedure (ie, identified with the SOP number).

15. SOP History

15.1 General Information

Step	Action
1	The last page included with each SOP is the SOP history page, which is used to document pertinent information about the procedure.
2	This SOP history page must be present with the master copy of the procedure.
3	This page documents the change control of the SOP.

15.2 Generating an SOP History Page

Step	Action
1	A new SOP history page should be generated for new SOPs or SOPs that have had a significant change in title. *Note:* All copies of the procedure "history" are retained with the procedure until the SOP is permanently retired. At the time of retirement, the SOP history pages should be archived with the retired procedure. The reason for retirement should be noted at the bottom of the SOP history page.
2	Information to be included on the SOP history page: • SOP number • SOP title • SOP author • Manual in which master copy of this SOP is located • Distribution to which manual(s) • Approval by supervisor/specialist and the medical director
3	The effective date of SOPs will change with each revision. This will identify when the change became effective.
4	Distribution of copies of the SOPs: • If copies of the master SOP will be used in other locations, identify the primary functional area and the areas where additional copies are located. • It is the responsibility of the author to distribute authorized copies of an SOP at the time of any revision and to notify the recipients of any changes that have been made.

RELATED PROCEDURES

SOP #	Procedure Name
QM 610	Standard Operating Procedure Policies
QM 620	Review and Implementation of SOPs
QM 625	Revising or Archiving an Existing SOP
QM 630	Exceptions to SOPs

Reference

Laboratory Documents: Development and Control. Approved Guideline. 5th Ed. Wayne, PA: Clinical and Laboratory Standards Institute; 2006. Document GP2-A5.

Addenda

- Example of an Acceptable Procedure Format
- SOP History Page

Example of an Acceptable Procedure Format

Department of Pathology and Laboratory Medicine Procedure ####
Los Angeles, California 00000   Effective Date: mm/dd/yy

Page 1 of #

TITLE

PURPOSE/PRINCIPLE

SCOPE

SPECIMEN

REAGENTS AND EQUIPMENT

CALIBRATION

QUALITY CONTROL

PROCEDURE

CALCULATIONS

INTERPRETATION AND REPORTING RESULTS

PROCEDURE NOTES

RELATED PROCEDURES

REFERENCES

SUPPLEMENTAL MATERIALS/ADDENDUM

SOP HISTORY PAGE

SOP History Page

SOP HISTORY PAGE
Department of Pathology and Laboratory Medicine

SOP Number: SOP Title:

Written By:

Manual in which Master Copy of this SOP is located:
Distribution:
Supersedes Procedure:

SOP CHANGE CONTROL

Approvals				Action	Effective Date	
Mgmt	Date	**Director**	Date		**SOP**	**Form**

Date Archived: _____
Reason: _____ Initials:_____

CHAPTER 4

Personnel Management

Elizabeth A. Wagar, MD
Richard E. Horowitz, MD

Contents

Human Resources

Creating jobs and job descriptions, hiring employees, managing the rules and standards for employees in a given work environment, evaluating employee performance, and facilitating promotions and terminations are all within the scope of human resources. In some respects, the term *human resources* seems to be a somewhat cold and impersonal term for what is, in fact, a very sensitive and occasionally problematic activity that closely touches the daily lives of an institution's employees. The primary goals of human resources are to work with employees, motivate them, and allow them to contribute, develop, and achieve.

Given the complex rules and regulations of the work environment and the specialized knowledge and experience required to manage employment issues, most health care institutions and independent laboratories have a human resources department that assists laboratory management in performing the functions of job development and performance evaluation, managing work rules, and facilitating promotions and terminations. In a broader sense, however, laboratory personnel management requires involvement at all levels of management, from the institution's chief executive officer to the laboratory's section supervisor. Hospital administration is responsible for addressing overall strategic planning, budgeting, and compensation issues. The human resources department develops personnel policies (including job classifications), publishes the employee handbook (see Appendix 4-3), manages employee recruitment, and assists in the selection and, when needed, termination of employees. The pathologist or laboratory director, together with the laboratory manager or chief technologist, is responsible for defining the job, establishing performance standards, selecting candidates, establishing a reward system, and ensuring employee retention and satisfaction. The section supervisors may help develop performance standards; provide new employee orientation; assess competencies; provide training, development, and feedback; and complete annual performance evaluations.

Rights and Responsibilities of Management

Management has certain rights to ensure that employees work effectively and follow rules and regulations. These rights include:

- Organizing or reorganizing work
- Defining jobs with job descriptions
- Selecting employees to fill job vacancies
- Developing quality and performance standards
- Disciplining or terminating employees for poor performance
- Rewarding strong performance
- Eliminating unnecessary jobs
- Establishing or changing work schedules

Management also has certain responsibilities to ensure that employees have the opportunity to succeed. These responsibilities include:

- Selecting the candidate best qualified to perform the job without regard for age, gender, race, ethnicity, or national origin
- Providing new employee orientation to the job
- Assessing competencies of new and existing staff on an annual basis (a Joint Commission requirement)
- Providing training, development, and opportunities for employees to attain maximum competency (eg, on-the-job training)
- Providing ongoing constructive feedback (positive or negative) regarding employee performance
- Providing annual criteria-based performance evaluations
- Communicating the organization's mission, goals, projects, and events to employees

Human resources management can employ some generic "good practices"—some of which might simply be perceived as "good manners"—to most employees. However, work cultures vary considerably among health care institutions, and the correct ways to interact with employees should always be considered. One good practice is to openly solicit ideas, concerns, and issues from the staff. This can be done in regularly scheduled staff meetings for each shift or less formally when rounding in the laboratory. For example, while walking through the laboratory, the laboratory director may hear one employee say that it seems uncomfortably hot in one area. The laboratory director may also notice that it seems unusually warm around a rather large piece of automated equipment. After investigation, it may be determined that better ventilation and air conditioning is needed in that particular area of the laboratory.[1-3]

In terms of relationships, it is good practice to apply policies, work rules, and human resources practices uniformly and equally to all employees. Also, while pathologists and laboratory directors should remain flexible under unusual circumstances, they should only make exceptions that are defensible. Pathologists often enter into an existing human resources organization without knowing many of the details related to work rules and policies. If a given circumstance is not carefully considered, pathologists can find themselves in an awkward position. For example, a pathologist might support a technologist who complains about an evening or graveyard shift assignment. But before taking a position, the pathologist should fully investigate the operation of this human resource process and the policies by which it is governed.

Pathologists should also respect employees' privacy and confidentiality, and demonstrate genuine caring and empathy. Work is a conundrum; employees juggle how much of their personal lives interface with their work lives, and yet life events and work have major effects on each other. In Western culture, except for defined opportunities such as holiday parties, there is relatively little interface between work and personal life. Some human resources policies, for example, family and medical leave, may intersect with employees' personal lives. However, if employees share personal life issues at work, pathologists should remember the two C's—confidentiality and caring—and govern their behavior appropriately.

Government Regulations

Human resources departments are governed by a number of federal and state regulations. This section focuses on federal regulations. However, many states have their own statutes related to employment, which may be more definitive and legally binding. Some of the federal statutes and regulations that impact laboratories are listed in the chronological order of their passage in Table 4-1.

Only the more common regulations are provided in this section. Certain geographical locations may require a review of other areas of employment law; for example, immigration law may be more relevant to employment practices in some states. However, the several core laws and regulations described in this section likely account for why many personnel management activities are performed in prescribed ways. Becoming well-versed in these procedures can help pathologists protect themselves from making errors while navigating complex layers of employment legislation.

National Labor Relations Act

Congress enacted the National Labor Relations Act (NLRA) in 1935 to protect the rights of employers and employees, encourage collective bargaining in union shops, and curtail certain private-sector labor and management practices. After a generation of tumultuous relationships between unions and manufacturers, the NLRA provided stability to employment areas involving labor unions. The law provides protection for employees who wish to organize and bargain collectively, and encourages negotiation practices that are fundamental to the amicable resolution of industrial disputes that arise regarding wages, hours, and other working conditions. The intent of the NLRA is to provide equality of bargaining power between employers and employees.

Most of the NLRA's provisions apply to employee groups initiating efforts to organize as a union and union activities within work environments. Several major unions may organize laboratory staff. If an institution is a "union shop" (ie, under a union contract), pathologists must have an awareness of the rights held within the union contract. One such right may be the right of an employee who files a discrimination complaint to have union representation present during the human resources hearing. Employers are restricted from interfering with certain labor organizational and election activities. The union contract defines employees' right to strike as well as the jurisdiction of the courts related to socioeconomically necessary industries. Pathologists who work in institutions with unions should be knowledgeable about union contracts and understand what can and cannot be said and done relative to union activities. Human resources can provide advice regarding any labor-contract–related questions.

Fair Labor Standards Act

In 1938, Congress passed the Fair Labor Standards Act (FLSA), which defines the minimum wage, federal overtime, and other requirements related to

Table 4-1. Human Resources Legislation and Regulation

1935	National Labor Relations Act (NLRA)
1938	Fair Labor Standards Act (FLSA)
1963	Equal Pay Act
1964	Civil Rights Act, Title VII
1965	Equal Employment Opportunity, Executive Order 11246
1967	Age Discrimination in Employment Act (ADEA)
1970/1991	Occupational Safety and Health Act (OSHA)
1990	Americans with Disabilities Act (ADA)
1990	Immigration Reform and Control Act (IRCA)
1991	Civil Rights Act
1993	Family and Medical Leave Act (FMLA)
1994	Uniformed Services Employment and Re-employment Rights Act

From Harmening DM. *Laboratory Management. Principles and Processes.* 2nd ed. St. Petersburg, FL: FA Davis Co; 2007.

employee salaries and wages as well as the terms *exempt employee* and *nonexempt employee*. Exempt employees are typically employees in administrative, executive, or professional positions who receive salaries instead of hourly wages. Nonexempt employees receive hourly wages. The FLSA also makes provisions for overtime hourly pay; for example, nonexempt employees receive wages at the rate of 1.5 times the employees' regular hourly pay rate each hour over 40 hours in 1 work week. However, the FLSA includes a special provision for an 80-hour workweek for health care workers. The provisions of the FLSA are quite complex, and each FLSA-related question may require specific investigation by the human resources department. Also, some states may have additional statutes that further define overtime wages, exempt status, and nonexempt status. For example, California law provides a stricter definition of "exempt" that implies that only employees with administrative, executive, or professional job titles are exempt, while employees who perform labor as well as administrative duties are not. Significant fines can be imposed for violating the FLSA.

Equal Pay Act

The Equal Pay Act (EPA) is actually part of the FLSA and is enforced through the Equal Employment Opportunity Commission. The EPA prohibits wage discrimination between men and women who are performing similar work under similar working conditions. The difficult part of any gender-based wage discrimination case is to establish what constitutes "similar work" and "similar conditions." Equal pay discrimination cases can move forward easily if a difference in pay exists between a man and a woman who have the same job title, have the same job description, have the same responsibilities, and work under the same conditions (eg, during the same shift at the same laboratory). Cases are not restricted by gender; a man can be the plaintiff in an equal pay discrimination lawsuit. However, if the titles and job descriptions (see "The Job and the Job Description," below) are "similar but different," the case may become complicated. Human resources representatives should be consulted if any questions regarding equal pay cases arise.

Civil Rights Act, Title VII

Title VII of the Civil Rights Act prohibits discrimination based on race, color, creed, religion, national origin, or sex. The plaintiff is responsible for the burden of proof in Title VII discrimination cases. To move forward with a discrimination complaint, the plaintiff must be a member of a protected class. A protected class is a personal characteristic for which someone cannot be targeted for discrimination or harassment. Different types of employment actions can be considered; these include hiring, firing, demoting, or promoting. An employer can be held responsible for discrimination based on an employment action. An employment action may be discriminatory if the adverse action was based on unlawful discriminatory intent or if the reason for the action provided to the plaintiff was untrue, in which case the employer's motive may be inferred as unlawful discrimination. Discrimination law is a complex area of law and relies heavily on "bona fide occupational qualifications." An employer may limit employment if an employee or applicant lacks the actual qualifications required for performing a job. However, if a baccalaureate degree is not actually required to perform a job, it may not be a bona fide occupational qualification requirement.

Executive Order No. 11246

Executive Order No. 11246 is more commonly known as affirmative action. There are several misconceptions regarding this order. For example, affirmative action does not require employers to hire certain numbers or percentages of people of a

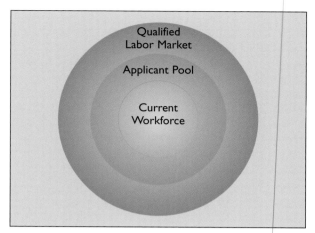

Figure 4-1. Affirmative Action Plan: Areas of Assessment. An affirmative action plan should include information about races and genders in the qualified labor market, the applicant pool, and the current workforce.

protected class. Instead, affirmative action stipulates that qualified candidates will be sought from a wide pool of potential applicants during the hiring process. Thus, the listing of job opportunities should be distributed in such a way as to be representative of the qualified applicant pool. The US Department of Labor or state labor representatives can advise employers on how wide a distribution may be required. Advertisements for employment should indicate that the employer is an equal opportunity employer.

Employers receiving federal funding (ie, federal grants) are obligated to create and maintain an affirmative action plan. As part of the plan, employers maintain the files of all job applicants that include information on the applicants' races, genders, and the positions for which they applied. In 2004, a category for e-applicants (electronic web-based applicants) was also recognized. Typically, the human resources department maintains an internal computerized tracking system for this information. Employers should keep similarly tracked records of interviewed candidates by race and/or gender. Employers who do not receive federal funding can voluntarily create affirmative action plans. Proactively soliciting "diversity candidates" has been a controversial area of law in recent years, however. A diagram of the affirmative action areas of assessment is shown in Figure 4-1.

Americans with Disabilities Act

The Americans with Disabilities Act (ADA) prohibits discrimination based on disability. The ADA defines a disability as any physical or mental condition that substantially limits major life activities such as walking, talking, maintaining active employment, and practicing daily hygiene. The ADA requires employers to provide a qualified candidate or employee, as determined by job description and responsibilities, with reasonable accommodations, for example, providing ramps, larger bathroom facilities, and wheelchair-accessible doors.

Family and Medical Leave Act

The Family and Medical Leave Act (FMLA) provides eligible employees with up to 12 weeks of paid or unpaid leave to address their own serious health conditions; care for a seriously ill or impaired spouse, child, or parent; or care for a newborn or newly adopted child. The FMLA applies to private companies that employ 50 or more employees each working day for 20 calendar weeks and all public agencies (eg, schools, government agencies) regardless of the number of employees. Employees must work for the employer for a specified period of time to be eligible for the benefits provided by the FMLA. Some states may have additional regulations related to the FMLA. Because the interpretation of the FMLA can lead to many questions, it is always wise to consult with human resources regarding any FMLA-related issues.

Unions and Civil Service

The National Labor Relations Act established the primary law governing the formation of unions and their relationships with employers.[4] In 2004, unions represented only 7.9% of the private-sector workforce, down from 35% to 40% in the 1950s. This is still a sizeable workforce, estimated at more than 12 million employees.[4] The NLRA enables employees to participate in concerted activity, including union activity, without employer and/or union interference, restraint, or coercion. If a private-sector employer is regulated by federal law (a designation based on the employer's gross volume of business in annual sales), the NLRA preempts any state legislation regarding union–employee relationships. Under the NLRA, employees have the right to form, join, support, and assist unions; choose unions to represent them in labor negotiations; and engage in "group conduct."

The NLRA also gives employees the right to refuse to engage in union activities. Some types of employment are excluded from the union definition of an "employee." Supervisors and managers are typically excluded from this definition because they engage in management actions, including hiring and firing employees and providing advice regarding such activities.

In some states, unions are permitted in government agencies. In other states, state employees are not allowed to unionize. If the employees of state institutions such as public universities are permitted to unionize, the union may be a factor in negotiating salaries and benefits for clinical laboratory employees. Employees have the right to decide if they wish to have union representation in such negotiations.

Employers and employees have the right to campaign for or against union representation. However, employees ultimately choose whether they wish to be represented by a union. Most employers now take a stance of neutrality in the course of a union campaign. During a campaign, employees have the right to distribute information and hold meetings to discuss unionization. A secret ballot election can be initiated if at least 30% of employees express interest in unionization by signing authorization cards. If a particular union wins an election, it does not necessarily represent every employee in the institution. Thus, clerical workers may not be included in a union that represents laboratory technologists. It is important to understand how different unions represent different types of employees.

Union members have the right to withhold work, or strike, under certain circumstances. Typically, a union contract will have a "no strike" clause stipulating that union members will not strike while the contract is in effect. However, when a contract expires, a strike is a legal "collective action." If a strike is initiated at an institution that performs services for the public welfare, such as a hospital, the employer can request a court-ordered injunction against the strike. Employers also have the right to hire replacement employees during a strike. However, difficult scenarios can arise if a picket line forms. The human resources department should be consulted regarding questions about proper conduct during a strike. Pathologists and laboratory management should use good judgment when encountering union activities and refrain from making comments or directives related to employee union actions.

Union contracts also affect the actions of individual employees. A contract may require that employers show "just cause" for counseling or disciplining personnel and define the procedures by which counseling and discipline will occur. Just cause requires the employer to do the following:

- Notify the employee that they may be disciplined.

- Explain the reason for the disciplinary action (eg, repeated tardiness).

- Undertake a fair, impartial, and comprehensive investigation, indicating a work rule has been violated.

- Apply the disciplinary action uniformly to all employees of the same category.

- Assure that the discipline is proportionate to the violation involved.

Typically, union employees have the right to file grievances against employers regarding a work action. For example, one laboratory technologist may file a grievance if he believes that he is doing the same work as another, higher-paid technologist and believes they are not being treated fairly at work. Legal and/or union representatives for the employee and representatives from the employer's human resources department evaluate the grievance and, if mediation between an employee and supervisor is not successful, bring the grievance to arbitration to determine an outcome for the grievance. The arbitrator is a designated neutral third party. The entire grievance–arbitration process may be avoided if proper evaluation occurs in the early stages of review.

Civil service laws, which are meant to protect government employees from discriminatory work practices, are premised on the concept of just cause to terminate. Government employees are allowed to appeal a discharge action through civil service commissions and thus undergo a termination action review process that is somewhat similar to that of union employees. Federal regulations governing governmental employment activities operate under the Federal Labor Relations Act. Some differences from typical union activity may exist, however. For example, the categories covered by civil service laws may be broader than those of unions. The Federal Labor Relations Act prohibits government employees from bargaining for wages; it instead requires employees to negotiate for conditions of employment or circumstances of the work environment. Finally, many governmental entities have "no strike" clauses to protect the public welfare from labor actions. Pathologists in county or state institutions, such as a county hospital, may encounter civil service rules. Pathologists should know which employees in the clinical laboratory are covered by civil service rules.

The Job and the Job Description

The American Society for Clinical Pathology Board of Certification recognizes the following laboratory job categories and positions:

Technician ASCP Certification
Phlebotomy Technician (PBT)
Histotechnician (HT)
Medical Laboratory Technician (MLT)
Donor Phlebotomy Technician (DPT)

Technologist ASCP Certification
Technologist in Blood Banking (BB)
Technologist in Chemistry (C)
Technologist in Cytogenetics (CG)
Cytotechnologist (CT)
Technologist in Hematology (H)
Histotechnologist (HTL)
Medical Laboratory Scientist (MLS)
Technologist in Microbiology (M)
Technologist in Molecular Biology (MB)

Specialist ASCP Certification
Specialist in Blood Banking (SBB)
Specialist in Chemistry (SC)
Specialist in Cytotechnology (SCT)
Specialist in Hematology (SH)
Specialist in Laboratory Safety (SLS)
Specialist in Microbiology (SM)
Pathologists' Assistant (PA)

Diplomate ASCP Certification
Diplomate in Laboratory Management (DLM)

International ASCPi Certification
International Medical Technologist (MT)
Tecnólogo Médico Internacional en Español (MT)
International Medical Laboratory Technician (MLT)
International Phlebotomy Technician (PBT)
International Technologist in Molecular Biology (MB)
International Technologist in Gynecologic Cytology (CTgyn)

Qualifications
Cytometry
Immunohistochemistry
Laboratory Informatics
Laboratory Operations (International)

Certification requirements for medical technologists and laboratory assistants vary from state to state. For medical technologists (clinical laboratory sciences), certification typically requires a bachelor's degree, specific courses, and a 1-year internship. Schools that award medical technologist certification are typically accredited by the National Accrediting Agency for Clinical Lab-

Job Title: Medical Technologist   **Classification:** Level II   **Exempt Status:** Nonexempt

Education / Experience: Baccalaureate degree in biologic science, chemistry, medical technology, or related science. ASCP Board of Certification certification as a Medical Technologist or categorical certification. Two years of relevant clinical experience.

Knowledge: Knowledge regarding performance of routine and complex laboratory tests on a variety of instruments including trouble-shooting. Knowledge regarding quality control and assurance, proficiency testing, and reagent and equipment maintenance. Ability to develop and maintain policies and procedures.

Duties: Performs moderate and high complexity testing using approved procedures and quality protocols. Reviews and verifies results, reviewing specimen integrity, clinical history, delta checks. Takes corrective actions as necessary. Reviews new and existing procedures. Operates, calibrates, repairs, and maintains laboratory equipment and reagents. Performs phlebotomy (venipuncture and capillary). Maintains knowledge of applicable regulations (federal, state, and local) and accreditation requirements. Participates in performance improvement. Maintains knowledge/skills and participates in a minimum of 12 hours of continuing education. Assists in orientation and training of new staff and trainees. Performs other related duties as required.

Interactions: Interacts with the Supervisor of the laboratory section. Also interacts with physicians, nurses, and other laboratory staff.

Safety: Frequent sitting/standing. Walking and bending. Occasional lifting 25 lbs for 10 ft. Repetitive hand motions and frequent hand washing. Possible handling of hazardous chemicals and sharps. Biohazardous handling of patient specimens. Protective gear use (face shields, gloves, fluid-resistant coats).

Reporting: Reports to the Supervisor of the laboratory section as direct report. Does not direct or supervise laboratory activities.

Approvals:

Employee Signature/Date: Supervisor Signature/Date: Human Resources/Date:

Figure 4-2. Sample Job Description.

oratory Scientists. Many hospitals participate in the internship step of medical technologists' training, which provides hospitals an opportunity to evaluate trainees for future positions. Medical laboratory technician (MLT) certification typically requires an associate's degree. MLTs are often hired to perform moderate-complexity testing. In some states, MLTs do not have to meet specific requirements, and a bachelor's degree in the life sciences may be sufficient.

Other laboratory jobs include administrative assistants, pathology transcribers, and couriers or drivers. In some settings, there may also be job descriptions or position charters for the higher-level professionals in the laboratory, including pathologists, doctoral scientists, and research scientists.

The job description is probably the single most important document in human resources, and writing a good job description is one of the greatest challenges laboratory management faces. The job description justifies the need for the position, drives the recruiting process, and is used during employment interviews to determine whether candidates are suitable for specific positions. The

job description also tells new employees what is expected of them; it is used to evaluate employees' performance and determine whether merit pay, promotion, or termination is warranted. The job description is the culmination of an accurate assessment of work needs aligned with the prevalent human resources job categories.[5-7]

A job description should include the following seven sections. A sample job description is shown in Figure 4-2.

Job Title. A job title is usually one of the categories listed above. The precise name may be different in some situations, but the job will be the same; for example, a clinical laboratory scientist (CLS) may also be called a medical technologist or a laboratory technologist. Within each category, there may be levels indicating increasing proficiency. Thus, a CLS I is the entry level position, while a CLS IV is the highest-level position. Each job category may also include rankings. For example, there could be a CLS for a bench technologist or a Supervising CLS for a section supervisor, and within each of these ranking there would be additional levels, so that a CLS Supervisor I could be in charge of a small laboratory section, while a CLS Supervisor III could supervise several laboratory sections (eg, both the evening and graveyard shifts).

Further complicating the job title is the step; for each job there are steps indicating progression within a category. Thus, an entry-level employee would begin working as a CLS I, Step 1, and then be promoted to a CLS I, Step 2, after a year of satisfactory work. There are generally four to five steps in each category, and these steps provide management with the ability to reward good employees without necessarily promoting them to the next level. Information about the job location, shift, hours, and exempt or nonexempt status may be included with the job title. The exempt categories are generally administrative, supervisorial, or professional workers that are exempt from hourly wage and overtime laws, while nonexempt workers are the hourly wage earners for whom the various wage laws apply. Thus, the job title might be: Clinical Laboratory Scientist II, Step 3, Shift 3, Full Time, Nonexempt.

Basic Requirements. This section of the job description includes basic requirements related to citizenship, education, licensure, certification, recertification, and experience. Organizational requirements such as foreign language proficiency may also be listed in this section.

Knowledge or Competencies. This section might first summarize the job, describing the major or general duties involved. The specific knowledge or skills required and the specific duties and tasks to be performed are then listed, along with any specific performance expectations. The more details provided in this section, the more likely it is that the recruiting office will find the perfect candidate, the new hire will have realistic expectations, and the probation evaluation and performance evaluation will be reality-based. Any unusual requirements regarding teaching, research, or administration should be listed here as well.

Interactions. Interactions identify the personnel with whom the employee interfaces. This includes employees external to the laboratory (eg, nurses and physicians), employees within a given laboratory or laboratory section, and patients and the public.

Safety. The job description should also include any safety requirements and fully disclose any hazardous materials, physical activities, or ergonomic constraints that are part of the employee's work environment.

Reporting Lines. Reporting lines indicate the line of authority and the position of the employee in the line of authority. This section may be written or be a part of a sectional organizational chart.

Approvals. The final section of the job description is the Approvals section, which is required to ensure that the author of the job description has reviewed it with the appropriate authority (eg, a laboratory manager or a human resources officer) to ensure that the job description represents the work performed.

The direct supervisor should review and update job descriptions annually. This can often be accomplished as part of the employees' annual performance reviews because employees are likely to be most familiar with the current tasks and duties and can account for any changes in instrumentation or skill requirements.

Recruitment and Selection

Employee recruitment and selection usually begins with a request from a section supervisor and the pathologist in charge of that section to the laboratory manager and the pathologist/director, followed by approvals from the human resources department and hospital administration. Laboratories are expected to justify the need for new or replacement positions. Generally, new or replacement positions are needed so things can be done faster, better, and/or cheaper. To provide a convincing justification for a new or replacement position, the request for the position should document the laboratory's increased workload; explain how the position would improve service, shorten turnaround times, increase productivity, or decrease costs (for example, by decreasing send-out tests); and/or note that the position would help provide a new service or procedure that clinicians critically need.

After the new or replacement position has been approved, the job description becomes paramount in candidate recruitment and the subsequent selection process. A well-developed job description provides the criteria for the selection process as well as the basic elements to be included in an employment advertisement. Candidates are recruited or attracted by in-house postings, advertisements, employment agency listings, and word of mouth. Although the human resources department usually writes the advertisements, it is critical that the pathologist review and approve any advertisements or job postings. Ideally, high-level positions should be filled by qualified persons already working in lower-level positions in the laboratory. Such a "promotional ladder" concept is a major tool for retaining employees and maintaining departmental esprit de corps. Affirmative action must also be considered. Hopefully, the recruiting process generates enough interest that the human resources department can screen applicants by matching the applicant's resume or curriculum vitae to the job description. Often, the human resources department will conduct preliminary interviews and check references before sending the applicants to the department.

Interviews

The job interview gives management the best opportunity to evaluate a candidate. However, interviewing has its pitfalls. Offensive or even unlawful questions should not be asked. Typical questions to avoid during an interview relate to the protected categories, ie, race, religion, national origin, sex, age, and disability. Questions to avoid include questions related to the interviewee's age (eg, "What is your date of birth?"), marital status ("Are you married?" "Do you intend to have children?"), disability ("Do you have or is there a history of a disability?"), and previous work-related actions ("Have you ever filed a workers' compensation claim or sexual harassment complaint?"). The interview process may include individual interviews or group interviews.

Group interviews have the advantage of using standardized questions, usually based on the criteria for selection. However, they can also be a bit overwhelming for some candidates, and candidates' personal responses to the process may alter the assessment. Interviewers should include other employees (staff or supervisory) in some aspect of the interview process to gain a wider perspective of the candidate's skills. However, everyone involved in the interview should be cognizant of the legal and regulatory pitfalls. In some circumstances, for certain positions, the interview may include testing for special skills such as cytogenetics analysis. Appendix 4-1 lists some specific tips for interviewing.

Some organizations may include drug testing and psychological testing as part of the interview process. If the applicant survives the interview process, a position is offered to the successful candidate. In some institutions, the pathologist or laboratory manager will offer the position; in other institutions, the human resources department will offer the position. In either case, the position offer should detail the salary and other terms of employment, provide the job description, and specify the performance criteria that will be used to evaluate the new employee.

Compensation

Compensation is governed by the Fair Labor Standards Act. This federal law defines minimum wage, overtime, and other requirements related to nonexempt employees. States may have additional specific laws and regulations related to minimum wage, overtime, meal periods, rest periods, vacation, holidays, allowable deductions, and other work-related activities. Individual institutions may have additional policies for shift differentials (eg, greater pay for employees working evening or graveyard shifts), overtime pay, and on-call pay.[6,7]

Employees' salaries are usually determined by the hospital administration and are based on the employment market for laboratory employees and comparisons to the salaries provided for other jobs of comparable worth. Salaries are also determined with attention to maintaining internal equity. In some communities, standard or common salaries are published annually, usually for the mid-range position in a specific job category (eg, Medical Technologist II); an institution can use these data to construct its own salary schedule accordingly.

One of the more difficult management issues a pathologist or laboratory director must face is a request from a very good employee for a salary increase. Usually, such an increase is based on an offer the employee has received from another institution. To retain that employee, changes in pay need to be made. Several options for increasing the employee's pay are available, including increasing the cost-of-living allowance or merit-based pay. The employee may receive an early promotion to the next step in the job category or be promoted to the next job category, for example, from a Medical Technologist II to a Medical Technologist III. Another possibility is to assign the employee additional duties that would justify a new job category, ask that the employee's current position be reclassified, and then provide the employee with additional pay. Monetary incentives, profit-sharing plans, and/or spot bonuses could be used if the institution permits them. In some instances, the laboratory can appeal for category-wide salary increases by invoking inequity adjustments. For example, the starting salary for a nurse in a community hospital may be higher than the starting salary for a medical technologist in the same hospital, even though nurses have lower educational requirements, no national certification, and no licensure requirements. The laboratory director may be able to show that this constitutes salary inequity, and the salary schedule for the entire medical technology category could then be raised.

The pathologist or laboratory director must be aware of other components of the compensation package, including pension and retirement plans; health, life, and disability insurance; tuition reimbursement and other educational benefits; uniform allowances; and hiring bonuses. Other benefits, such as childcare, a gym membership, and free parking or parking allowances, are benefits that can complement compensation.

Hiring and Orientation

After the candidate is hired, the start date is established and he or she is provided with keys, a parking space, a uniform, computer access codes, tax and benefits forms, etc. In a standard hospital setting, orientation provides information about both the hospital and the laboratory. Orientation training should include several elements, including confidentiality training (including a review of the Health Insurance Portability and Accountability Act [HIPAA]), sexual harassment training, fire prevention training, and employee safety training (including a review of Occupational Safety and Health Administration [OSHA] guidelines), as well as a review of institutional work rules and dress codes. An employee handbook should be provided to new employees either directly or through electronic links. (See Appendix 4-3, "Employee Handbook Contents.") Human resources or the supervisor should complete a sign-off of the employee's review of the handbook. The new employee's immediate supervisor is responsible for orienting the employee to the laboratory section and the hospital and laboratory information systems. The immediate supervisor is also responsible for reviewing the job description with the employee, assessing the employee's competence, and reviewing the criteria that will be used to evaluate the employee's performance during the probation period and at annual reviews. New employees can also be assigned to a "buddy"—a long-term employee who can answer any questions the new employee may have; introduce the employee to his or her new colleagues; show the

employee where the lockers, bathrooms, cafeteria, and other important places are located; and be available for breaks and lunch with the new employee. There should also be a departmental policy for introducing new employees to the staff, either by a memo or by introducing them at a monthly social event such as a birthday party.

Scheduling and Staffing

The manager or the supervisor is responsible for scheduling work assignments to meet the needs of the clinical laboratory in a safe and cost-effective manner.[5] The number of hours scheduled for an employee depends on whether he or she is classified as a full-time, part-time, or per diem employee. Depending on the work rule used, full-time employees work 40 hours in 1 week or 80 hours in 2 weeks.[5] The 8/80 work rule, which has been used by hospitals for many years, covers a 2-week time frame. During the 2-week period, an employee works 8 hours per day for any number days up to 10; any hours worked beyond 80 hours in the 2 weeks is considered overtime. According to the 40-hour work week rule, an employee is allowed to work any number of hours per shift as long as the total number of hours does not exceed 40 hours in 1 week. The day conveniently divides up into three shifts: day shift (7 AM to 3 PM), evening shift (3 PM to 11 PM), and night shift (11 PM to 7 AM).

A part-time employee works a predefined number of hours that is less than that of a full-time employee. The work is scheduled and could be as few as 8 hours each week. The number of hours worked will typically determine whether an employee is qualified to receive benefits. A per diem employee, also known as a *pro re nata* or "as-needed" employee, is not regularly scheduled and has no set number of hours. Per diem employees work only when needed, for example, to fill in for regular employees who are on vacation or leave or who are unexpectedly absent.

The staffing process begins with determining how many and what type of staff are needed to perform the average workload per shift. Staffing should be applied in an impartial manner. There are several ways to approach staffing. One can start with the "ideal" situation in the clinical laboratory. The supervisor should identify the number of employees in each category (eg, phlebotomists, laboratory technicians, laboratory technologists) required per shift and review the categorical number of employees to ensure that there are sufficient employees for each category and that they are accounted for appropriately. The categories should then be reviewed to confirm that the employees meet the CLIA '88 requirements for category types in a clinical laboratory.

In any pay period in a 24/7 operation, 14 24-hour days need to be staffed. Depending on institutional work-rule adoption, all employees are subject to the 8/80 rule or the 40-hour rule. The day is typically divided into three 8-hour shifts. After creating a generic schedule, the supervisor should take employees' specific work needs, leave requests, vacation requests, and special coverage into account before completing the schedule. Scheduling is a flexible process and changes over time according to the needs of the organization and individual employees. Typically, schedules are based on a pay period or are created monthly. Advance planning is required to accommodate all special employee requests. Scheduling is a frequent source of employee discontent and should be approached seriously, impartially, and in a timely manner.

Performance Appraisal, Annual Review, and Competencies

A performance evaluation, conducted at least once a year, is a standard human resources procedure.[7,8] The annual performance evaluation documents the employee's success, or lack thereof, in several major categories; these may include education, knowledge, duties, interactions, and safety performance. In some institutions, supervisors grade employees by noting whether the employees exceed, meet, or do not meet expectations. Supervisors at other institutions may use different terms or a grading scale (eg, a 5-point scale in which 5 indicates that the employee exceeds expectations, 3 indicates that the employee meets expectations, and 1 indicates that the employee does not meet expectations). Some job descriptions include a column for these grading activities to ensure that all essential activities are accounted for at the annual performance review. Regardless of the system used, pathologists and laboratory directors must be familiar with the appraisal and evaluation.[5]

An employee's performance evaluation should be completed by a supervisor who directly observes the employee on a daily basis; usually, the pathologist only reviews and approves the performance evaluation. The evaluation, which is based on a detailed review of the job description and specific performance criteria, competency skills, or other standards that are detailed in the job description, should provide specific examples of the ways in which the employee is meeting, exceeding, or failing to meet the job requirements or standards. The employee's accomplishments should be recognized, and failures should be clearly defined. Goals or action plans suggested on previous performance evaluations should be reviewed and evaluated; new goals and plans for achieving those goals should be established for the next year, and the consequences of not fulfilling such goals or skills should be clearly explained. Wage and promotion decisions can be made on the basis of the evaluation and competencies. The performance evaluation process should be documented, and the employee should sign the performance evaluation to acknowledge the evaluation.

If the person performing the evaluation anticipates that the evaluation will be negative or that the employee will be contentious, having another person sitting in on the evaluation may be warranted. This person could be the next-highest supervisory technologist or the pathologist in charge of the laboratory section. If there had been previous problems or negative prior evaluations, a representative of the human resources department should be consulted.

Competencies, which are an annual requirement for certification by both the College of American Pathologists and the Joint Commission, can be performed at the same time as an annual performance review. Competency is having the knowledge, skill, ability, or characteristics associated with adequate job performance. Competency assessment must be recorded because it is an explicit requirement of CLIA '88. Competencies can be assessed by an examination, an employee demonstration of skills, or by observing an employee perform required laboratory tasks. Aspects such as safety; analytical procedures; specimen adequacy, collection, and processing; and point-of-care testing may be examples of relevant competencies.

Competencies for new employees should be assessed at 3 months, 6 months, and 1 year after their hire date. Thereafter, competencies should be documented in personnel files at least annually. The College of American Pathologists Competency Assessment Program and the Medical Training Solutions at the University of Washington, Seattle, are examples of commercial competency management systems that a laboratory may employ to document and manage their competency training program.

Employee Retention

One measure of managerial competence or success is the employee turnover rate (number of exiting employees divided by the average annual total employees multiplied by 100). A laboratory with a high turnover rate—for example, a rate of over 25% in the medical technologist category—is a poorly managed laboratory. Every time a long-time employee leaves and is replaced by an inexperienced employee, productivity is reduced for at least 3 months. Thus, employee retention is a major task of management and must be monitored on an ongoing basis.

Everyone in the laboratory, from the director to the bench technologist, must take responsibility for employee retention. Laboratory leadership must be continually aware of Maslow's needs categories and Herzberg's satisfiers and dissatisfiers (see Chapter 1, "Management Principles"). The laboratory should have an active program that emphasizes worker relevance and achievement; recognizes productive work; establishes mechanisms for recognition and reward; maintains a career ladder for promotional opportunities; provides continuing education, adequate compensation, and special benefits such as child care; ensures a pleasant work environment; and supports outside training and educational opportunities. Peter Drucker's admonition to management cannot be repeated often enough: In addition to providing a product or service, in addition to making a profit and being cognizant of societal responsibility, it is the task of management to assure productive work and worker achievement. This does not happen by chance—it must be planned and implemented.[2]

Counseling and Discipline

Counseling and discipline events occur frequently in the workplace. Counseling may occur as a positive event, identifying where, with further training, an employee could be promoted. Scenarios where employees do not abide by work rules or demonstrate less than adequate competencies are other scenarios for counseling and discipline. The counseling and discipline procedure begins with, and has as its basis and justification in, the job description and the performance standards described therein. An employee's immediate supervisor is responsible for gathering and documenting the performance data used in any counseling or disciplinary action. If an employee's performance is unsatisfactory, the counseling should be timely, specific, and private; it should not be left until the employee's annual performance review. If the counseling is for a performance deficiency, there should first be an analysis in which the following questions are answered: Were the performance standards known? Is there an issue of inadequate training? Is motivation an issue? Is it a matter of competency, or is it just a bad fit between person and job? Once the data have been gathered, the formal counseling procedure can begin.

Most institutions employ a formal progressive process for counseling, disciplining, and dismissing employees. Within a set of human resources rules (often referred to as work rules), the prescribed steps taken typically correspond to the severity of the employee's violation of the work rule or law. Progressive discipline may involve, in succeeding order: verbal counseling, verbal counseling with consequences, a verbal warning, a written warning, penalties (such as fine imposition, demotion, or leave without pay), and finally termination.

The essentials of a written warning or disciplinary report are:

- Description of the problem
- Record of previous verbal warnings
- Record (and copies) of previous written warnings
- Employee's response
- Penalties or remediation currently being instituted
- Description of expected future performance with timeline
- Signatures of rater, employee, and witness

Supervisors may forgo progressive discipline when illegal actions, harm to patients or others,

One of the more unpleasant duties of the pathologist/director is participation in counseling or disciplinary sessions. Most people do not like to bring up anything negative in an annual performance evaluation. But it cannot be overemphasized how important it is to be honest and up-front and to thoroughly document all that is said. One pathologist encountered a severe disciplinary problem and discharged an employee. It was well known that this was a problem employee; however, the previous pathologist was always reluctant to record anything negative, and the employee had been given satisfactory performance appraisals for years. In subsequent litigation, the employee was awarded damages because no pattern of misbehavior could be documented.

breach of HIPAA or confidentiality agreements, or other institutionally-defined reasons are involved. Usually, progressive discipline occurs within a defined time period. For example, a written counseling memo may reside in the employee's personnel file for 3 years. If no further progressive discipline is required for that employee, the memo can then be removed. This process may vary if employees are members of a union, in which case the union contract may direct the discipline process as well as involvement of union representation and arbitration.

In well-run human resources departments, each level of progressive discipline has described education, remediation goals, and possible penalties. Carefully managed counseling and discipline applied with the appropriate education and thoughtful corrective action can benefit employees and employers in the long term by providing a means for improving employee performance. However, discipline processes may require serious penalties, including unpaid leave or demotion for more egregious violations. The keys to managing counseling and discipline are following human resources rules and carefully documenting each step in the process. Should a discrimination complaint later be filed, this documentation will verify the steps of the progressive disciplinary action.

Termination

There should be well-defined processes for the several types of termination of, or separation from, employment. Employees often resign voluntarily to seek higher-paying jobs. Because laboratory employees are "knowledge workers" who are highly trained, highly knowledgeable, and highly sought after, they are likely to move from one job to another. Employees may also resign voluntarily because they are ready to retire or wish to develop skills or obtain additional education, or because of personal reasons unrelated to their work. In the event of an employee's retirement, the human resources department should manage any details regarding the employee's accumulated pay or leave time, pension and insurance plans, and retirement benefits. Whenever there is a voluntary retirement, the employee's contributions to the laboratory and the hospital should be acknowledged at a retirement party or in a notice in the laboratory bulletin.

Involuntary termination can occur if a job ceases to be available—for example, when a laboratory downsizes or when a section of the laboratory closes. Involuntary termination can also occur as the final step of progressive discipline. To understand this type of termination, the pathologist or laboratory director needs to understand the definition of at-will employment as well as for-cause employment. At-will employment is a doctrine of US law that defines an employment relationship in which either party (employee or employer) can cease a relationship with no liability, provided there was no express contract for a defined term of employment, and the employer and employee are not part of a collective bargaining (union) contract. For-cause termination is the dissolution of an employee/employer relationship based on the terms of a previously agreed-to contract under the provisions of a termination clause. It is important for pathologists and laboratory directors to know whether they are working in an at-will employment state and whether employment contracts (union or pathologist) govern employee relationships. Justifications for involuntary terminations for cause include incompetence (based on the job description and its performance standards), insubordination, repeated violation of employee rules, verbal or physical abuse of patients or co-workers, breach of HIPAA or confidentiality regulations, falsification of records or tests, and criminal activity.

In cases of involuntary termination, the employee has certain rights and may appeal the decision to terminate his or her employment. The rules that govern this appeals process vary depending on the state and any union contracts that may be in effect. In such situations, the pathologist or laboratory director should seek guidance from the human resources department and possibly the hospital's legal counsel.

An exit interview should be conducted any time an employee is terminated, whether voluntarily or involuntarily. For an involuntarily terminated employee, the purposes of the exit interview are to document the problem(s) leading to the employee's termination, restate the progressive disciplinary actions taken, explain the employee's rights, describe how the termination will be announced, and describe how inquiries from the employee's future potential employers will be addressed. A thoughtful and sensitive exit interview will minimize employee hostility and help avoid legal challenges. The employee who leaves voluntarily may be a source of vital information about the department, its staff, and procedures.

Challenge Questions

What laws govern sexual harassment?
Answer: See pages 61 to 62.

What is the at-will standard?
Answer: See page 71.

What are the essential elements of a job description?
Answer: See pages 64 to 66.

Describe a proactive program for employee retention.
Answer: See page 70.

What are the components of a progressive discipline process?
Answer: See pages 70 to 71.

References

1. Practice Management Committee. *Professional Relations Manual.* 12th ed. Northfield, IL: College of American Pathologists; 2003.
2. Drucker PF. *Management.* Revised ed. New York, NY: Harper Collins; 2008.
3. Travers EM. *Clinical Laboratory Management.* Baltimore, MD: Williams & Wilkins; 1997.
4. *The American Bar Association's Guide to Workplace Law.* 2nd ed. New York, NY: Random House Reference; 2006.
5. Harmening DM. *Laboratory Management. Principles and Processes.* 2nd ed. St. Petersburg, FL: F A Davis Co; 2007.
6. Muller M. *The Manager's Guide to HR. Hiring, Firing, Performance Evaluations, Documentation, Benefits, and Everything Else You Need to Know.* New York, NY: AMACOM; 2009.
7. Armstrong S, Mitchell B. *The Essential HR Handbook.* Franklin Lakes, NJ: The Career Press Inc; 2008.
8. Halstead DC, Oblack DL. Performance appraisals and competency assessment. In: Garcia LS, ed. *Clinical Laboratory Management.* Washington, DC: ASM Press; 2004.

Appendix 4-1.
Interviewing Strategies

- Prepare beforehand; review the candidate's resume or curriculum vitae ahead of time.
- Ensure the facility in which the interview is being held is in compliance with the Americans with Disabilities Act. (For example, is the facility handicap-accessible?)
- Allow enough time for the interview.
- Avoid interruptions; hold phone calls.
- Welcome the candidate and make him or her feel at ease.
- Explain the interview process.
- Avoid stress interviews (interviews intentionally designed to challenge the candidate in some way).
- Avoid controversial issues. Do not ask illegal questions.
- Use the job description as a basis for interview questions
- Assess specific competencies, interpersonal and communication skills, professional appearance, and mandatory requirements (eg, licensure, CME).
- Do not make promises you cannot keep.
- Don't do all the talking.
- Explain what follow-up the candidate can expect and when, including the expected chronology for additional interviews and notifications.

Based in part on: Kurec AS. Recruiting, interviewing, and hiring the right person. *Clin Lab Manag Rev.* 1999;13:251-261.

Appendix 4-2.
Sample Questions for a Behavior-Based Interview

- Describe a stressful situation and how you coped.
- Give an example of when you used judgment and logic in solving a problem.
- Describe a time when you had too much to do and explain how you prioritized.
- Describe a time when you anticipated a problem and developed preventive measures.
- Give an example of how you have dealt with conflict or a difficult co-worker

Adapted from: Casassa M. Hiring for the future. *Advance for Administrators of the Laboratory.* Sept 2009; 18(9):14.

Appendix 4-3.
Employee Handbook Contents

Standard Employment Practices
- At-Will Employment
- Equal Opportunity Employment
- Sexual and Other Unlawful Harassment
- Evaluation Period
- Standards of Conduct
- Personnel File

General Policies and Procedures
- Orientation
- Reporting Changes
- Job Classifications (Exempt, Nonexempt)
- Pay Periods
- Hours of Work
- Breaks
- Time Keeping
- Overtime
- Salary Increases
- Payroll
- Performance Reviews
- Bonus Structure
- Expense Reimbursement
- Attendance and Punctuality
- Availability for Work
- Mandatory Meetings
- Telecommuting
- Job Sharing
- Holidays
- Vacations
- Drugs and Alcohol
- Violence and Weapons
- Smoking
- Food and Beverage
- Recycling
- Visitors
- Workplace Attire
- Telephone Use
- Voice Mail and Electronic Mail
- Use of Company Vehicles
- Use of Company Property
- Postage, Shipping, and Office Supplies
- Personal Property
- Personal Safety (OSHA)
- Confidential Information (HIPAA)
- Conflicts of Interest

- Non-Solicitation
- Competing Employment
- Employment of Relatives

Leave Policies
- General Policies
- Sick Leave
- Short-Term Disability Leave
- Family and Medical Leave
- Personal Leave of Absence
- Jury Duty
- Military Duty
- Funeral Leave
- Emergency Closings and Severe Weather

Employment Benefits
- Benefits Eligibility
- Medical Insurance
- 401(k)
- Stock Options
- Employee Discounts
- Tuition Reimbursement
- Workers' Compensation
- COBRA

Disciplinary Policies
- Problem Resolutions
- Discipline
- Corrective Action

Separation Policies
- Job Abandonment
- Termination
- Termination Process
- Employment References

Laboratory-Specific Content for New Employees
- Department Mission and Vision
- Laboratory Organizational Chart
- LIS Instructions
- Standard Precautions, Infection Control, Safety, and Quality Procedures
- Key Names and Phone Numbers

Adapted from: Employee Handbook Template. Available at http://www.sampleemployeehandbook.com. Accessed Nov 17, 2010.

Appendix 4-4.
Sample Performance
Evaluation Template

Performance Factors	Employee Rating	Supervisor Rating
Knowledge of Work: Understands assigned duties and responsibilities, establishes priorities and plans work, uses appropriate procedures, tools, equipment, and materials for assigned work.		
Quality of Work: Work is complete, neat, accurate, timely, and thoughtful.		
Quantity of Work: Completes all assignments within specified time limits, adjusts to unexpected changes in work demands to meet timetables.		
Initiative: Self-starter, requires minimal supervision, requests additional assignments or responsibilities, suggests and implements improved work methods.		
Cooperation: Projects a positive work attitude; relates effectively with co-workers, supervisor, and others; uses tact and diplomacy; acts professionally at all times.		

Rating Descriptions

1 = Consistently failed to meet performance standards. A remedial action plan is being developed.

2 = Occasionally failed to meet performance standards.

3 = Consistently met performance standards.

4 = Frequently exceeded performance standards.

5 = Consistently exceeded performance standards.

Source: Muller M. *The Manager's Guide to HR. Hiring, Firing, Performance Evaluations, Documentation, Benefits, and Everything Else You Need to Know.* New York, NY: AMACOM; 2009:39-40.

CHAPTER 5

Equipment, Supplies, and Space

Richard E. Horowitz, MD
Elizabeth A. Wagar, MD

Contents

Introduction

Successful administration requires that pathologists be knowledgeable not only about planning, operations, finances, and personnel, but also be familiar with equipment, supplies, and laboratory design. In that role the pathologist must interact with a variety of experts including health care administrators, purchasing agents, architects, lawyers, and manufacturers and suppliers. Effective communication with them demands fluency in their nomenclature. This chapter provides an introduction to the terminology and processes that are critical for optimal equipment, supply, and space deployment.

Equipment Acquisition

Unlike most other medical specialists, pathologists are closely tied to, and dependent upon, their instruments and equipment; only radiologists have a similarly symbiotic relationship with their technology. The acquisition of equipment is an integral part of the pathology laboratory's strategic plan. If done thoroughly and prudently, equipment acquisition helps facilitate successful laboratory operation.

The acquisition of new instrumentation requires an assessment of the laboratory's needs, a request for information (RFI), a preliminary cost analysis, a request for proposal (RFP), a site visit, a final cost analysis, a contract, and a budget request. The initial step is assessing the laboratory's needs, which also is commonly known as the technology assessment. It should be performed whenever methodology changes significantly or new tests that require new equipment are instituted.

Technology assessment and the subsequent equipment acquisition are the responsibility of the laboratory director. Some hospitals have a systemwide acquisition committee that makes equipment decisions for all the laboratories in the system; pathologists should be represented on such committees to help ensure that the equipment needs of individual laboratories are met. In other hospitals, an acquisition committee consisting of physicians and administrators may make final purchasing decisions; again, it is critical that pathologists be members of such committees. All acquisitions are typically accomplished through the hospital's purchasing department. Thus, laboratory directors should maintain a good relationship with the purchasing office. Similarly, laboratory directors should be on good terms with their hospitals' legal advisors, who may review and approve major purchase or lease contracts.

The first step in acquiring new equipment is determining the need or justification for the new equipment. Pathologists must show that new equipment meets one or more of the following criteria:

- Replaces existing worn or obsolete equipment to continue operations
- Provides marked improvement in patient care
- Improves quality
- Enhances productivity and efficiency and/or reduces costs
- Improves patient or employee satisfaction
- Is necessary for patient or employee safety
- Is necessary for the laboratory to meet governmental requirements

An important adjunct to the justification is the clinical utility assessment, which is provided by clinicians. Also important is input from clinicians regarding new technology, including any advantages provided to patient management. It is always useful to obtain clinicians' support, preferably in writing, when acquiring new equipment.

Once the need for new equipment has been established, the pathologist works with the purchasing department to issue an RFI to potential vendors. An RFI is a request, typically made during the project planning phase, in which a buyer requests preliminary information about a vendor's product. It does not require as much detail in the response and may not provide full product requirements, specifications, and purchase options. RFIs should clearly indicate that receipt of the RFI does not guarantee the vendor will be awarded a contract. The five common elements in an RFI are:

- Statement of purpose (eg, "To gather information to evaluate vendors for issuance of a subsequent RFP")
- Description of the laboratory and/or hospital issuing the RFI
- Description of the needed technology and its general operating characteristics, such as the methodology or methodologies required, testing capacity (volume), turnaround time, implementation requirements, maintenance and scheduled down time, personnel limitations, and computer interface requirements
- RFI procedures (ie, guidelines for how vendors should format their response to the RFI, when the vendors' responses are due to the issuing hospital or laboratory, and how soon the responses will be evaluated after they are returned)
- Statement of confidentiality

Vendors' responses to an RFI should include:

- Description of the vendor, including ownership, history, and financial information
- Description of the product, including its operating characteristics, cost, and installation requirements; training, service, and maintenance provisions; and guarantees and warranties
- Number and location of installations of products similar to the one requested
- References (ie, contact information for customers using similar equipment)

Upon receipt of the RFI responses, the laboratory director, and some combination of purchasing department personnel, the pathologist in charge of the domain, and the technologist who supervises the section in which the equipment will be used, should evaluate and rank the vendors. Usually, the three vendors who submit the RFI responses that best reflect the needs of the laboratory are then selected for further review.

Before issuing an RFP, pathologists should visit the laboratories indicated by the vendor to have comparable equipment. Site visits may be arranged directly with the other laboratory's pathologist or administrator or through the vendor's representative. The team that visits the site should include the technologist who supervises the section where the equipment will be used. Before the site visit, pathologists should review their own laboratory's operating requirements and the stated functionality in the RFI. At the site, in addition to speaking with the pathologist or laboratory director who chose the vendor's equipment, the visiting team should also speak with the technologists operating the equipment. Questions to ask the technologists may include:

- Were there any problems with delivery, installation, or connection to the laboratory information system (LIS)?
- How much time did it take to make the equipment fully operational?
- Does the equipment meet the requirements for test volume and turnaround time expectations?
- Is the equipment reliable? Is there unexpected down time?
- Did the manufacturer provide adequate training?
- Do the technologists find the equipment easy to use?
- Are the pathologists satisfied with the equipment's performance?
- Is there availability (order to delivery) of reagents and supplies?
- Is there satisfaction with the vendor's technical support and maintenance?
- Did the equipment have any unexpected consequences on laboratory operations?

The pathologist should ask several other questions that can assist in the equipment review. For example, has the equipment been on the market for at least 5 years? Is the equipment mechanically simple, with few moving parts? Is there a local parts warehouse and readily available repair support? Are the reagents inexpensive? Is the new equipment compatible with the laboratory's current instrumentation (same methodology, reference ranges, etc)? Is the equipment inexpensive enough to buy two units? (Duplicate instruments provide back-up for down-time.)

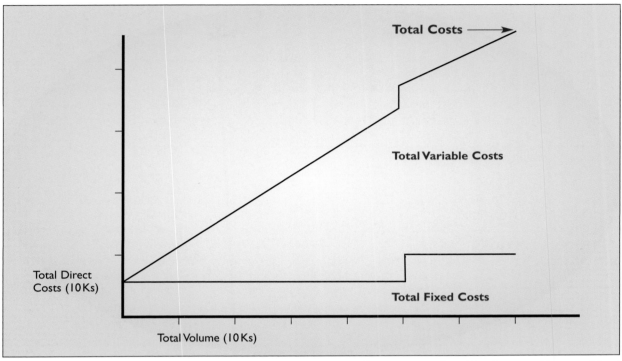

Figure 5-1. Graph of Total Direct Costs. The graph demonstrates the nonlinear aspects of total fixed costs and how total fixed costs contribute to total costs.

- Does the equipment meet projected operating costs?
- Does the equipment meet the laboratory's needs regarding volume, turnaround time, and test menu?
- Would they recommend buying or leasing the equipment again? Why or why not?

The vendor's responses to the RFI should include acquisition cost data for purchase, lease, and reagent rental. Reagent rental combines reagent purchase and equipment leasing with an assumed increase in reagent costs to cover the expense of the lease. The institution's chief financial officer can help perform a thorough cost analysis. Other factors must also be considered, including fixed and variable costs (see Chapter 9, "Financial Management of the Laboratory"). Briefly, variable costs are the total cost of variable (direct) inputs; total fixed (indirect) costs describe the cost of fixed factors. The total cost is the sum of total variable costs and total fixed costs. Typical variable costs include costs that increase with increased output (eg, reagents, increases in technologist support). Total fixed costs include general facilities overhead, lease of the building, and utilities. An example of total costs related to fixed and variable costs is shown in Figure 5-1. The economics of technology acquisition are thoroughly detailed in Travers'

Clinical Laboratory Management, appendix 22-A, "Laboratory Materials Cost Worksheet Summary," and table 22A-2, "Laboratory Indirect Cost Worksheet Summary."[1]

The costs of new equipment must be weighed against its benefits, such as increased productivity or revenue, decreased cost per test, and reduced turnaround time. Perhaps the most important calculation for this analysis is the return on investment (ROI) rate, also referred to as the rate of return (ROR). In a for-profit environment, the ROI is the net profit after taxes divided by the total assets. In a non-profit environment, the margin may be increased by reducing expenses, raising prices, producing more tests for less cost, increased charges for professional fees, improved billing collections, or increasing reimbursement rates. Thus, if other costs remain stable, new automated equipment that allows a higher test volume with fewer technologists may result in an improved margin and ROI. Institutions must understand how long it will take to recoup their investment in a given technology. A simplistic formula for ROI is as follows:

$$ROI = \frac{(\text{Gain from Investment} - \text{Cost of Investment})}{\text{Cost of Investment}}$$

New equipment in the pathology laboratory may also bring cost savings or benefits to other areas in the institution; for example, decreased turnaround

Rank from 1 to 5, with 5 being best match.	Vendor 1	Vendor 2	Vendor 3
Acceptable operating characteristics			
Maintenance contract and warranties			
Emergency maintenance			
Reagent rental options			
Lease/purchase option			
Estimated cost/test and ROI			
Required technologist expertise			
Provision of training to technologists			
LIS interface cost			
LIS interface implementation plan			
Overall reputation of the manufacturer			

Figure 5-2. Request for Proposal Grading Grid Example.

times for test results may hasten patients' discharge from the emergency room or reduce patients' lengths of stay. Although difficult to quantify, improved patient care must also be included in a cost analysis. Before issuing an RFP, the hospital and/or medical staff equipment committee, system equipment committee, if any, and hospital administration should agree that funds are available for the purchase of the new equipment.

Typically, the purchasing group (including administration, pathologists, and laboratory manager and supervisors) selects three vendors on the basis of findings from the site visit, the cost analysis, and the vendors' responses to the RFI and issues RFPs.

The RFP is a publication of detailed requirements by a prospective buyer in order to receive firm vendor offerings. The RFP, which is also known as a request for bids or a request to tender, includes the following:

■ Statement of need
■ Vendor responsibilities
■ Performance and operating standards
■ Deliverables, hardware, software, training
■ Contractual requirements
■ Payment requirements, incentives, penalties
■ Proposal format
■ Evaluation and award process
■ Schedule

Final vendor selection should be based on a checklist that may include the following questions:
■ Does the equipment fulfill the laboratory's need or justification?
■ Does the equipment fulfill the laboratory's operating characteristics?
■ Does the equipment work at other laboratory locations or sites?
■ Can the equipment be tested in the laboratory?
■ Does the vendor have a reputation for providing quality products and services?
■ Are service, parts, and reagents readily available?
■ Is training available?
■ Does the vendor offer any warranties?
■ What are the costs and benefits of the equipment?
■ What is the projected profit or return on the investment?

Ideally, to help ensure that the three competing vendors will be graded unbiasedly, the purchasing group should establish such criteria before the vendors return the RFPs. An example of an RFP grading grid is shown in Figure 5-2.

After the laboratory director and institutional purchasing agent make the final selection, they work with the institutional attorney to write the contract to purchase or acquire the necessary equipment. The contract details all the elements in the RFP, including complete specifications (equipment description, functionality, and operating performance, characteristics, and standards), requirements for installation (space, utilities, code requirements, computer compatibility), cost to purchase or lease (including reagent rental), and delivery (insurance, liability, replacement, acceptance testing, warranties, maintenance contract, and penalty and lemon clauses). An experienced purchasing officer or attorney should help write the contract to ensure that no detail is overlooked. Overlooked details can cause problems in the future.

Equipment Maintenance

Equipment maintenance is an integral part of laboratory operations and quality management. Maintenance as well as maintenance records and documentation are required by accrediting and certifying agencies. Although technologists are generally responsible for equipment maintenance, the laboratory director has an obligation to approve a maintenance program and ensure its implementation. Maintenance is scheduled work aimed at preventing equipment failure. Repair is the unscheduled work required to bring equipment back on-line after it fails. First-line maintenance, which is performed by the technologists who operate the equipment, consists of frequent inspection, cleaning, disinfecting, lubricating, simple parts replacement, calibrations, and other adjustments. In some institutions, the staff of the biomedical engineering unit may perform these functions; in all instances, such functions must be recorded in an electronic or paper maintenance log. Second-line maintenance, which is performed by the manufacturer's field service representatives, consists of more complex replacements, alignments, and adjustments. Third-line maintenance involves a major overhaul or refurbishment of the equipment and is usually performed in the factory.

The acquisition process for major equipment should include the negotiation of a maintenance

It is important to have an experienced person assist in the writing of the contract so that nothing is overlooked. A pathologist once went through a thorough process, as described in the text, and purchased a new laboratory computer. It was delivered to the hospital loading dock in several very large crates. When the vendor's technicians arrived to begin the installation, they asked why the computer was still in crates; they did not do "un-crating," and the contract did not specify who was responsible for the un-crating. It was not a major problem, but it did cause delay and certainly some loss of goodwill.

contract. Maintenance contracts should be reviewed by an experienced attorney and should detail the following:

- Scope of equipment to be covered, including hardware and software
- Frequency of preventive maintenance
- Other types of service, including remote, on-site, routine, and emergency services
- Availability of service technicians and replacement parts
- Availability of equipment loans or backup equipment
- Expected response time, including the hierarchy of response if initial service is unsuccessful
- Exclusions (eg, electrical or computer connections)
- Parts, labor, travel, and out-of-pocket expenses

Supply Management

The management of supplies is largely handled by the laboratory's administrative and technical staff with the assistance of the institutional purchasing department. However, the laboratory director is ultimately responsible for sufficient supply management to provide for patient care testing. When a chemistry analyzer runs out of reagent and test results are delayed, or when phlebotomy supplies are not delivered to a physician's office, the complaints are not directed to the technologists or the purchasing department but rather directly to the pathologist. Therefore, the laboratory director must understand the systems and nomenclature of supply management and establish a working relationship with purchasing department leadership. The traditional responsibilities of an institution's purchasing department are to obtain a continuous and adequate supply of materials at a reasonable cost and deliver these materials to the laboratory in a timely fashion. Laboratory personnel should use intelligent demand planning to determine and forecast what supplies are needed, and at what time. The purchasing department should have knowledge of the marketplace, a broad range of supplier contacts, and good supplier relationships to obtain the best prices and discounts; make "buy-or-make" recommendations; negotiate volume discounts; and ensure that supplies are properly received, stored, and distributed. Generally, vendor selection is delegated to the purchasing department; however, the laboratory must establish and approve the specifications of any purchases.

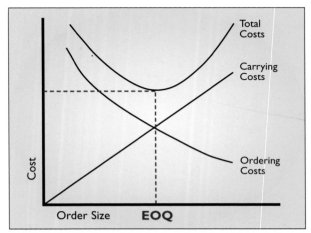

Figure 5-3. Economic Order Quantity (EOQ). This figure demonstrates the relationship between ordering costs, carrying costs, and total costs.

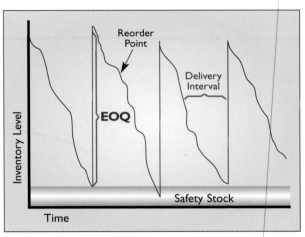

Figure 5-4. Level of Inventory Over Time. This figure shows the dynamic relationship of supplies to the economic order quantity (EOQ), reorder point, and delivery interval.

The laboratory's role in supply and equipment acquisition may be restricted by the institution's purchasing agreements, by requirements for competitive bidding, or by membership in a group purchasing organization (GPO). A variety of GPOs are available to health care institutions. University Health System Consortium (Oak Brook, Illinois) has aligned with some GPOs in representing academic health care centers. Other GPOs are Novation (Irving, Texas), Amerinet (St. Louis), and Essensa (New York). Laboratory directors should be aware of the GPOs their health care institutions use. Regardless of the purchasing agreements, the laboratory is ultimately responsible for providing accurate test results, and this charge cannot be compromised by mediocre supplies. As with equipment, the laboratory must define the specifications for supplies, including their description, functionality, and performance standards; and the laboratory, together with the purchasing department, should insist on warranties and recourse or replacement procedures.

Once purchasing decisions are made, the laboratory must establish a system of supply chain management that is based on the synchronization of supplies. Such a system should have blanket ordering, online ordering, and order inquiry capabilities; shipping documentation and tracking capabilities; inventory tracking, delivery, receiving, inspection, and invoice verification; warehousing; and "just-in-time" delivery to the laboratory. Large orders of supplies may require an understanding of the economics of material management and warehousing. Two basic concepts are involved in supply management: (1) economic order quantity (EOQ) and (2) just-in-time inventory. The goal of just-in-time inventory management is to reduce inventories to quantities needed precisely at the time of production needs.

EOQ is the optimum amount of goods to order each time so that total inventory costs are minimized. EOQ is calculated as the square root of:

$$\frac{2 \times \text{Supply} / \text{Month} \times \text{Price} / \text{Order}}{\text{Cost} / \text{Unit}}$$

Using this equation requires an understanding of carrying costs and ordering costs. Ordering costs typically decrease with an increase in the number of units ordered from the supplier. The carrying costs are the costs to inventory supplies, including space expense (ie, a lease), personnel to manage the inventory, facilities (refrigeration), and other storage costs. The EOQ is the order size (units) at which carrying cost equals ordering cost (Figure 5-3).[1] A dynamic graph showing the interaction of EOQ with order quantity, re-order, and delivery intervals is shown in Figure 5-4.[1] Obviously, planning is important, but circumstances beyond a laboratory director's control—for example, withdrawal of reagents by the US Food and Drug Administration—may circumvent all efforts. Contingency plans for inadequate supplies are always appropriate.

Many laboratories have recently participated in Lean review of their supply chain. Lean is the process of recognizing what the customer values and applying flow thinking to any activity, including ordering and receiving supplies.[2] Lean also standardizes the ways in which supplies are managed and inventory assessed. In addition, the use of Lean allows hands-on–level employees to make suggestions and improvements on a continuous basis. Lean is discussed in greater detail in Chapter 7, "Quality Management in Laboratory Medicine."

Contract Services

Pathology and laboratory medicine departments engage a number of contract services. In most laboratories, the single largest purchased service is reference laboratory testing. However, several other common contracted services must be considered, including a courier service to deliver supplies and pick up specimens from outlying facilities, an autopsy diener service to provide autopsy assistants when needed, and a billing service for billing and collecting the pathologists' professional fees. The laboratory director is medically and legally responsible for the contract services, and it is important to establish criteria and performance standards for these contracts. An example of the importance of planning all delivery steps is shown in the case example.

As with supplies, contract services may be determined by group purchasing agreements and may be subject to competitive bidding procedures. The purchasing department contracts for hospital-related services, such as reference laboratory testing, while the pathology group contracts separately for its own services, such as billing.

The following is an example of the due diligence required of a laboratory director and purchasing department before contracting for reference laboratory services:

- Licensure, accreditation
- Personnel credentials
- Test menu (scope of services)
- Quality management program
- Proficiency testing results

Case Example

A woman underwent a skin biopsy at a dermatologist's office. The dermatologist claimed that he placed the specimen in one of the laboratory's formalin tissue containers, which was to be picked up by the courier service and brought to the laboratory for processing and diagnosis. However, the laboratory had no record of having received the specimen. The patient sued the laboratory and the laboratory director because she did not have a diagnosis and therefore did not know what the possible sequelae might be. The insurance carrier elected to settle the case rather than litigate. There was no system in place that documented specimen pick-up and delivery by the courier. Needless to say, the laboratory revised performance standards for the courier service immediately.

- Test ordering system (LIS interface)
- Specimen pick-up, frequency, supplies
- Test turnaround time
- Evening and weekend availability
- Test reporting format (LIS interface)
- Stat capability and reporting
- Billing (LIS and hospital information system interface)
- Consultation/interpretation availability
- Client (customer) support services
- Cost

A thorough analysis of reference laboratory contracting is available through the CAP website in *Laboratory Medical DirecTIPS*.[3] The Joint Commission requires that all laboratories review their reference laboratory contracts and have the list approved annually by medical staff leadership. The laboratory director should personally review the reference laboratories under consideration and conduct a site visit for each, where appropriate.

Space Planning, Renovation, and Construction

Space planning is essential to effective and efficient laboratory operation. The layout of a laboratory is much more than its floor plan. The layout of the laboratory reflects the organizational structure of the laboratory and is the culmination of the operational goals integral to the mission of the laboratory and its leadership. Thus, the layout of a specialty reference laboratory with isolated areas for sensitive molecular techniques is very different from a laboratory in a high-volume, acute-care hospital with a busy emergency room and intensive care unit requiring seamless, around-the-clock, stat testing.

A publication of the National Academy of Sciences identifies four critical factors that characterize a successful laboratory construction or renovation project: (1) a "champion" who is strongly committed to the success of the project, has the confidence of the entire client group, and stays with the project from beginning to end; (2) a design professional, often an architect, who has experience and demonstrated success in laboratory design and construction; (3) a well-defined and well-articulated process for carrying out the project from the predesign through postconstruction phases; and (4) clear lines of communication and authority for all participants throughout the process.[4] Attention to all of these factors is basic to achieving a successfully designed and built laboratory facility.[5,6]

Ideally, the champion of a laboratory construction or renovation project is a pathologist with at least 5 years pathology practice experience beyond training in the laboratory that will undergo construction or renovation, and superior interpersonal and communication skills. Experience in laboratory management is essential; the champion must have the complete confidence of the laboratory director and the respect of the laboratory staff. In addition to coordinating the various needs, desires, and limitations of the multiple constituencies in planning and implementing a successful laboratory construction or renovation, the champion must continually emphasize that the ultimate goals of the project are to provide a more efficient and effective laboratory service to patients and physicians and a more productive and pleasant workplace for laboratory staff. To ensure a successful laboratory design and renovation or construction project, the champion, laboratory staff, and others should take the following steps:

1. The champion should review the institution's strategic plan to determine whether there are any plans that might impact laboratory operations (eg, a new breast center, a new neonatal intensive care unit, a new inpatient drug rehabilitation unit, a new hospital information system, an increase or decrease in the number of hospital beds).

2. The champion should review the vision the laboratory director and pathologists have for the future of the laboratory; determine whether it involves new technology in anatomic pathology (digital imaging, telepathology, DNA microarrays, genetic analysis), new technology in clinical pathology (PCR microbiology, flow cytometry, microfluidics, biochips), or new organizational philosophy (eg, silo elimination); and determine the space implications of the new technologies and philosophies.

3. The champion should revisit the laboratory's strategic plan, including environmental assessments, SWOT (strengths, weaknesses, opportunities, and threats) analysis, and the above visions, and prioritize what the laboratory will do, ie, continue as usual, change existing activities, downsize or eliminate functions, or begin new projects and programs. This prioritization by the director and the pathologists will determine the priorities of the construction project.

4. The champion should perform a preliminary cost analysis to determine the amount of money available for the project and the rough costs of the project (eg, the remodel cost per square foot, the cost of purchasing or leasing new equipment). By determining how much can be reasonably accomplished with the funds available, the champion can help dispel unrealistic expectations.

5. The champion should meet with senior laboratory staff, including section directors (pathologists and/or postdoctoral scientists) and supervising technologists, to introduce the construction or renovation project, review the hospital and departmental vision and strategic plans, and define the departmental priorities and the scope of the project. The champion should also introduce the group to the concept of function sequencing and explain staff's role in the various phases of the project.

6. The champion should conduct workflow analysis or function sequencing for each work station in each section of the laboratory (see Chapter 3, "Laboratory Operations"). This is the champion's first major task, and it is the best way to learn the laboratory's current operations, the ideal way to determine the wishes or needs of the laboratory staff, and the only way to determine what changes are needed and whether such changes can be incorporated into a new laboratory. The function sequence forms the basis of how, what, where, and when things will be done in the new laboratory. It will determine the floor plan, instrument locations, work sequence, staffing, etc.

7. The champion should prepare a rough design or "wish layout" for each section of the new laboratory using the information gleaned from the function sequence. The rough design, which should be performed by the supervisor and pathologist in charge of each section, should include an estimate of bench requirements in linear feet, total space requirements in square feet, and size and location requirements for major equipment.

8. The champion should transmit the wish layout information to the project architects, who will draw the first of several iterations of the schematics or floor plans for the new laboratory.

9. The champion should determine whether the architects require additional information from the laboratory, eg, equipment lists detailing instrument size, power requirements, utility locations, and air conditioning, phone, and computer needs, and make certain the laboratory staff provides the necessary information.

10. The champion should determine whether other departments in the institution—eg, Safety, Engineering, Materials Management, Information Technology—need to be involved in space planning and encourage communication between these departments and the architects.

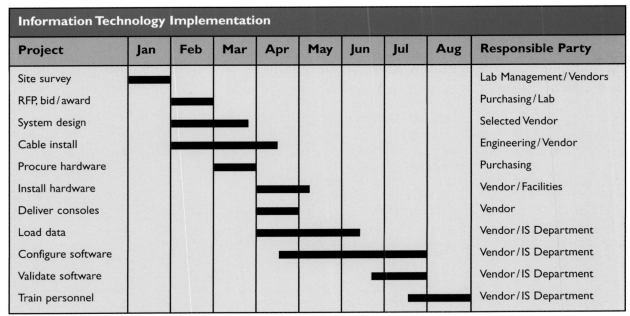

Information Technology Implementation									
Project	**Jan**	**Feb**	**Mar**	**Apr**	**May**	**Jun**	**Jul**	**Aug**	**Responsible Party**
Site survey									Lab Management / Vendors
RFP, bid / award									Purchasing / Lab
System design									Selected Vendor
Cable install									Engineering / Vendor
Procure hardware									Purchasing
Install hardware									Vendor / Facilities
Deliver consoles									Vendor
Load data									Vendor / IS Department
Configure software									Vendor / IS Department
Validate software									Vendor / IS Department
Train personnel									Vendor / IS Department

Figure 5-5. Gantt Chart Example. A Gantt chart organizes activities, working backward from a defined endpoint.

11. The champion should schedule a series of individual meetings with the architects, laboratory planners, the laboratory director, and supervisors of each laboratory section to rework the wish layout into an architecturally viable schematic that improves workflow, facilitates efficiency, meets codes, and does not exceed budget. These initial meetings will take between two and three hours apiece.

12. At this point in the process, the architects might have a better idea of the costs involved; if the costs appear to exceed budget, laboratory leadership may have to set some priorities or make some cuts in programs.

13. The architects prepare a revised schematic and transmit it to the laboratory staff for review. The laboratory staff offers suggestions and transmits their ideas back to the architects for a final or sign-off meeting.

14. The champion should schedule another series of individual meetings between architects, laboratory planners, the laboratory director, and supervisors of each laboratory section to finalize and approve the schematic or floor plan design of the new laboratory so that it can be sent out to bid.

15. The champion should schedule a series of additional meetings between architects, laboratory planners, the laboratory director, and supervisors of each laboratory section to specify casework, furniture, finishes, plumbing fixtures, etc, to ensure that the needs of individual laboratory sections are met.

16. The champion should review the documents the architects send to prospective construction bidders, review the bidders' responses, and carefully scrutinize the details of the winning bidder.

17. The champion should act as the central coordinating entity during the construction phase. The champion should coordinate all communication to or from the laboratory director, laboratory staff, and/or architects as well as any and all communication between the construction crew and the laboratory staff.

18. The champion should serve as the laboratory's representative in the approval and acceptance process once construction is complete.

Some individual space projects require analysis of the time required to complete the project. For such projects, a diagram such as a Gantt chart may be valuable in expressing the progress and expenses of a long-term project. Some activities may need to be performed in a specific sequence; other work can be provided in parallel. The Gantt chart and recent refinements such as network analysis have become mainstays of major capital projects such as building programs. The philosophy of the Gantt chart begins with the end product. For example, the delivery of a new building is required on a given date. Each step backwards is analyzed in terms of parallel bar graphs for the various activities required to complete the project. Projects that extend over a considerable time period or that include a number of different activities that occur at the same

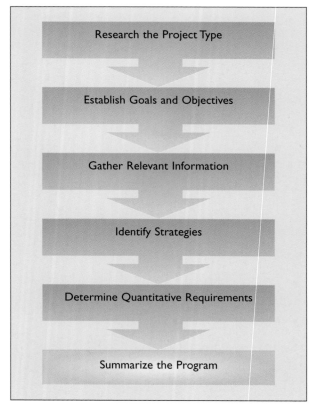

Figure 5-6. Architectural Programming Steps. Architectural programming establishes a process by which users (organized in user groups) can sequentially interact with architects over the course of a space renovation project.

Table 5-1. Clinical Laboratory Facilities Requirements

Ventilation requirements
Biosafety requirements: biosafety containment, anticipated biosafety level
Power: back-up power source, generator location, emergency outlet locations, power pole locations
Plumbing requirements: location of drains and sinks
Water type, type 2 reservoirs, type 1 requirements
Refrigeration options and locations: walk-in versus stand-alone, alarm systems, blood bank requirements
Storage: short-term versus long-term, accessibility, organization of storage
Loading dock: location, access to laboratory storage, management of biohazardous and other waste, supply delivery management system
Security: locked doors, location of key-code/card required locks, phone lines, management of access to phlebotomy supplies
Air conditioning: relationship to refrigeration, large equipment, and personnel
Pneumatic tubes: stations, layout, number, point-to-point lines, vendor support

Some laboratory-specific requirements are shown.

time or in the same space should always include a Gantt chart in addition to an appropriate budget. A simplified example of a Gantt chart for a laboratory information system upgrade is shown in Figure 5-5. Gantt charts are also frequently used in other larger projects such as information technology implementation and automation installation.

Another process sometimes encountered in the course of building or space design is architectural programming. Architectural programming is the research and decision-making process that identifies the scope of work to be designed. Synonyms include "facility programming," "functional and operational requirements," and "scoping." Architectural planning can be used in laboratories that have to account for multiple functions in space planning and maintain communication and links with multiple hospital or institutional sites.

The six basic steps to architectural programming are shown in Figure 5-6.[6] Laboratory personnel typically encounter architectural programming in the early stages of planning, when general discussion about objectives, strategies, and other rele-

vant information is very important to the success of the project. The architects or planners should be familiar with laboratory design and appropriately research the project type. Also, the architects should evaluate the quantitative requirements and translate those requirements to gross square footage for the earliest phases of evaluation. Pathologists, who may first encounter programming as part of a selected "user group," should be prepared with design ideas and comments. Also, to prepare for programming, pathologists should develop a table of current square footage and the functional assignment of current space for comparative purposes. As previously described, the champion should stay in touch with all programming steps, including the summarization.

Clinical laboratories have some specific facilities requirements to become operational after any renovation or space design project is complete. Some of the specific support requirements that may impact clinical laboratories are shown in Table 5-1. For example, if power outlets are located distant from large equipment, or if the air conditioning is insufficient to support multiple refrigerators and freezers, considerable expense may be generated to make the required corrections to the new laboratory.

Ultimately, space planning is a continuous activity for anyone in a position of clinical laboratory leadership. It is important to maintain communication through all intervals of building design and construction. Without continuous communication, change orders (changes in the planned design) can occur to the detriment of laboratory services.

References

1. Travers EM. Technology acquisition. In: Travers EM. *Clinical Laboratory Management.* Baltimore, MD: Williams and Wilkins; 1997:333-375.

2. Womack JP, Jones DT. *Lean Thinking. Banish Waste and Create Wealth in Your Corporation.* New York, NY: Free Press; 2003.

3. Practice Management Committee. Are you buying premium when regular will do? Getting a handle on send-outs. *Laboratory Medical DirecTIPS.* Northfield, IL: College of American Pathologists; Dec 14, 2009. Available at: www.cap.org. Accessed Nov 17, 2010.

4. National Research Council. Commission on Physical Sciences, Mathematics, and Applications. *Laboratory Design, Construction, and Renovation.* Washington, DC: National Academy Press; 2000.

5. Elin, RJ. Consideration for the design of a new laboratory. *Am J Clin Pathol.* 1986;85:61-66.

6. Koenig AS. *Medical Laboratory Planning and Design.* Chicago, IL: College of American Pathologists; 1985.

Challenge Questions

The laboratory supervisor always seems to be running out of supplies for the chemistry instrument. What tool might the pathologist use to investigate the problem?
A. Request for information (RFI)
B. Group purchasing organization (GPO)
C. Economic order quantity (EOQ)
D. Return on investment (ROI)
E. None of the above
Answer: C; see pages 79 to 80.

The hospital's chief operating officer is assisting in the development of an RFP for a new automation line for the core laboratory. Three vendors have been selected to receive the RFP. The chief operating officer asks the pathologist to develop the evaluation tool for the RFP submissions. Which of the following items would the pathologist include in the evaluation tool?
A. Acceptable operating characteristics
B. Maintenance contract and warranties
C. Required technologist expertise
D. LIS interface cost
E. All of the above
Answer: E; see pages 75 to 78 and Figure 5-2.

How should space be reallocated in a laboratory renovation project?
Answer: See pages 82 to 83.

CHAPTER 6

Management of Pathology Information Systems

James H. Harrison Jr, MD, PhD

Contents

Definition of Pathology Informatics

Pathology informatics is a subdomain of biomedical informatics, the science that underlies the academic investigation, optimization, and practical application of computing and communications technology in health care, health education, and biomedical research. Biomedical informatics includes, as broad areas: (1) bioinformatics, the use of computer technology in basic research, especially for the study of gene, protein, and cellular structure and relationships; (2) medical or clinical informatics, the application of information technology to health care delivery and clinical research; (3) public health informatics, which focuses on population health; and (4) health knowledge informatics, which is concerned with managing clinical and research literature and health information for patients. Pathology informatics is primarily a subset of clinical informatics that focuses on optimizing the acquisition, management, communication, and use of information related to anatomic and clinical pathology analyses and laboratory operations.

Early Development and Growth of Laboratory Information Systems

The use of information systems in pathology predated the formal recognition of the field of biomedical informatics and contributed to its development. The initial impetus for clinical laboratory computerization occurred in the 1960s as a result of the transition to primarily third-party (insurance) payment for medical care and the adoption of automated analyzers for chemistry and hematology testing. These developments created a demand for increased testing and the capacity for laboratories to meet that demand, except that manual specimen tracking, data management, quality control, and reporting were limiting factors. Automation of these functions using early computers was a natural step, and the capital to create those systems was available because laboratories were a major revenue source at the time. The initial work in the 1960s led to a consensus by the end of the decade that laboratory computer systems could be cost-justified and should be implemented as in-laboratory minicomputers with local terminals (a laboratory information system [LIS]) rather than as a component of hospital information systems (HISs) implemented on large mainframe computers.[1] The first vendor systems began to appear at this time.

Interest in LIS development was stimulated in the 1970s by national workshops and increasing hardware and software capability. Systems became more flexible, allowing users to manage test names, normal ranges, and report formats without re-programming. The concept of "turn-key" vendor systems was developed, ie, LISs that were almost complete and required only relatively simple configuration and "a turn of the key" to use. The systems remained primitive by modern standards, though, and installations were not always successful. A review in 1975 defined an "optimal" laboratory system as one that had electronic connections to at least some chemistry and hematology instruments and at least three of the following five features[2]:

- Test requests could be imported or entered through a terminal.
- Collection lists with labels could be printed.
- Test results could be entered without manual re-entry of a patient identifier.
- Ward reports could be printed.
- Cumulative summaries could be printed.

Only about half of installed systems met this benchmark, and many attempted system installations failed completely, with substantial loss of effort and funds.

Technical progress in the latter part of the 1970s substantially improved the uncertain success of early systems. LIS programming moved from assembly language (LCI) and FORTRAN (Medlab, CHC) to MUMPS (Meditech, Sunquest) and COBOL (Cerner), which freed systems from ties to particular computer models, handled variable-length text efficiently, and facilitated faster software development. Systems were modularized around key laboratory functions, new modules were developed to handle non-automated laboratory sections such as microbiology and blood bank, and system interfaces to, for example, HIS and billing systems became more common. Recognizably modern vendor systems appeared

during this time. By the end of the 1970s, the basic design of LISs had been established, with a modular architecture supporting multiple laboratory sections and working from a common database, and greater than 90% of installations were successful. Separate systems supporting anatomic pathology began to appear in the late 1970s and early 1980s, with features such as specimen accessioning, workload recording, capture and display of patient demographics and history, in-terminal text editing and report formatting, searching and printing of SNOMED-coded reports, and billing.[3-5]

The challenges and progress of LISs provided background for a paper published in *Science* in 1980 by Lincoln and Korpman titled "Computers, health care, and medical information science."[6] The authors used the clinical laboratory as an illustration of the larger challenges in the application of computer technology to health care delivery and argued that meeting these challenges required a new approach that blended medical knowledge with information science and engineering. They termed this approach *medical information science,* foreshadowing the field that ultimately became prominent as medical informatics in the 1980s and 1990s.

Maturation and Adoption

As automation of laboratory procedures advanced in the 1980s, LIS adoption became widespread and was essentially a requirement for clinical laboratories of any size. Commercial LISs added features and refinements that took advantage of increasing computer hardware capabilities, though at the cost of increased complexity and occasional reliability problems. Standardization of electronic communications improved the ability to interface laboratory instruments and other systems such as the hospital information system to the LIS. The American Society for Testing and Materials (ASTM) developed standards for instrument interfaces, and the Health Level Seven International (HL7) standards organization was created. In 1987, HL7 released the second version of its messaging standard, which became widely used for instrument and system interfaces in the United States. A shift from terminals to networked microcomputers (single-user personal computers) running terminal emulators occurred by the end of the decade. Microcomputers increased the usefulness of workstations and saved space by effectively combining multiple terminals into one device, but they also increased end-user support requirements and decreased overall reliability and security.

The important role of pathologists in managing pathology information systems and using pathology information to optimize patient care was highlighted by Korpman in 1987,[7] and these concepts formed the basis for the field of pathology informatics. Friedman[8,9] and Beck[10] subsequently provided strong quality, strategic, and financial arguments for establishing pathology informatics as a distinct component of pathology services and a subspecialty of pathology. This early work, which defined a role for pathologists in ensuring the accurate and understandable communication of electronic data to clinicians, is reflected in the current College of American Pathologists (CAP) laboratory accreditation checklist requirements that pathologists validate both laboratory computer system operation and pathology data display in downstream information systems such as electronic health records (EHRs).

By the 1990s, clinical laboratory systems were relatively mature, and development centered on workflow and system integration. Improvements included automated specimen handling, calculations and rules storage and execution, and communications and data standards to support LIS incorporation into developing medical enterprise information architectures. The SNOMED medical terminology system, which grew out of the pathology community, was substantially expanded through several releases, culminating in SNOMED CT in 2002.[11] Development of the Logical Observation Identifiers, Names and Codes (LOINC) code set for identifying laboratory tests began in the mid-1990s.[12] As microcomputer hardware and operating system capabilities advanced, LISs offered client software that provided graphical user interfaces (GUIs) as a replacement for scrolling textual displays on terminal emulators. Although GUIs provided easier training and aided in the use of unfamiliar functions, they were not clearly more efficient—and were often demonstrably less efficient—for laboratory workflow than textual displays with expert users. For this reason, terminal-style displays remain in use in LISs at some sites today. Anatomic pathology laboratory information systems (APLISs) largely adopted GUI client software, with some systems embedding commercial word processors for text editing and printing, and report design focused on printing on paper. Continuing orientation to paper reports is a limitation in APLISs as medicine transitions to fully electronic systems; however, report formatting recommendations as late as 2008 dedicated only limited space to formatting for electronic use

Acronyms

APLIS: anatomic pathology laboratory information system; **ASCII:** American Standard Code for Information Interchange; **ASP:** application service provider; **ASTM:** formerly American Society for Testing and Materials; **DBMS:** database management system; **DICOM:** Digital Imaging and Communications in Medicine; **DSL:** digital subscriber line; **EHR:** electronic health record; **GUI:** graphical user interface; **HIS:** hospital information system; **HL7:** Health Level Seven International; **HL7 CCD:** HL7 Continuity of Care Document; **HL7 CDA:** HL7 Clinical Document Architecture; **HL7 RIM:** HL7 Reference Information Model; **IHTSDO:** International Health Terminology Standards Development Organization; **IT:** information technology; **JPEG:** Joint Photographic Experts Group; **LIS:** laboratory information system; **LOINC:** Logical Observation Identifiers Names and Codes; **MUMPS:** Massachusetts General Hospital Utility Multi-Programming System; **NIC:** network interface card; **NIST:** National Institute of Standards and Technology; **PNG:** Portable Network Graphics; **RAM:** random access memory; **RFID:** radio frequency identification; **SNOMED CT:** Systematized Nomenclature of Medicine Clinical Terms; **SQL:** Structured Query Language; **SSL:** Secure Sockets Layer; **TCP/IP:** Transmission Control Protocol/Internet Protocol; **TLS:** Transport Layer Security; **UML:** Unified Modeling Language; **VPN:** virtual private network; **XML:** Extensible Markup Language.

and noted that most ambulatory reporting in anatomic pathology remained on paper.[13]

Advances in hardware speed and storage capacity in the 1990s enabled experimentation with telepathology and digital imaging of microscope slides. Telepathology may be classified in order of increasing computing and communication requirements as static, in which selected images from a slide are transmitted to a remote pathologist for diagnosis or consultation; dynamic, in which remote real-time microscopic images are viewed; or virtual, in which the entire tissue content of the slide is digitized, often in multiple focal planes. During the 1990s, radiology underwent a transition from film-based imaging to digital imaging, but pathology did not. Though the technical challenges in digitizing routine pathology practice are substantial, the primary difference between these two applications is related to financial impact and turnaround time. Digital radiology eliminated the use, processing, storage, and transport of film, with substantial financial savings, and decreased the time to image availability. In contrast, digital pathology did not eliminate slide processing and, because it added digitization time to the existing workflow, tended to lengthen the time to image availability. With potential benefits limited to the possibility of more rapid consultation, and with some regulatory barriers related to interstate licensing, there were inadequate financial or quality incentives to spur investment in the engineering and process change required to develop routine digital pathology for widespread use. In settings where access to necessary pathology expertise is limited, however, telepathology can provide substantial value for diagnosis and consultation.[14,15]

Recent Developments and Challenges

The progression to greater automation in the laboratory continued in the first decade of the 21st century. The advancement of automated sample handling systems with associated instrument clusters created a need for specialized instrument management software that was not met by the standard LIS. Instrument management software, often referred to as "middleware" because it mediates between the LIS and instruments, represents a new class of LIS software that specializes in the management and quality control of high-volume analyzers. These systems' modern user interfaces and databases, quality control capabilities, and ability to execute stored operational rules have proven valuable outside the limited setting of automated sample handling; thus, they are now encountered as part of automated testing sections in many laboratories. LISs and related systems are also being extended to improve testing-related workflow in non-laboratory settings. Point-of-care (POC) systems support the downloading of data from mobile devices, quality control management, and the uploading of patient results to the LIS for final reporting. Patient recognition and label printing has also become automated; "positive patient identification" tokens such as barcoded armbands and radio frequency identification (RFID) tags have improved sample acquisition workflow and simplified in-lab sample processing.

Unfortunately, data in pathology systems continue to be represented primarily as locally defined codes and free text, and report formatting and content in anatomic pathology is idiosyncratic. The use of standard terminologies to represent patient characteristics and diagnoses or test identities is limited. While idiosyncratic systems may function adequately for local patient care—particularly when reports are printed on paper—they do not optimally support emerging health system priorities such as communicating data across care delivery systems, providing data that can be summarized automatically, or contributing data to large-scale comparative effectiveness and post-marketing surveillance studies of therapeutics. Current APLISs are particularly weak in providing reports that communicate well when displayed electronically in downstream systems such as EHRs. Recent progress in standardizing the content and presentation of anatomic pathology reports—for example, the CAP cancer protocols[16]—is a positive sign that suggests increasing support for report standardization. As EHRs become widespread and the use of paper reports declines, the need for accurate data sharing and effective display within these downstream systems will increase. Appropriate data representation and formatting standards exist to meet these needs; their incorporation will likely be one of the next steps forward for pathology systems.

More profound changes in pathology informatics are on the not-too-distant horizon. The migration of microarray technologies, whole genome sequencing, and other high throughput methods from research to the clinical laboratory will generate an enormous amount of data for which computer storage, analysis, and diagnostic interpretation is essential. Management and processing of the raw data from these methods to yield predictions of disease risk and therapeutic response requires a fundamentally different architectural and processing strategy than exists in current LISs and APLISs. Software and data standards development in this area is very active and will ultimately yield a new class of data processing, storage, and reporting applications. Pathologists will manage these applications and integrate their output into the LIS and, ultimately, the EHR.

Computer Basics

Digital computers are available in a wide variety of sizes and configurations, from large mainframe systems and warehouse-sized computing clusters to devices that can fit in the palm of one's hand or be embedded in other small devices. Across this wide physical range, the basic principles and features of computers are remarkably consistent (Figure 6-1). Data contained in a computer's working memory (random access memory [RAM]) are transformed in a central processing unit according to instructions contained in application programs, which are also stored in RAM (for example, word

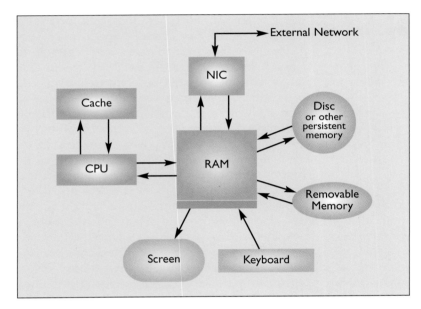

Figure 6-1. Simple Diagram of the Major Components of a Digital Computer. Binary data stored in random access memory (RAM) are transformed in the central processing unit (CPU). A smaller set of high-speed RAM called cache memory is used to store commonly accessed instructions and data temporarily. If the computer is connected to a screen and keyboard, sections of RAM (which may be separate from primary RAM) hold data that are written to the screen and receive data from the keyboard. Data for long-term storage are transferred to persistent memory, such as magnetic or optical discs, flash memory, or tape, which can be removable and portable. Data for transmission across networks to other computers are processed by a network interface card (NIC) and passed to the network using communication protocols such as Ethernet.

processors, spreadsheets, and LISs). Application programs are managed by a controlling program called the operating system. Windows, Mac OSX, Linux, and Unix are familiar examples of operating systems. Data and programs that need to persist when the computer is shut down are written as files from RAM to persistent storage, such as magnetic or optical disks, flash memory cards, or tape, and the files are read from those media back into RAM when they are needed. Data files can be exchanged between computers using removable persistent storage media or by transmission across communication networks. Physical devices are generally referred to as hardware, while programs are referred to as software. Data stored semipermanently in computers in flash memory, usually used for basic device configuration settings or system startup, are sometimes called firmware.

Data Representation

Computers store and process sequences of binary digits, or bits, that have values of either 0 or 1. For speed and simplicity, bits are usually used in groups of 8, called bytes, that together can represent integers from 0 to 255. Larger integers and other kinds of data, such as floating-point (decimal) numbers, text characters, and images, are represented by using defined patterns to string bytes together in long sequences. Those sequences can then be processed in RAM or saved as files. Large data sets may require many bytes, and thus the byte sizes of files and computer memory capacity are generally referenced in thousands (kilo-

bytes), millions (megabytes), or billions (gigabytes).

Medical systems generally store patient demographics, diagnosis codes, test codes, test results, textual descriptions and interpretations, etc, as characters—including any numbers these data types contain. Most systems represent characters with the American Standard Code for Information Interchange (ASCII), which uses one byte per character and assigns numerical values to 128 characters, including the lower- and uppercase Roman alphabets; Arabic numerals from 0 to 9; and a limited number of punctuation and "white space" characters, including the space, tab, and return. ASCII is very limiting, particularly in non-English settings, and is being replaced by a newer standard called Unicode, which can use two bytes per character. Unicode supports a much larger character set, including all alphabets and number representations in use; a large set of business, mathematical, and scientific symbols; and a large number of Japanese and Chinese characters. Current microcomputers support Unicode, and medical information systems will support Unicode in the future.

Computers can represent images as vector graphics or bitmaps, also known as raster images. Vector graphics are drawn as combinations of shapes from mathematical instructions contained in a data file and are commonly used for graphic art. Bitmaps are two-dimensional arrays of dots called pixels that vary in brightness and recreate an image when displayed in aggregate (Figure 6-2). Images captured by digital cameras or scan-

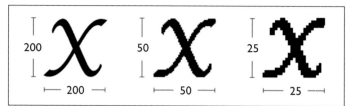

Figure 6-2. Bitmap Image Resolution. The images of the letter X are formed from black and white dots (pixels) at resolutions of 200 x 200, 50 x 50, and 25 x 25. As resolution decreases, the image loses its ability to represent fine detail. Full-color images of these resolutions would require a minimum of 120 kb, 7.5 kb, and 1.9 kb, respectively, assuming 3 bytes per pixel.

ners, including most images used in medical and pathology systems, are bitmaps. In a full-color image, each pixel is defined by three bytes whose values represent the brightness of red, green, and blue; the remaining colors are created as mixtures of these primary colors. Modern systems may include a fourth byte that can be used for additional purposes, such as indicating whether the pixel should represent transparency if it is layered over another pixel by allowing a variable amount of the underlying pixel's color to be averaged with the color of the overlying pixel.

The resolution of a bitmap image is the number of pixels it contains and is usually expressed as the vertical and horizontal pixel dimensions (Figure 6-2). The minimum size of an image's data set is the product of the pixel dimensions and the number of bytes used per pixel; for example, a full-color, medium-sized image (1024 x 768 pixels) would require a minimum of about 2.4 megabytes. Higher-resolution images appear sharper at a given image size (Figure 6-2) but require more storage space and take longer to transmit over a network. Images that represent pathology slides at multiple levels of magnification appropriate for diagnosis usually have a very high resolution and are thus very large.

Image Compression

Image compression techniques, which mathematically describe groups of pixels in an image rather than representing each pixel separately, reduce the size and transfer time of images. Image compression may be lossy or non-lossy. Lossy compression methods eliminate less important data and reduce the size of the remaining data. If the method is applied correctly, the regenerated image, while not identical to the original image, does not show significant differences. Non-lossy methods compress all the data, and regenerated images are identical

to the original images. The most common lossy method is called JPEG because it was developed by the Joint Photographic Experts Group. This method is very effective for compressing continuous tone images such as photographs or scans—ie, images that contain color gradients with few abrupt edges. The JPEG method allows variable compression with greater artifacts at higher compression levels; thus, compression can be adjusted to suit a particular use. Because lossy methods introduce artifacts each time they are used, images that are repeatedly compressed will degrade. It is best to use a lossy compression method for the "final form" compression of an image that will not be further edited and re-saved. The most common non-lossy compression method is PNG (Portable Network Graphics), which is used optimally for bitmap graphic art with large areas of identical color and few gradients. PNG allows one compression level; the method compresses photographic images, albeit much less effectively than JPEG. However, because it is non-lossy, PNG allows images to be repeatedly compressed with no loss of quality. JPEG and PNG files are typically denoted by .jpg or .png file-name extensions, respectively. JPEG is most useful for pathology images as long as they are not overly compressed and repeated compression is avoided.

Data Standards

ASCII, Unicode, JPEG, and PNG are data standards that have been defined and approved by standards organizations, and their specifications are generally available. A number of organizations are active worldwide in producing data standards, including professional societies, government agencies, and consortia comprising vendors, users, and other interested parties. Standards development typically includes a requirements definition, an initial trial implementation, a period of comment and refinement, and a vote leading to approval for general use and publication. Standards may be copyrighted and licensed for fees that support their ongoing maintenance, or they may be freely available. Any vendor or programmer can review the specifications in a data standard (subject to applicable licensing fees), design a computer program to work with the standard, and share data with other programs that adhere to the same standard. Pathology information systems use several standards for medical data representation that support the basic interchange of information between systems for regulatory reporting and electronic

Table 6-1. LOINC Example for Cardiac Troponin I

Code	Component	Property	Time Aspect	System	Scale	Method
10839-9	TROPONIN I.CARDIAC	MCNC	PT	SER/PLAS	QN	

Definitions: MCNC, mass concentration; PT, point in time; SER/PLAS, serum or plasma; QN, quantitative.
Fully-qualified name: TROPONIN I.CARDIAC:MCNC:PT:SER/PLAS:QN.
Short name: Troponin I SerPl-mCnc (LOINC short names are for convenience but may change over time).

Table 6-2. SNOMED CT Data Elements for the Concept of Bronchial Pneumonia (Simplified)

Concept ID	Name	Synonyms*	Relationships**	
67814005	Bronchopneumonia	Bronchial pneumonia Lobular pneumonia Segmental pneumonia Bilateral bronchopneumonia ...	is-a	pneumonia
			associated-morphology	inflammation
			finding-site	lung
			finding-site	bronchus

*Each synonym also has a numerical ID.
**Representative examples shown; a SNOMED record would contain additional relationships. Relationships may connect two SNOMED concepts within a hierarchy (is-a) or across hierarchies (associated-morphology, finding-site). A SNOMED record connects concepts by associating the primary concept code with a second concept code through a relationship code.

billing. The most important of these standards are the International Statistical Classification of Diseases and Related Health Problems (commonly known as ICD) and the Current Procedural Terminology (CPT). Both are controlled vocabularies that associate well-defined medical concepts with numeric codes. ICD, currently ICD-9-CM, is a hierarchical list of about 6000 diagnoses published by the World Health Organization. CPT represents medical services and procedures, such as laboratory testing and pathology interpretation, and is maintained and licensed for use by the American Medical Association. In billing claims, procedures must be identified by CPT codes and justified by ICD codes. A new version of ICD, ICD-10-CM, is scheduled to go into use in October 2013. ICD-10 is more complete (about 155,000 codes) but contains changes that will require upgrades of many medical systems.

Though ICD and CPT have been useful for communications related to billing and reporting, they are not complete medical vocabularies capable of describing laboratory tests, results, and interpretations in adequate detail in clinical summaries. Future health-data–sharing goals, including the transport of clinical summaries between care providers, and population health surveillance will require more comprehensive medical data standards such as LOINC and SNOMED CT. LOINC is maintained by the Regenstrief Institute and is available for use at no cost.[17] It provides standard names and codes for clinical observations, including laboratory tests as well as components of the physical exam, radiology exams, EKG studies, etc. A laboratory test is designated in LOINC by a "fully qualified name" that includes the analyte (component), the property being measured, the timing of the measurement, the type of specimen (system), the general measurement scale, and an optional method descriptor (Table 6-1). Each name defines a type of test and is designated a numerical code with a hyphenated last digit. SNOMED CT (Table 6-2), a large clinical vocabulary that was originally developed under CAP management and is currently maintained and developed by the International Health Terminology Standards Development Organization (IHTSDO), has been licensed for national use in a number of countries including the US.[18] It contains over 300,000 concepts represented by numeric codes and is organized into 18 topic-oriented hierarchies (clinical finding, body structure, organism, specimen, social context, etc). It also includes rules for combining its codes into higher level concepts. SNOMED defines relationships between concepts such as "is-a," "finding-site" (body location), and "associated-morphology" and includes almost 1 million specified relationships within and across its 18 hierarchies. Notably, SNOMED includes the notions of uncertainty and severity, which are absent from ICD.

Table 6-3. Good Password Practices

Use at least 8 characters (more is better).
Do not use words from the dictionary or names (even with numbers appended).
Do not use common number sequences.
Do not use current or past personal information.
Use upper and lower case letters, punctuation, numbers, and spaces.
Passwords derived from phrases can be good, especially if numbers, punctuation, and spaces are added.
Passwords should be changed periodically to limit access if a password is broken.
Never share your password with others.
Do not enter your password in front of an observer.
If you write down your password, keep it in a safe place; do not keep passwords where they can be seen or easily found.

General Characteristics of Laboratory Information Systems

Modern LISs are deeply embedded in laboratory operations, managing data and supporting workflow required for preanalytical tasks, testing, reporting results, and laboratory administration. LISs receive patient demographics and test orders, and print work lists with container requirements and specimen labels for phlebotomy teams, histotechnologists, or clinicians. Specimens are tracked, usually by scanning a barcoded label at each step, from creation through transport, accessioning in the lab, preparation, aliquotting, analysis, and storage. LISs provide testing instructions to automated analyzers and worksheets for manual methods, and receive results from both sources. Quality control data are tracked and compared with acceptable values on a run-by-run basis and accumulated into reports for periodic review. Initial results of tests may be processed using rules that calculate derived results, initiate reflex testing, or provide decision support; interpretive or explanatory comments from stored libraries of text may be manually or automatically added to selected results. Reports containing results and associated text in electronic or paper form are routed to a clinical information system, the patient's location, and/or the ordering physician. LISs may create requisition forms or electronic orders to accompany send-out tests to reference laboratories and receive and report the results of such tests. They may also receive orders from and transmit results to other laboratories and physician offices to support outreach activities. A variety of predefined, scheduled reports support quality assurance, workload analysis, and resource use, and ad hoc reports are often created to address special questions from laboratory management, an associated health care system, or medical researchers. LISs provide data necessary for billing pathology services, and billing systems may be closely associated with an LIS under pathology management, or the LIS may provide procedure information and diagnostic codes to an institutional billing system through an electronic interface.

LISs receive, create, store, and report many different data elements as they carry out the tasks listed above. While some of these data elements are represented using standard vocabularies such as ICD and CPT, many more are defined locally and thus are not meaningful outside their local environment. For example, most laboratories use locally invented codes to designate laboratory tests. This practice developed because in the past there was no standard way to represent tests, and because short, mnemonic, locally memorable codes were useful as commands for terminal displays. The disadvantage of local codes is that they are meaningless if they are sent to another system unless explicitly translated to the appropriate data representations used by that system—a process that requires effort and time. Standard vocabularies such as LOINC and SNOMED CT, which could

Figure 6-3. Database Structure. Hierarchical databases (A) connect data elements in tree structures. Looking up test results on a particular patient by traversing the tree is very fast. Finding all instances of Test E across a population of patients in an ad hoc report, in contrast, would be very slow because each patient and visit would need to be evaluated to see if Test E were present. Relational databases (B) maintain data in multiple tables that share values. Each patient in the Patients table is assigned a unique patient ID (pID), and the table also contains other information about patients. Each visit has a unique visit identifier (vID) in a separate Visits table, and also the pID from the Patients table and other information about the visit. Each test has a unique test identifier (tID) in a separate Tests table, along with the pID from the Patients table and the vID from the Visits table, plus other information about the test and result. Test results for a particular patient can be found by searching the tests table using the patient's pID. This is reasonably efficient but not as fast as traversing the hierarchical tree. Instances of Test E can be found by searching the Tests table, and any necessary in-

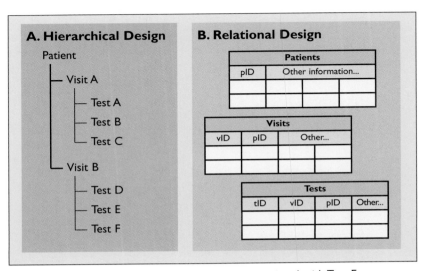

formation about visits or patients associated with Test E can be found by searching the other tables with the ID values associated with Test E in the Tests table. This is much faster than evaluating all patients and visits and illustrates the flexibility of the relational design.

potentially solve this problem, are not yet widely used.

Database Applications

LISs store standard and locally defined data elements in databases, which are organized data files that are managed by application programs called database management systems (DBMSs). DBMSs provide access control, audit trails, transaction support for data modification, and searching/reporting tools. DBMS access is typically managed via password-protected accounts. Good password practices are crucial for system security (Table 6-3). The network environment may provide additional security. Descriptions of users' actions, including viewing or updating data, are captured to log files called audit trails that identify users by login account. Transactional databases allow multiple data items to be updated together so that all data are confirmed to be correctly updated; otherwise, the state of the database is rolled back to the point prior to the transaction so that the transaction succeeds or fails as a whole. Concurrent transactions are managed in such a way that they do not conflict with one another. Transaction support is important in receiving an order, which adds a number of new data elements to the database that should be accepted only as a complete set. Medical databases have several additional transaction requirements: once accepted, transactions should not be deleted because the information could have

triggered actions that affect patients. Corrections should be accomplished via an annotated replacement record while maintaining the previous version. DBMSs also provide a method for defining database searches, formatting and scheduling reports, and saving searches and report formats for future use. LISs typically provide predefined, modifiable reports that are useful for laboratory management and allow the creation of additional scheduled and ad hoc reports.

Several types of DBMSs are used in transactional LISs. MUMPS databases first appeared in commercial LISs in the 1970s and are still used in a number of systems. MUMPS databases—efficient, fast, and able to support high transaction rates in large laboratories or multiple sites with a consolidated LIS—are essentially hierarchical data structures that update and report very rapidly when the update or search "fits" the design of the hierarchy (Figure 6-3). Ad hoc searches that do not fit the hierarchy may be very slow, lasting for hours, and may require substantial system resources. Several LISs and instrument managers use an alternative relational database design that organizes data in multiple tables that are associated through shared data elements (Figure 6-3). Relational databases also use structured query language (SQL), a powerful, relatively standard programming language for specifying searches and reports. Because they are flexible and applicable in many different settings, relational databases are the most widely used type of database outside of medicine.

However, relational databases are slower and more demanding of computer hardware than MUMPS databases when the latter are used optimally for their hierarchical design, and thus are not as well-suited as MUMPS databases for very large applications and high transaction rates. On the other hand, their flexibility allows relational databases to provide much better average performance than MUMPS databases across a range of arbitrary searches. Some MUMPS databases provide adapters that allow searches to be specified in SQL to take advantage of SQL's convenience and familiarity, but the performance of those searches remains subject to the hierarchical structure of the database.

A data dictionary is the set of individual data elements a database contains. The internal organization of data elements in different databases with the same data dictionary can differ, yielding advantages or disadvantages for particular applications. The structure of a database is called its schema, which is often depicted graphically, similar to Figure 6-3. A broader and more general term for the definition of a set of data elements and their relationships is a data model. Databases have data models that describe their data elements and organization; on a smaller scale, individual reports, insurance claims, and any other grouping of data elements designed for a particular purpose also have data models.

Database searches usually yield lists of data elements in meaningful groups, for example, a work list of specimens with requested tests or a list of test results with patient names and medical record numbers. The entries in these lists are often called records, and their constituent data elements are called fields. A list of records is often displayed as a table, with one record per line and one field per column, but records also might be displayed as one record per page or screen, with the content of fields arranged logically in the display area. The fields of a record may contain single data elements with well-defined representation and meaning that are either local or derived from a standard, known as structured data (eg, dimensions of a tissue specimen captured in separate fields using a defined syntax), or they may contain uncontrolled narrative text with embedded data elements that have variable position and wording, known as unstructured data (eg, dimensions of a specimen captured as part of a textual gross description). Unstructured data are difficult to search quickly

and reliably because their presence and content may vary unpredictably across large numbers of records. Methods have been developed to add structure to narrative text, including the use of defined templates or markup (eg, Extensible Markup Language [XML]), and to process these textual patterns in databases; however, pathology systems have not yet implemented such technology.

Although LISs and anatomic pathology systems share many similarities, the systems differ in several important ways. Because LISs support a flow of clinical data that includes orders, specimens, discrete results, and locally standardized textual comments, most data in LISs are structured. In contrast, anatomic pathology systems support extended textual descriptions and interpretations with fields representing general report sections, such as clinical history, gross description, final diagnosis, and comments—a design that yields a substantial amount of unstructured data. Anatomic pathology systems usually allow standard coding of diagnoses (using SNOMED, for example), but there is little incentive to perform detailed coding since it is not required for billing or patient care, and because clinical data sharing has consisted primarily of transporting complete printed reports. In lieu of using defined data elements to search results, anatomic pathology systems generally offer "free text" (character string) searches of unstructured fields whose reliability is dependent on the local site's ability to standardize text descriptions by convention. The use of uncontrolled text has serious drawbacks, but it does have the benefit of flexibility. In recent years, this flexibility has enabled anatomic pathology systems to support relatively complex reports from, for example, molecular diagnostics and flow cytometry, when LISs did not offer structured data models adequate for these purposes.

Some anatomic pathology systems also associate selected images with cases. Since images are often large and do not need to be searched internally, it is most efficient to store them as files outside the textual case database, with links in the database that lead to the image files. In some cases, images are maintained on a separate image server, a computer optimized for the storage and transmission of large data files. Data standards for representing pathology images with associated information such as measurements and interpretations have been developed recently by DICOM, the organization that also develops standards for digital radiology.[19]

Data Warehousing and Mining

Databases such as LISs that are used in daily patient care are typically transactional systems with schemas designed to support efficient data lookup and updating for individual patients. Databases are also useful for finding populations of patients with similar characteristics, for example, for retrospective research, population health surveillance, or quality improvement studies. Because transactional schemas are not efficient for these types of tasks, data are often exported from transactional systems to large databases called data warehouses that have schemas optimized for population searches.[20] Data warehouses may be searched directly to find patients with particular attributes, or statistical techniques collectively known as data mining may be used to discover previously unknown associations in data or to create data-driven predictive models.[21] These techniques appear to have substantial potential for application to pathology data,[22-24] but so far they have seen limited use in the field.

Computer Networking

LISs were developed initially as standalone systems, with most data entered manually through multiple, directly connected terminals and results communicated through printed reports. This situation has changed dramatically, and most laboratory systems now communicate directly with instruments and other computer systems through computer networks. Networked computers are connected to each other by media such as coaxial cables, twisted pair copper wires, fiberoptic cable, or radio frequency signals. Network interface cards (Figure 6-1) inside the computers send and receive binary data to and from the media in the appropriate form (eg, impulses of electricity, light, or radio waves). For convenience, local networks that use physical media are usually configured in star patterns, with a network hub or switch at the center and computers at the ends of the branches (Figure 6-4). The hub or switch is located in a protected spot such as an electrical closet and may service 48 or more branches leading to workstations, instruments, the LIS itself, other hubs, and/or external connections. Basic hubs allow all network communications to travel to all branches. Switches are more expensive and allow communications to travel only to the branches containing the devices to which they are addressed. Switches have speed and security advantages because they

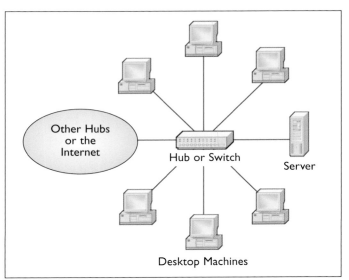

Figure 6-4. Basic "Star" Network. The connected devices are arranged like the points of a star around a central hub or switch. Workstations, servers, printers, scanners, and other devices may be connected to the network, and a branch of the network may connect to other local networks or to an Internet connection point. Hubs support a common network in which all communications go to all branches, and devices ignore communications addressed to others. Switches actively sort communications so that data only enter a branch if they are addressed to a device on that branch. Wi-Fi base stations function similarly to standard hubs but use radio frequencies instead of wires. All devices within range can "hear" all communications but ignore communications addressed to other devices.

reduce overall network traffic and prevent devices from reading each others' network communications surreptitiously (ie, eavesdropping). Computers and application software that provide shared resources or data to a network are called servers; computers and application software that users work with directly to access server-provided resources across a network are called clients. Thin clients are a class of client software that is designed primarily to display server-generated views of data rather than receive and process data from servers.

Successful communication between two computers requires that both computers use the same strategy for encoding, addressing, and exchanging data, and these shared network protocols are established by standards organizations. Ethernet and Wi-Fi are two of the most common data transport protocols used in local networks. Most current devices implement these protocols directly, but some older instruments and printers may use other protocols such as the RS-232 serial communications protocol for direct connection to computers. These devices can be connected to local networks using a hardware adapter, which is essentially a small computer that gives the device a network address and translates the protocols. Additional protocols are used to transmit data greater distances between local networks, and data transmitted across the Internet between widely separated computers may cross many different media and be translated through many protocols. Computers or local networks in homes and small businesses may be connected to the Internet via digital subscriber lines (DSL) from telecom vendors, cable television networks, or satellite connections in remote locations. These low-cost, relatively high-speed connections for end users are collectively termed broadband. Larger organizations may lease higher-capacity lines from telecomm vendors at higher cost.

Network performance is generally measured as data transmission rate in bits per second and is referred to as bandwidth. "Standard" Ethernet over twisted pair copper wire runs at a theoretical maximum of about 10 megabits per second. Updated versions of Ethernet available in most networks and current desktop and laptop computers run at 10 to 100 times that speed (eg, gigabit Ethernet). Protocols running over the national network backbones yield even higher bandwidth. Radio frequency networks are somewhat slower, with Wi-Fi (the 802.11 family of standards) running at about 10 to 150 megabits per second, depending on the specific protocol in use. In reality, the theoretical maximum achievable with one computer transmitting at the maximum rate is rarely approached in local networks. In the usual situation, multiple computers on a network communicating individually occasionally interfere with each other by transmitting simultaneously. When these network collisions occur, both devices wait a random length of time and retry their transmissions. Such collisions reduce the efficiency of communication, and they become more common as overall network usage increases. When this happens, the network appears to slow down from an individual device's perspective. Network usage and collision frequency can be monitored, and excessive numbers indicate a need to reduce network usage through policy, segment the network to separate traffic, or upgrade the network.

A suite of standard communication protocols called transmission control protocol/Internet protocol (TCP/IP) was originally developed for use on the Internet but is now almost universally used across a variety of networks. TCP/IP works in combination with data transport protocols and defines how data are addressed to remote computers (IP addresses), how data are transmitted, and how transmission errors are resolved. In TCP/IP communications, data are divided into packets (short bursts of network activity) that have destination and return addresses plus a data payload, and the packets are numbered in sequence. They are transmitted independently to the destination, and the data are reassembled into the correct sequence by the receiving device.

System Interfaces and HL7

TCP/IP and related protocols allow binary data to be transmitted reliably across networks, but data standards are necessary to allow the binary data to carry meaningful information between application programs such as an LIS and an instrument control program or an EHR. A connection between application programs is called a system interface. Interfaces may be unidirectional (one system always transmits and the other always receives) or bidirectional (systems can exchange data in both directions). Bidirectional interfaces are typical in modern systems; unidirectional interfaces are used with laboratory instruments that require manual test setup but can transmit results and with some hospital administrative systems that only broadcast admit/discharge/transfer information. In the United States and increasingly in the rest of the world, standards for both instrument and system interfaces used in health care are developed and approved by the HL7 standards organization. ASTM also provides standards for instrument interfaces.

Current system interfaces use version 2 of the HL7 standard, which defines a set of text message formats for transferring information related to particular health care tasks. For pathology, important message types include admit/discharge/transfer (patient demographics and location), order entry (new orders to the laboratory), and results (pathology data for reporting). Each message type has a data model that defines its overall structure, the type of data elements (fields) it contains, and the placement of the fields in the message (Figure 6-5). HL7 v 2 does not specify the data representation to be used in the fields because many of these data elements are locally defined. This content flexibility allows HL7 interfaces to be used without data standardization, but it also means that the interface must transform nonstandard data elements between representations used in the

```
MSH|^~\&|IDXLAB|UVAHSC|DADD||DateTime||ORU^R01|DateTime|P|2.2|||||
PID|||xxxxxxxx||lname^fname^mi||Date|M|^^|||||||||3116488572||
PV1||OP|STFM^||||483230^lname^^fname mi.(4201)|^|||||||||||OP||||||||||||||||||||||||||...
ORC|RE|320532-0^0|||||||||||4201^lname^^fname mi.(||||^||||
OBR||320532-0^0||CPBAS^BASIC METABOLIC PANEL^^CPBAS|||DateTime|||^||||DateTime|^|...
OBX|1|NM|NA^SODIUM|1|137|mmol/L|136-145||||F|||DateTime|UVA^|2886^AUTO^VERIFY|
OBX|2|NM|K^POTASSIUM|1|4.0|mmol/L|3.5-4.5|||F|||DateTime|UVA^|2886^AUTO^VERIFY|
OBX|3|NM|CL^CHLORIDE|1|101|mmol/L|98-107||||F|||DateTime|UVA^|2886^AUTO^VERIFY|
OBX|4|NM|CO2^CO2|1|24|mmol/L|23-31||||F|||DateTime|UVA^|2886^AUTO^VERIFY|
OBX|5|NM|BUN^UREA NITROGEN|1|23|mg/dL|8.4-25.7|||F|||DateTime|UVA^|2886^AUTO^VERIFY|
OBX|6|NM|CREAT^CREATININE|1|1.0|mg/dL|0.7-1.3|||F|||DateTime|UVA^|2886^AUTO^VERIFY|
OBX|7|NM|GLUC^GLUCOSE|1|135|mg/dL|74-99|H||F|||DateTime|UVA^|2886^AUTO^VERIFY|
OBX|8|NM|CALCM^CALCIUM|1|9.8|mg/dL|8.4-10.2|||F||DateTime|UVA^|2886^AUTO^VERIFY|
OBX|9|ST|GFRCAL^CALC GFR (mL/min/1.73m2)|1|>60||||||F|||DateTime|UVA^|2886^AUTO^VERIFY|
```

Figure 6-5. Representative HL7 Version 2 Message. HL7 messages are textual and adhere to a structure defined in HL7 v 2 Implementation Guides. This is an Observation Result message (ORU-R01) for a basic metabolic panel. Names and dates have been replaced to protect identities, and two long lines were truncated (indicated with "..."). Each line of an HL7 message is called a *segment,* and each segment starts with a three-letter identifier and then contains *fields* delimited by vertical bars. Fields may be subdivided with additional delimiter characters to produce *components* (carats are used as delimiters here). Not all fields are used, and unused fields are left in place but are empty (indicated by contiguous bars).

The segment structure of a message is defined by the HL7 standard; an ORU-R01 message contains a Message Header (MSH), Patient ID segment (PID), Patient Visit segment (PV1), Common Order segment (ORC), Observation Request segment (OBR), and a variable number of Observation Result (OBX) segments. It may also include Note (NTE) segments, which are not shown here. The type of information that a field should carry is also defined in the standard, for example, field 3 of an OBX segment should carry the service identifier (test name), but there is no specification of how that name should be expressed. Thus, HL7 v 2 is a partial standard defining message structure, but much of the data carried by these messages is not in standard form.

connected systems. This is usually done with hand-constructed mapping tables that associate equivalent data elements and must be edited and tested whenever data elements in either system change. The interface must also catch and log transformation errors that occur when mapping edits are omitted or incorrect. In addition, HL7 messages carry textual reports as a series of text lines, one line per data element. There is no provision for display formatting instructions such as those used by word processors, and such instructions could include inappropriate characters such as field delimiters that would disrupt HL7 messages.

These characteristics mean that current HL7 interfaces are unique for a particular installation, expensive to create and maintain, and severely limited in transmitting textual reports. A new version of HL7, HL7 version 3, addresses these problems by implementing a comprehensive data model for medical care, the Reference Information Model (HL7 RIM), as a basis for defining both the structure of a message and the allowable content of its fields. Messages are expressed using XML markup,[25] and a standard XML-based Clinical Document Architecture (HL7 CDA) is available that supports textual reports including clinical summaries (HL7 CCD) containing both formatted narrative text and structured data.[26-28] Future systems incorporating HL7 v 3 will transmit and re-

ceive data using common syntax (data representation) and semantics (data meaning). Such systems will be interoperable and easily interfaced using a generic HL7 data connector, with minimal configuration and data mapping.

LISs that serve large health care delivery enterprises typically implement many (mostly HL7) interfaces. Within the laboratory, interfaces connect the LIS with automated instruments and instrument manager middleware. From an enterprise perspective, LISs are one of a number of ancillary systems that support specialized services and are interfaced to hospital information systems, clinical information systems (eg, EHRs), and billing systems. Enterprises often implement an automated communications manager, sometimes called an interface engine, to provide a consistent connection point for communications and to organize and support a large number of HL7 interfaces. In aggregate, the core systems, interface engine, ancillary systems (as well as their local environments), and external connections make up the physical architecture of a health care enterprise information system (Figure 6-6).

LISs may also use HL7 interfaces to exchange orders and results with external systems via the Internet. Such systems may include reference or other LISs, EHRs in physician offices or remote clinics and community hospitals, and/or special-

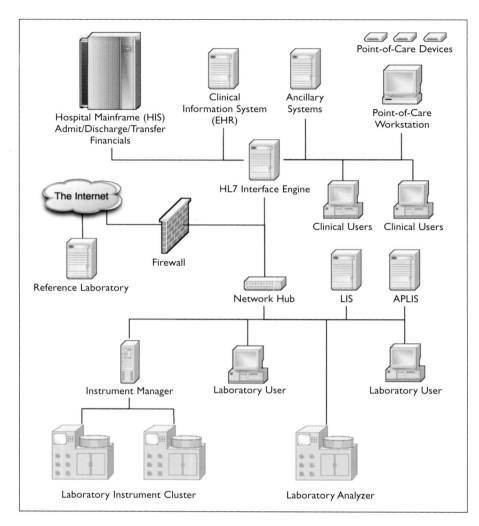

Figure 6-6. Health Care Enterprise System Architecture. This diagram illustrates the participation of laboratory systems in the larger health care information ecosystem. The laboratory information system (LIS) and anatomic pathology system (APLIS) on the right side of the figure are accessible to laboratory users and instruments over the network.

This laboratory implements an instrument manager ("middleware") that manages a cluster of instruments and connects to the LIS. HL7 interfaces between the major systems (HIS, EHR, and ancillary systems such as radiology, point-of-care devices, and the laboratory systems) are managed by an HL7 interface engine. Non-HL7 network traffic, such as email and web communications, also travels on this network.

One of many network hubs in a system this size is illustrated. External communications with a reference laboratory, other outside systems, and the web are available through a firewall that protects the internal network.

ized laboratory outreach support systems. Remote health care delivery sites may also offer local laboratory services with workstations and instrument interfaces that connect to the central LIS. Some vendors, called application service providers (ASPs), provide analogous off-site LIS services and support by subscription, usually to smaller sites. Participating sites connect instruments, workstations, and local administrative and clinical systems to the remote LIS via HL7 interfaces provided by the vendor. This arrangement reduces the local requirement for managing hardware, the LIS application, and interfaces, and may be financially attractive depending on a site's size. However, the ASP vendor must be able to provide an ongoing, adequate level of service and a viable plan for exporting data in an interoperable form in the event that the level of service is inadequate or if a site wishes to change vendors or bring the LIS in-house.

System and Data Security

System security is important because of the importance of LISs in supporting laboratory workflow and the importance of pathology information in reaching a diagnosis and in patient care. Security has two aspects: (1) pathology systems must deliver data reliably and correctly or patients may be harmed, which means that LISs should not fail or allow data to be deleted or modified surreptitiously by malicious activity or inadvertent errors; and (2) pathology data contain patient identifiers and thus qualify as protected health information under the Health Insurance Portability and Accountability Act (HIPAA)—which means that identified pathology data are confidential; should be displayed or transmitted only when necessary for medical care/billing, quality control/improvement, or formally-approved research; and should be viewed only by the individuals involved in those tasks. As a practical matter, most inappropriate data access involves local personnel and local devices. These problems can be limited by rigorous information system practices such as user training, good password security (Table 6-3), timely removal of retired accounts and passwords, automated logout and screen blanking of inactive workstations, regular review of audit trails listing data accesses and changes by personnel, and the use of network switches rather than hubs to limit eavesdropping.

Connection to the Internet raises the possibility of remote attacks that divert computers from LIS tasks, steal data, and/or disrupt network communications. Recent tests indicate that susceptible computers on unprotected networks connected to the Internet are compromised in about an hour on average.[29] Attacks may attempt to take over control of computers or capture sensitive data such as passwords or credit card numbers by targeting operating system or application defects or by tricking users into installing malicious software (malware). Compromised computers may be diverted to unwanted or malicious processing, communication, or data storage tasks, which reduces their performance and may render them unreliable. Alternatively, malicious external computers and compromised local computers may intentionally flood a local network with data packets, preventing legitimate communication (a denial-of-service attack). Any of these events can be very disruptive to laboratory operations and require substantial effort for recovery, and they should be prevented by good computer and network security practices. Basic good practices include keeping software updated to fix identified security problems (small corrective updates are sometimes called patches; note that LIS vendors may need to verify operating system and other software patches and updates before they are applied), doing routine work in user accounts with limited access privileges rather than in administrator accounts, using malware detection programs to block and remove known problem software, and limiting the use in the laboratory of removable data storage media (eg, flash memory drives) and portable computers that have been connected to external networks.

Computers and networks can be protected from malicious communications using firewalls that filter and route communications packets (Figure 6-6). The simplest firewalls are application programs that block all types of communication to the computer they are running on except for those that are explicitly allowed. More complex firewalls are used to protect local networks, and they may be separate devices or computers that are located between sections of a network or between a local network and the Internet. These firewalls may examine the target addresses, return addresses, sequence, size, and even content of communication packets, and block those without authorization or those with evidence of malicious content or usage patterns. These firewalls can keep track of communication sessions and, for example, allow external packets to pass only when they are responses to internally initiated communications. Firewalls may implement a proxy server through which all communications to and from the outside must pass. These proxies prevent an outsider from gaining knowledge about specific devices inside the network and thus make it difficult to target devices and vulnerabilities for attack. Firewall configuration and network security should be managed by an expert and may be handled by the general information technology support unit at enterprise sites or by a security consultant at smaller sites.

Routine Internet communications, such as email, file transfer, and data submission using Web forms, are insecure. The packets that carry those communications are stored and forwarded between many devices as they pass from origin to destination. Logs from those devices may be copied, or eavesdropping software may be used to copy the contents of packets to text files. Those files can then be searched automatically to find information of interest. Packets could even be altered or replaced prior to reaching their destination. For many types of communication, a low level of security is acceptable. It is not acceptable, however, for the transmission of protected health information, online commerce, or many other types of business communications. Such data require encryption, a process by which the bit sequence carrying the data is scrambled using a special second sequence called a key and, depending on the form of encryption, can be unscrambled only with the same or a related key. The protocol currently used to encrypt Internet communications is called Transport Layer Security (TLS), which is an extension of the Secure Sockets Layer (SSL) protocol developed by Netscape in the mid-1990s.

A full review of cryptography and TLS is beyond the scope of this discussion, but the following is a brief sketch of the logical process. Pairs of cryptographic keys can be created such that if one is used to encrypt data, the other can be used for decryption (asymmetric encryption). These keys

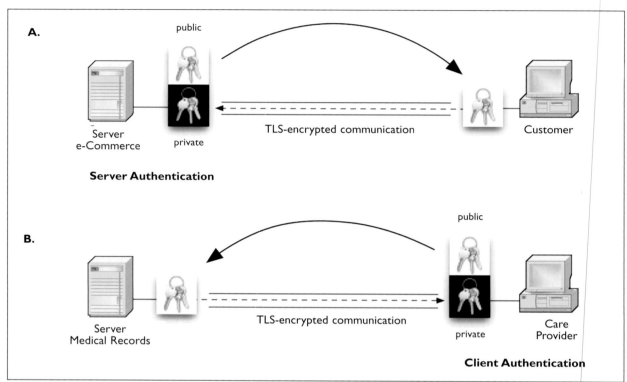

Figure 6-7. Public Key Encryption. In typical e-commerce applications (A), it is important to authenticate the vendor server because the customer sends the server sensitive information such as credit card payment instructions. The server has a digital certificate containing public and private keys. The public key is sent to the customer, who may check it for authenticity with a certificate authority. The public key is then used to encrypt the data, and the data are sent to the vendor. Only the private key that matches the public key and is owned by the vendor can decrypt the data. In health care applications (B), it is usually most important to authenticate the client, such as an external health care provider, because they will be sent sensitive medical records information. The client must have a digital certificate installed on their computer, which will provide its public key to the medical data server. The server can validate that key with a certificate authority or its own records and then use it to encrypt sensitive data. The data are then sent to the client and can be decrypted only with the private key that matches the public key, which only the client owns. Virtual private network (VPN) connections are established similarly, creating a persistent encrypted connection to a remote network. TLS: transport layer security.

are incorporated into a digital certificate that is provided to a recipient by a certificate authority, which also verifies and registers the recipient's identity according to a standard protocol such as NIST SP 800-63.[30] The certificate is stored on the certificate owner's computer, and one key is made public, while the other is kept private (public key encryption). When another computer wishes to communicate securely, it requests the public key, verifies it with the certificate authority, and uses it to encrypt the data to be sent (Figure 6-7). After that, only the matching private key can decrypt the data, and only the computer holding the certificate has the private key. Thus, the certificate provides an encryption method that both protects the data and authenticates the identity of the certificate holder. In online commerce, the vendor's Web server holds the certificate, because the goal is to authenticate the vendor so that the client's

payment is directed correctly. (The client's successful credit card validation is regarded as adequate authentication for the vendor's purposes [Figure 6-7, A].) For access to protected health information or other enterprise network resources, the goal is different: the greatest need is to authenticate the client, though both sides should ideally be authenticated. Thus, to identify and encrypt communications from trusted outsiders, the latter should download and install digital certificates on the client computers they will use to access the sensitive data or resources (Figure 6-7, B). Some health care systems implement their own certificate authorities to provide these certificates, or they may be purchased from commercial certificate authorities. In addition, many sites require two-factor authentication for external access to protected health information. Two-factor authentication requires something the user knows (a password) and an identifiable object the user has (a hardware token that can be plugged into a computer or a smart card with a number that changes according to a unique pattern).[30]

Encrypted communications from trusted clients may be sent directly to a server, or they may be passed through a firewall into the local network of the enterprise. The latter essentially extends the local network to the authenticated client through an encrypted "pipeline" called a virtual private network (VPN). Alternatively, a server at one location with a local network may establish a VPN connection to a second server at a remote local network, creating a virtual network that connects the two local networks securely and allows free communication between their computers. Encrypted communications are thus very useful for connecting enterprise networks with workers from home, physician offices, affiliated health care systems, vendors, or ASP sites that provide subscription services. Public key encryption is also used in digital signatures, in which documents are signed by encryption with an individual's private key. If a document can be read with an individual's public key, it is proven to be signed by the individual (authentication) and not modified after signature (non-repudiation, ie, the individual cannot deny signature or claim modification). The actual protocols for encrypted communications and digital signatures are a bit more complex than described here, but the general idea is accurate.

Disaster Recovery

Problems may occur with hardware, software, and security even in systems that are optimally designed and managed, and there can be physical plant failures or natural disasters. Thus, it is critical to have a well-designed plan for data backup, interim operation without the LIS (downtime operation), and rapid rebuilding of systems (disaster recovery). Backups are often made to tape cartridges because tapes are relatively inexpensive and reliable. A typical backup plan will rotate seven tapes (one for each day of the week), with tapes that are not in use rotated among several storage locations, including at least one off-site storage facility. Some systems may copy data directly to off-site storage. Because replacing hardware and restoring a system from a tape backup takes significant time, depending on the nature of the problem, some sites implement two complete systems with data replicated on both systems. Optimally, the systems are in different locations.

One system is used as the primary production LIS, and the other is a hot backup to which operations can switch rapidly. Making this switch still requires setup time because interfaces and clients must be reconfigured to point to the backup system. The most critical systems that require very high availability can implement automatic failover, which manages a rapid, automated shift of operations to the second system if a switch is necessary. The laboratory should have a planned downtime operations mode, usually a paper process, that can be used for ordering, accessioning, analysis, and reporting if the LIS is down for any significant period. The disaster recovery plan should include procedures for evaluating the nature and scope of the problem, establishing an appropriate management process, determining when downtime operations should be activated, returning the system to functional status, deactivating downtime procedures, and entering all work done during the downtime into the recovered system.

Systems and Personnel

An LIS installation may include the main clinical laboratory system, the anatomic pathology system, and related software such as instrument managers, fax and print servers, etc. Because blood bank systems manage therapeutic products, they must be approved by the Food and Drug Administration (FDA) and are thus sometimes separate from LISs. Not all LIS vendors provide an FDA-approved blood bank module; sites using those systems may implement a stand-alone, FDA-approved blood bank system that communicates with the LIS and other local information systems through system interfaces.

Laboratory systems are usually managed by a technical group that should be led by a pathologist and includes a supervisor with one to eight staff, depending on the size of the site. There should be at least two technical staff members, even for small sites, to provide continuity during staff turnover and to support after-hours call schedules. LIS staff may be recruited from the medical technology or IT fields. Because the design and implementation of LISs are so deeply intertwined with laboratory operations, it is useful for at least some of the staff to have medical technology backgrounds. These individuals may be identified as strong LIS users among laboratory staff and further trained internally. The interface between the laboratory system group and the hospital information group is criti-

Table 6-4. Key Responsibilities of the LIS Management Team

Evaluation, recommendation, installation, configuration, testing, and validation of software and hardware that supports laboratory operations, including the LIS, anatomic pathology system, and related systems
Hardware and software installation or updates to improve performance, add new capabilities, or fix problems, with documented formal testing, review, and approval prior to implementation
Creation and maintenance of a comprehensive LIS procedure manual, with documented annual review (see Table 6-6 for additional detail)
Documented regular system checks and proactive maintenance to confirm that the LIS and associated systems are stable, operating within established parameters, and have adequate data storage capacity
User account management, including addition of new users, deletion of inactive users, and resolution of password and other account access problems
Problem and issue resolution for LIS users, including 24-hour night and weekend support
Maintenance of data stored in the LIS, including definitions of laboratory tests, worksheets, and reports; system configuration data; information about the local laboratory and reference laboratories; personnel data; information about the medical practice environment; etc (see Table 6-5 for additional detail)
System interface management, including initial implementation, updating, and data mappings maintenance with documented testing, validation, and acceptance
Documented description, follow-up, and resolution of computer system and interface error logs and error messages, performance problems, and unscheduled downtime
Ensuring or carrying out an appropriate backup plan, and restoring and verifying the system from backup files if necessary
Managing software licenses, hardware acquisitions, and service contracts, including need forecasting and budgeting
Management and updating of test reference information for online or print distribution to laboratory users
Training of laboratory technologists in use of the LIS and any software or hardware modifications, with documentation of training
Data validation and quality assurance
Demonstration of procedures and documentation for laboratory accreditation inspections

cal, and one way to cement good relations is to have the pathologist volunteer to be the medical consultant to the hospital's chief information officer. Pathologists are uniquely qualified to do so because they are experts in instrumentation and automation, have a broad knowledge of medical practice, and are typically the most knowledgeable physicians about quality management.

Application Management

At larger sites, LIS staff specialize in application management tasks, ie, managing the LIS software. The LIS computers are often located in a protected environment such as a machine room with other enterprise information systems. System administration, the management of the hardware and operating system, and network management tasks may be carried out by enterprise IT teams or consultants who collaborate with the LIS staff. At smaller sites, LIS staff may be responsible for LIS system administration tasks, the laboratory network, laboratory workstation support, management of associated printing devices, and other technical tasks. Thus, the requirements of different sites may vary widely, and it is important to match the skill set of the LIS staff with these requirements. Some sites that implement laboratory systems that are part of larger EHR systems recently have moved LIS management to the general-enterprise IT support staff. The early consensus seems to be that this arrangement reduces the quality of LIS support and that it is beneficial to have individuals with laboratory backgrounds manage the LIS application under laboratory medical leadership.

The primary job of the LIS staff and medical leadership is to provide an information management application that is adequate in capability and reliability for patient care, and meets the local laboratory's workflow and data communication needs. Evaluating and installing LISs and related systems is part of this job, though LIS installation is

Table 6-5. Data Tables Contained in the LIS and Maintained by LIS Support Staff

Table	Description of Contents
Tests and batteries	List of tests and test groupings with ID codes and descriptions
Test limit values	Reference ranges, delta checks, technical limits, auto-validation limits
Cumulative headers	Result summary formats (becoming less used with EHR displays)
Worksheets	Specimen lists for analyzers or manual workstations
Text comments	Standard comments that can be added to results
Default text	Comments that automatically add to results
Laboratory departments	Main laboratory sections
Laboratory locations	Sites performing testing that are part of the local laboratory
Terminals	Data entry and display devices connected to the LIS
Diagnoses	ICD codes for diseases
Tube types	Specimen container descriptions
Reference laboratories	Outside laboratories performing testing not done locally
Tech accounts	Laboratory technician demographics, ID codes, and passwords
Locations	Sites where samples will be obtained and/or results will be reported
Physicians	Physicians who may order tests on patients and receive results
Workstations	"Benches" or work areas of the laboratory
Test logs	Listings of specimens, tests, and results
Quality control	Definitions of controls and target values
Calculations and rules	Instructions for automatically calculated values, reflex testing, etc
Reports	Definition of the names, content, and formatting of reports
Event types	Inpatient, outpatient, and other designations
Alternate facilities	Other health care providers
Species	Codes for veterinary specimens
Sex	Codes for gender
Performing laboratory	Other laboratories from which data may be entered or received

such a large project that these systems often remain in place for 10 to 20 years. After installation, the LIS staff is responsible for maintaining the LIS and its connections to other systems, training laboratory staff in its use, resolving problems that users encounter, and selectively enhancing the LIS and associated systems as needed. A formal change control process must be followed for hardware and software modifications and should include validation and approval prior to releasing new systems or modifications into routine use. Validation includes formal testing using a selected testing library of data that demonstrates all functions of the system, with documented review and approval of results. Systems that support transfusion have particularly extensive validation requirements.

Table 6-4 provides an overview of a typical LIS staff portfolio of responsibilities. LIS staff must monitor error logs/messages and system performance on an ongoing basis and document problems and their resolution. System maintenance includes maintaining software (patches and upgrades) and contained data, which include a large amount of information that the LIS requires to operate in the local environment. These data are held in a section of the LIS database often called maintenance tables (Table 6-5), and managing these maintenance tables is an ongoing activity as the laboratory and health care organization evolve. Feedback is important to determine whether the LIS is meeting the needs of its users, and most LIS management groups follow user feedback provided directly through the LIS and in regularly scheduled meetings between the LIS leadership, laboratory section supervisors, and laboratory leadership. Laboratories that have an LIS off site, either through affiliation with a larger laboratory or by use of an ASP vendor, will have fewer technical responsibilities but will still need to perform data maintenance, application configuration, error resolution, and documentation related to local use.

Interface Management

System interfaces that are used in health care are built using a partial standard (HL7), and much of the transmitted data use local representations that may need to be translated with mapping tables between systems. When the interfaces are between commercial systems, the vendors of each system are contracted to develop their sides of the interface at an additional licensing and maintenance cost. If the site uses an HL7 interface engine (Figure 6-6), the vendors will develop the portion of the interface that runs between their systems and the interface engine. For LIS interfaces, the LIS staff will take delivery of the LIS side of the interface and collaborate on its installation, develop a test data library, and carry out the interface testing and validation, confirming correct data transfer to and from the interfaced system. The LIS staff may then maintain the data mapping tables to ensure that they continue to correctly represent all the data elements that need to be transmitted across the interface. As discussed previously, when HL7 v 3 is generally adopted, vendors will be able to develop an HL7 data communication module that is applicable at any site and can be configured easily by local staff, with limited or no need for mapping tables.

When data are transmitted to other systems—eg, EHR systems—for patient care, laboratory accreditation requirements specify that the laboratory must confirm and periodically re-check that the data are being transmitted and displayed correctly and completely in a form adequate for clinical decision making. In practice, this requirement usually means that the LIS staff must periodically validate both the data transmission and data display for each system that is interfaced. This validation is most commonly carried out by identifying a set of test data that includes representative data elements (textual and numerical results, categorical results, result flags, comments, etc) and then documenting medical director review and approval of the data display (obtained as screen prints or report printouts) of the "downstream" systems.

Though a receiving system could transmit data to another system, the display validation is required only for the first downstream system that would reasonably present the data to a clinician for patient care decisions. Each separate system must be validated individually; however, if several sites use a common display system, the system need not be validated for each site.

Other Systems

LIS staff may also have responsibilities outside the laboratory. Laboratories that offer outreach programs may provide software that allows outside laboratory users to order tests and receive results electronically. Such software may support interfaces between the LIS and external systems such as a physician office's EHR, and/or it may support a user interface for manual order entry and results review. Outreach systems may be installed locally and managed by LIS staff, or the LIS staff may manage a contract with an ASP vendor to provide these services using a VPN connection to the LIS. Since some of these systems run in conjunction with the LIS, LIS staff may also manage positive patient ID systems that use armband barcodes to identify patients for specimen procurement. Point-of-care testing systems require data capture and processing from base stations for laboratory comparisons and quality control; the LIS staff may perform parts of this workflow beyond merely managing the interface between the LIS and base stations.

Record Retention

Patient records and laboratory documentation must be accessible for periods of time that are defined in the CLIA regulations; these regulations apply to both electronic and paper records.[31,32] Test orders and quality control data should be kept for at least 2 years. Routine laboratory results should be kept for 2 years from the time of reporting. Immunohematology and blood bank results should be kept for 5 years after reporting; records related to products with lifetimes longer than 5 years should be kept for 6 months past their outdate. Anatomic pathology reports should be available for 10 years after the reporting date. Medium-sized laboratories with a modern LIS and hardware can maintain data over these spans, and often longer, in their primary database, allowing immediate access. Very large laboratories that may need to purge data from their main databases before these spans are reached can fulfill this requirement by moving older data to an archival system.

Table 6-6. Typical LIS Procedure Manual Contents

Section	Topics*
General	Description of systems, operating environment, and operating requirements
	Overall change control policies for hardware and software
	System installation and updating requirements for hardware and software
	Personnel training (LIS staff and laboratory users)
	Monitoring and evaluating system and network performance
LIS	System description and vendor contacts
	Description of system functions and their use for laboratory tasks
	System backup and data archiving
	System startup and shutdown
	Downtime procedures (laboratory operation during downtime)
	Software error resolution
	Printer maintenance and error resolution
Interfaces	Installation, testing, acceptance, and periodic re-testing
	For each interface: purpose, data elements, operating conditions, start and stop procedures, maintenance procedures, vendor contacts
Reports	For each report: purpose, design, schedule, run instructions, distribution
Quality Assurance	Periodic system monitoring and documentation tasks
	Database verification for accuracy
	Report verification for accuracy and formatting
	Calculation / rule review
Security	User account and password management
	Client computer configuration and software installation
	Procedure for software updates related to security
Associated Systems	Topic lists similar to LIS but at a smaller scale, for example, an instrument manager
Disaster Recovery	Integrated plan including decision-making framework, initiation, limiting damage, downtime, restoration of hardware, restoration of software and data, startup, verification, entry of downtime data, and resuming operation

* This list is topic-oriented, and related procedures have been combined to save space. The organization of the actual manual will vary among laboratories.

Procedure Manual

The LIS staff is responsible for maintaining a complete, up-to-date procedure manual that covers the routine activities discussed in the previous section as well as downtime and disaster recovery procedures. The manual must be reviewed and approved according to standard clinical laboratory practice and must include the dates of initiation, yearly review, revision, and discontinuation of each procedure. Procedures must be available for 2 years after they are discontinued. The major sections and general topics that should be included in an LIS procedure manual are shown in Table 6-6.

System Evaluation, Selection, and Installation

The evaluation, selection, and installation of an LIS is a very challenging task, and the LIS team will generally be deeply involved in or lead any major project involving the laboratory. After the EHR, the LIS is usually the second-largest clinical system in a health care enterprise. The LIS is probably also the second-most challenging system to implement, with large installations often requiring 1 to 2 years to complete. Other laboratory information technology projects, such as installing instrument managers, outreach systems, and specialty laboratory systems, are of smaller scope but have analogous management requirements. Because laboratory procedure manuals do not normally include standard procedures for managing software evaluation, selection, and installation, these projects are approached on an individual basis by laboratory leadership. Nevertheless, there are well-described common patterns in successful projects. Some organizations maintain a project management office that employs people who have expertise in large projects and can be a valuable resource in designing a management strategy, helping keep the project on track, or collaborating on project leadership.

The following elements are found in most successful large system selection and installation projects, and they can be modified easily to fit the details and scope of a particular project. (See Chapter 5, "Equipment, Supplies, and Space.")

The administration, pathologists, and laboratory personnel should articulate the organizational goals and general scope of the project to provide a framework for discussion and identification of leadership. Large projects should have both enterprise and laboratory goals.

Based on the established goals, the leadership group should identify stakeholder groups who will be affected by the system and gain support from the leadership of these groups and enterprise leadership. As planning moves forward, continue to identify and include stakeholders proactively.

The leadership group should form a project management structure that includes a steering committee with stakeholder representatives and work groups for the major areas that will interact with the system. Identify sectional leadership and "champions" (project advocates) from each of these areas and from enterprise leadership.

The sectional leadership should define the functional and support requirements for the new system based on current workflow and project goals. Diagramming techniques for use cases and workflow sequences described in the next section of this chapter may be helpful in this task.

The primary leadership should identify potential vendors using generally available reference material, peers at other sites, and industry contacts. If open source (community-developed) software will be considered, an internal group or a commercial support vendor may act as the software vendor for the purposes of the evaluation.

The primary leadership group should create a request for information (RFI) to be sent to the most promising vendors based on the initial review. An RFI is a document that requests an initial assessment from a vendor of the suitability of their product for a customer's environment and goals. It is used for informational purposes in identifying vendors to review in detail. An RFI will generally contain the following:

- A description of the customer's organization and the current characteristics of the environment into which the product would go
- The goals of the project and the desired outcome
- An overview of known functional requirements for the software, constraints under which it will operate, and general support requirements
- Criteria for evaluation of software
- Questions about the philosophy, history, size, financial status, and overall stability of the vendor
- Questions about the number and characteristics of other installed sites, and contact information for sites willing to discuss their experiences with the software

An organizational project management or procurement office can be helpful in organizing and writing the RFI. If vendors believe their product is a good match for the environment and requirements, they will respond to an RFI with answers to the questions, a description of how their product would meet the organizational goals, and general descriptions of the installation process and the future working environment with their product.

On-site vendor demonstrations with a limited number of vendors (usually six vendors or fewer) can be scheduled based on the review and ranking of the returned RFIs. These demonstrations give a general feel for how the product supports workflows, but because they are controlled by the vendors, their utility in revealing product quality is limited.

Working-group members and other staff who will be system users should visit installed sites with similar complexity to review the system under operational conditions and discuss the sites' experiences with the product and vendor support. Because the quality of software engineering is difficult to measure in feature checklists, descriptions, and vendor-controlled demos, visitors should pay close attention to how well their key functional requirements are met in the installed software. Visited sites can include vendor-recommended references, and some contact with other sites can be beneficial. Appendix 6-1 lists a number of questions that should be answered during a site visit.

A request for proposal (RFP) is submitted to the top vendor or vendors after the demonstration evaluation and visit results. RFPs are generally prepared in collaboration with the enterprise procurement office and may include vendor-supplied templates. RFPs may contain similar information at a greater level of detail than the RFI, with the addition of requests for cost, installation, and support proposals from the vendor. The vendor will respond with a commitment to the functional requirements stated and a plan for hardware and software installation and support. The cost proposal may include licensing, installation, travel, training, and maintenance costs plus additional costs such as migration of data from older systems, any required custom development, and interfaces.

A vendor selection is made on the basis of the RFPs, followed by contract negotiations that are usually supported by the organizational procurement or business office.

When the contract is complete, the vendor should deliver a detailed implementation plan with an overall timeline, milestones for customer and vendor deliverables, and a projected "go-live" date. Components of the implementation plan generally include the following:

- Installation, configuration, and testing of new computing and network hardware.
- Software installation and initial testing.
- If old data will be brought into the new system, they must be exported, transformed, checked for consistency, and imported into the new database. Data representations commonly differ between systems, so data from a previous system must be converted to the new representations, and that conversion process must be validated both automatically and manually. In LIS conversions, old data are often stored in an accessible backup system rather than being imported into the new laboratory system.
- Analysis and modification of the local workflow to take advantage of the new system. In addition, systems usually provide some workflow and screen display flexibility, and these local options—for example, the sequence of screens associated with a task, the fields displayed on those screens, default values, and the terms used on tabs and menus—must be defined and configured.
- Maintenance table data collection and loading, for example, personnel, locations, reference laboratories, and other local data.

- Testing, initially of the new system's modules, and then of the full system, using a testing plan provided by the vendor and approved locally.
- Installation and testing of new system interfaces.
- Training for application managers, advanced users, and routine users.
- A go-live plan that provides a period of extra support and contingencies for problems.

Testing is generally carried out with test scripts supplied by the vendor, and the local site may supply data libraries for use in testing. Testing may be done in two stages: (1) unit testing, which evaluates a newly-installed software module independently for internal problems; and (2) integration testing, which tests the module in the setting of the whole system to catch problems in data transfer to and from the module. Testing, validation, and approval of the system and its interfaces must conform to established laboratory procedures.

Vendors generally provide three levels of training. Administrator or system manager training is designed for the LIS staff who will manage the application. This is usually offered relatively early in the installation process so that the staff can contribute to data loading and configuration. Superuser training is often offered about 6 weeks before go-live. Superusers are individuals chosen from key user roles who will become very knowledgable about the system and will later serve as resources or trainers for routine users. Standard user training is offered about 2 weeks prior to go-live, and superusers may participate as instructors or training aides. If user training is carried out too early, users will not retain the training information at go-live.

The new system is activated for production use at go-live, and old systems may be deactivated. Go-live is challenging and optimally is done at a time with lower workload. Extra staff and support personnel should be available to help work out problems, and contingency plans should be in place in case go-live cannot be completed successfully. After go-live, there is generally an extended period of reduced productivity until users gain familiarity with the system. Issues may appear with workflow or system configuration that require adjustment. As problems are resolved and the system becomes more familiar, the LIS staff will transition to routine maintenance and enhancement.

Performance Monitoring and Quality Assurance

LIS staff monitor the performance of the LIS primarily through routine quality measurements and regression testing. Routine measurements of LIS and network performance include:

- Network throughput, collision rate, and downtime
- Scheduled and unscheduled system downtime, total incidents, total time, and time per incident
- Interface transfer rates
- Stored data volumes and available disc space
- Total accounts used and available licensed accounts
- Resolution of error messages and error log entries for systems and interfaces

Benchmarks and response thresholds for these values are established by individual laboratories based on the local environment and are included in the LIS quality assurance procedure (Table 6-6). Some sites capture issues and report the problems to a separate issue-tracking system, which allows the enumeration and classification of issues for follow-up, resolution, and monitoring. The LIS may also be configured to identify and report cases that are useful for general laboratory quality assurance follow-up, such as values that are absurd or out of reportable ranges, apparent duplicate tests, etc.

Regression testing is the re-testing of previously tested functions to ensure that interim changes or upgrades have not introduced errors into data processing or transmission. Regression testing generally requires a test data library that contains a variety of data elements for which the correct system output has been established. Alternatively, it may be convenient when performing regression testing to identify current data with the necessary elements and compare output with expected behavior. Output is generally reviewed in printed reports or screen shots, signed on approval, and filed.

Regression testing is carried out biannually for calculations and executable rules, for data transmission across interfaces, for reports, and for the display of data in interfaced systems. The performance of calculations, interfaces, and reports are evaluated by comparison to expected performance using a test data set. Data display tests usually require the review of printed screen shots from the interfaced system and must include examples of surgical pathology reports, cytopathology re-

ports, clinical laboratory textual reports, quantitative results, categorial results, microbiology reports, and blood bank reports. The reports should include examples of all data elements and flags as well as corrected results. The results of testing should be available for 2 years past the life of the system tested.

Software Tools and Local Software Development

LIS groups may effectively extend the LIS by using additional software and programming tools to process reports or data extracts to offer greater analytic, data presentation, or automation capabilities. Spreadsheets are useful for the processing, formatting, and simple statistical analysis of tabular data. Spreadsheet plug-ins may offer additional capabilities useful in the laboratory, such as receiver-operating-characteristic (ROC) analysis.[33] Sophisticated programmable statistical and data display software is available at low or no cost from www.r-project.org,[34] and commercial software packages designed for specialized clinical laboratory data analyses are also available.[35,36] Some laboratories have written libraries of their own software to enhance their LIS or anatomic pathology systems; programming in MUMPS, Microsoft's Visual Basic, or .Net[37]; or programming in modern cross-platform scripting languages such as Python, Perl, and Ruby.[38] Microsoft's development tools and scripting languages such as Python are approachable and provide large libraries of prewritten code that enable self-taught, part-time programmers to create limited but very functional programs for local use. Commercial tools or locally developed software that become part of the routine laboratory operation have maintenance and change control requirements similar to those of the LIS, but if used judiciously, they can provide analysis capabilities and workflow improvements that justify the maintenance effort.

Diagramming Tools for Requirements Analysis and Workflow Redesign

Requirements and workflow analyses are important parts of planning the installation of a new system and improving existing systems. To effectively support a workflow with an information system, pathologists must understand the key tasks and actors in the workflow, their association

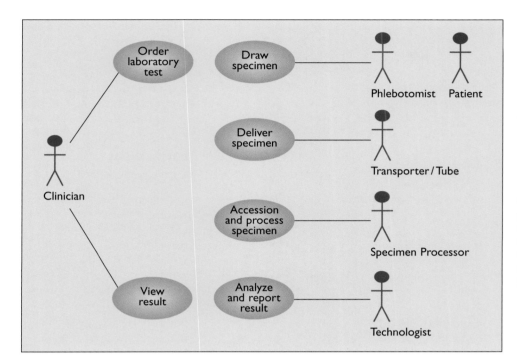

Figure 6-8. Use Case Diagram of Preanalytical, Analytical, and Post-analytical Laboratory Workflow. Key tasks are captured in bubbles, and actors (personnel and technical systems) are shown as stick figures linked to the tasks they perform. Use case tasks may be broad, as shown here, or specific, and analysis typically progresses from broad to specific. Task bubbles are often arranged in sequence, and brief textual descriptions may accompany diagrams.

with each other, and the data elements that are captured or communicated as part of that workflow. Documenting this information accurately is very challenging because it requires collaboration between individuals who normally play different roles in different work domains and often have different vocabularies and assumptions. These communication problems were the impetus for the development of the Unified Modeling Language (UML [www.uml.org]),[39] a standardized set of diagramming techniques designed for collaborative documentation and cross-domain communication of work processes and information system design concepts. Workflows and information models captured in UML diagrams clarify complex real-world environments and relate directly to information system requirements and design elements.

The most useful diagrams for clinical laboratory settings are use case models, activity diagrams, and class diagrams. Use case models (Figure 6-8) are very simple and are designed to clearly depict key tasks and actors (human and technological). They are easy to create during a discussion, and they may be supplemented with a brief paragraph providing details for each task. All requirements analysis and workflow redesign should be rooted in use cases. Activity diagrams (Figure 6-9), also known as swimlane diagrams, are flow charts in which each actor has a lane, and the sequence of events moves down the chart and across the lanes to indicate the flow of actions and information be-

tween the actors. Class diagrams (Figure 6-10) display data models that map all the data elements used in a workflow and their relationships with each other. Unlike activity diagrams, class diagrams are static; they do not specify a particular sequence of use of the data elements they depict. The combination of these three diagram types supplemented with some textual description can capture most of the information needed for the discussion and analysis of information flow in laboratory work processes. Most technical diagramming software includes templates for UML diagrams, and dedicated UML diagramming software is available commercially and in open source.

Discussion

LISs were an early and cutting-edge application of computer technology in medicine, and work with LISs contributed to the development of the broader field of medical informatics. LIS technology has been continually developing for 40 years, and well-managed LISs are now integral to the operation of modern laboratories. Pathology informatics is a subset of medical informatics that seeks to optimize the use of LISs and other pathology computing resources for pathology services, physician decision making, and patient care. Several recent books and monographs have covered aspects of pathology informatics in detail.[40-42] Concepts from

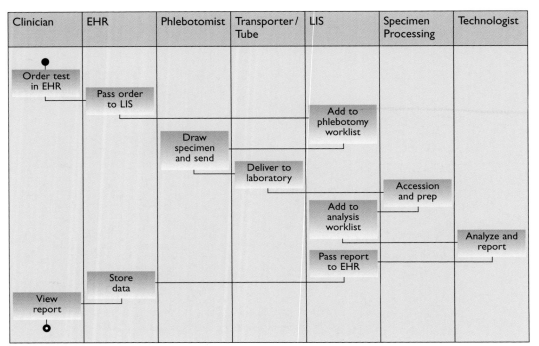

Figure 6-9. Activity Diagram of Laboratory Workflow. The actors and tasks from the use case diagram in Figure 6-8 are mapped in sequence to an extended flow chart, with one lane for each actor. Some additional actors that were not shown in the use cases (EHR and LIS) are included here to complete the information flow. Activity diagrams show the flow of tasks and information both in time and across participants and systems.

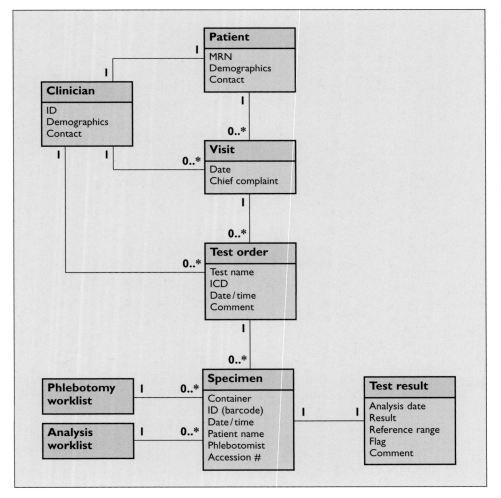

Figure 6-10. Simplified Class Diagram for Laboratory Workflow. This diagram shows data elements and their relationships from the simple workflow shown in figures 6-8 and 6-9. The boxes represent classes (entities for which data will be collected). Items within the boxes are simple data elements, sometimes called attributes. Classes can also contain other classes as complex data elements, and these associations are shown as lines. Multiplicity relationships are shown as numbers on the associations; for example, a patient can have any number of visits (the permissible range is shown as 0..*, where the asterisk indicates "any number"), but a visit can have only one patient. The clinician class is used in several settings; it represents the patient's primary physician, and it also represents the physician of record for a visit and the ordering physician for a test. These may be different physicians, but the clinician class provides a data model for all of them. Class diagrams express data models only and do not depict data flow or action sequences. Definitions: ICD, ICD-9-CM code; MRN, medical record number.

the pathology informatics community—for example, the necessary role pathologists have in ensuring that pathology information is presented to the clinician accurately and in a useful form—have become part of routine laboratory operation and accreditation requirements.

Most current pathology system designs are based on stand-alone systems that printed reports on paper for delivery to clinicians and for monitoring of laboratory operations. This previous environment allowed each system to define its own data representation, data models, and data presentation strategy. Without an incentive to standardize, vendors and local sites developed independent approaches to solve laboratory computer problems. As LISs and other systems became integrated into enterprise architectures (Figure 6-6), these once-independent systems required complex, expensive, and error-prone interfaces for translating their various differences. Accurately translating complex formatted reports between systems remains an unsolved problem. The second decade of the century will see a national push to broadly deploy EHR and electronic health data sharing; goals will include transferring clinical summaries containing actionable information between health care systems, enabling decision support across all data in clinical workflow systems such as EHRs,

Case Example

Dr. Henry Little is associate laboratory director and medical director of the LIS at a 400-bed hospital that has been actively pursuing relationships with regional clinics and small hospitals. A clinic about 30 miles away is forming a relationship with the hospital and is interested in sending testing to Dr. Little's laboratory but would like to be able to order tests and review results within its EHR.

What are the options for supporting the clinic?

Comments: There are several possibilities. The simplest, which could be appropriate for a physician's office or small clinic, would be to establish a broadband Internet connection such as a DSL line to the remote site, configure one or more of their office computers to establish a VPN connection with the LIS over the Internet, provide appropriate clinic staff with LIS accounts, and allow them to order tests and review results directly in the LIS user interface. The LIS should be configured to recognize users from that location and allow them to view results only on patients from that location. This approach would not satisfy the desire to use the clinic's EHR, and adding accounts to the LIS could require additional licensing fees that would need to be balanced against the anticipated test revenue.

Another approach would be to establish an HL7 interface running over a secure connection (similar to a VPN) between the LIS and the clinic's EHR. This would require creating and validating an HL7 interface with the participation of both systems' vendors, and Dr. Little's LIS group would probably spend significant time working with the remote site. However, this could also provide access to systems other than the LIS, which might be a benefit depending on the close-ness of the business relationship, and some of the cost thus might be picked up by other parts of the organization.

A third option would be to contract with a company that acts as an HL7 interface aggregator, ie, one that connects to systems at different sites and passes HL7 messages between them. Such a company would work directly with the clinic site and the LIS group to help set up interfaces to their locations, and the overall interface development time and cost might be decreased if the company had previously developed interfaces to the systems used by the clinic and the laboratory.

Finally, some reference laboratories offer a service similar to the HL7 aggregator companies at favorable pricing, if esoteric testing from the clinic will be sent to the reference laboratory. In this case, the reference laboratory establishes the interface with the clinic's system. If the hospital laboratory has an existing interface with the reference laboratory, it can be used to receive information on tests being sent from the clinic to the hospital laboratory and return results to the clinic through the reference laboratory system. This can be a good option if both the clinic and the hospital laboratory are willing to use the reference laboratory for esoteric testing.

Dr. Little should remember that laboratories are not allowed to offer material inducements or "kickbacks" to gain testing business and thus should be careful about, for example, low- or no-cost placement of computers and other communications equipment in the clinic. He should also consider that reporting directly to the clinic system means that his LIS group will need to do regression testing and validation of the interface and the data display in the clinic every 2 years.

Table 6-7. Data Standards Working Groups Pertinent to LIS and Anatomic Pathology

Group and Contact	Product/Activity
CAP Diagnostic Intelligence and Health Information Technology Committee (DIHIT) http://www.cap.org/	Monitoring and promoting standards development and general informatics in anatomic and clinical pathology
DICOM Working Group 26 (Pathology) http://medical.nema.org/DICOM/minutes/WG-26/	Imaging and image data standards for whole slide digitization
HL7 Clinical Genomics Working Group http://wiki.hl7.org/	Communication standard for genomics testing results, family history, and disease risk calculations, using genomic and other terminology standards
HL7 Orders and Observations Working Group http://wiki.hl7.org/	Communication standard for clinical laboratory orders and results, using terminology standards
HL7 Pathology Special Interest Group http://wiki.hl7.org/	Communication standard for anatomic pathology data representation and report formatting, using terminology and text markup standards
IHE Anatomic Pathology Domain* http://wiki.ihe.net/	Profiles** for anatomic pathology ordering, workflow, and reporting based on terminology and communication standards
IHE Laboratory Domain* http://wiki.ihe.net/	Profiles** for laboratory ordering, workflow, and reporting based on terminology and communication standards
International Health Terminology Standards Development Organization (IHTSDO) http://www.ihtsdo.org/	SNOMED CT medical and pathology terminology system
Logical Observation Identifiers Names and Codes (LOINC) http://loinc.org/	Standard terms for naming laboratory tests and other observations

Definitions: CAP, College of American Pathologists; DICOM, Digital Imaging and Communications in Medicine (dicom.nema.org); HL7, Health Level Seven International (www.hl7.org); IHE, Integrating the Healthcare Enterprise International (www.ihe.net).

*IHE Technical Frameworks for laboratory and anatomic pathology are available at http://www.ihe.net/Technical_Framework/. **Profiles are sets of existing standards that can be used to accomplish a particular information systems goal in the health care environment.

and aggregating large data sets across systems for population health research and surveillance, post-marketing studies for therapeutics and devices, and comparative effectiveness research. The ability of systems to support these goals is closely tied to their designation of allowing the "meaningful use" of data and thus their qualification for federal financial installation incentives.

The next major evolutionary step is achieving syntactic and semantic interoperability between pathology information systems and health care enterprise systems based on shared data representations and data models. Such interoperability will substantially reduce the cost and effort of creating and maintaining system interfaces and will increase the reliability of these interfaces. It will also allow pathology data of all types to be accurately communicated and clearly presented in systems that support clinical workflow and will enable those systems to more effectively incorporate clinical decision support. Data standards are avail-

able, but they are not yet complete or organized into generally accepted solutions to data-sharing problems. A number of working groups are actively developing and extending pathology-related standards in a collaborative effort that creates pathways for standards implementation by vendors (Table 6-7).[43] For example, groups within HL7 are developing data models and messaging syntax that incorporate existing terminologies such as LOINC and SNOMED. Representations of pathology reports that take advantage of the HL7 Clinical Document Architecture are being developed to carry both formatted text and processable data elements in sharable forms.[44] Groups within IHE (Integrating the Healthcare Enterprise) are gathering these standards into profiles (groups of standards used in particular ways) that accomplish real-world communication tasks. Multiple system vendors participating in IHE will be able to implement these profiles simultaneously, with confidence that a critical mass of systems using the standards is forthcoming.

Case Example

Dr. Little's hospital recently finished installing a new EHR system. About 6 weeks after go-live, the laboratory received a call from a clinician questioning several calcium values over 20 mg/dL. When the laboratory staff checked the results in the LIS, the values were normal, or, in some cases, no calcium assay had been done, but the clinician insisted that the high results were present in the EHR display. The laboratory staff could not review the display because the role-based security of the EHR had been configured so that only staff caring for a patient could see data on that patient. Laboratory staff members were not regarded as patient care staff and thus did not have access to the EHR data display. All interface validation had been completed with no problems before the EHR go-live. Further investigation revealed that a calculation rule had been implemented in the EHR to correct total phenytoin levels for albumin, based on clinician requests and without the knowledge of the laboratory, and the result of that calculation was being inserted erroneously into the calcium result display. The calculation was turned off.

Comments: This case raises several important issues. The most important is that a rule was created that produced a result, and the performance of the rule was not adequately validated. It is tempting to speculate that one reason for this outcome was that the rule was created by hospital computing personnel who were not familiar with patient data calculations and their validation. Though there are well established procedures in pathology for validating calculations with appropriate test data sets, the advent of EHR with rules engines that are managed outside of pathology raise the possibility of calculations and rules using pathology data that are not managed according to pathology standards. A case could be made that pathologists should participate in the implementation and review of any rule or calculation in a clinical system that uses pathology data and produces an actionable result. In this case, the hospital committee in charge of EHR rules previously did not include a pathologist; this incident yielded an invitation to Dr. Little to join the committee.

The inability of laboratory staff to review the data display is a second issue. Practically speaking, when problems are perceived in the display of pathology data, the pathology service will receive the call for assistance even though the display system may not be under pathology management. To resolve issues rapidly in support of quality patient care, the pathology service should be able to see the same display that the clinician sees and compare its content to their service records. This is also true for any other data-producing clinical service. Security of patient data is critically important, but it should be handled through methods, including appropriate training and access monitoring, that do not create barriers to problem resolution.

These changes will ultimately simplify the operation of LISs and anatomic pathology systems, and allow pathology services to contribute more actively to patient care through more flexible data display, increased decision support options, and systems that are able to respond in useful ways to test ordering and result patterns. Further development of pathology systems will include more sophisticated data analyses and data mining capabilities that monitor routine data to provide useful and actionable information. These capabilities will enhance pathology services' ability to tailor their offerings to clinical needs and individual patient characteristics and will improve analysis and decision-making in the management of pathology services. There will be demands and challenges associated with necessary changes in systems and work processes over the next decade, but there is also great potential for progress if these challenges are met.

References

1. Johnson JL. *Clinical Laboratory Computer Systems. A Comprehensive Evaluation.* Northbrook, IL: Lloyd Johnson Associates; 1971.
2. Johnson JL. *Achieving the Optimal Information System for the Clinical Laboratory.* Northbrook, IL: Lloyd Johnson Associates; 1975.
3. Aller RD, Robboy SJ, Poitras JW, et al. Computer-assisted pathology encoding and reporting system (CAPER). *Am J Clin Pathol.* 1977;68(6):715-720.
4. Foulis PR, Norbut AM, Mendelow H, Kessler GF. Pathology accessioning and retrieval system with encoding by computer (PARSEC): a microcomputer-based system for anatomic pathology featuring automated SNOP coding and multiple administrative functions. *Am J Clin Pathol.* 1980;73(6):748–753.
5. Pearson JM. A comprehensive software subsystem for anatomic pathology and cytology. *Proc Annu Symp Comput Appl Med Care.* 1982;2:274-281.

Challenge Questions

Which of the following statements regarding the HL7 version 2 standard is false?

A. It is a standard that supports data exchange between medical devices including information systems and laboratory analyzers.

B. The standard defines the structure of text messages.

C. The standard specifies standard terminologies for use in message fields.

D. HL7 version 2 interfaces usually require mapping tables to support data conversion between systems.

E. HL7 version 2 messages carry the character content of textual reports but not the page formatting.

Answer: C; see pages 98 to 100.

Which of the following are requirements for laboratory accreditation?

A. Validation of data display in the first downstream system used for clinical decision-making.

B. Maintenance of routine test results and quality control for 2 years.

C. Regression testing of interface data transmission every 2 years.

D. Verification of calculation results and executable rules every 2 years.

E. All of the above.

Answer: E; see page 110 and Table 6-6, page 107.

Which of the following is not part of the usual responsibilities of the LIS staff?

A. Regression testing.

B. Validation of data display in clinical systems interfaced to the LIS.

C. Monitoring interface transfer rates.

D. Carrying out method linearity and reportable range checks.

E. Resolution of error messages.

Answer: D; see pages 103 to 104 and Table 6-4.

6. Lincoln TL, Korpman RA. Computers, health care, and medical information science. *Science.* 1980; 210(4467):257-263.

7. Korpman RA. Using the computer to optimize human performance in health care delivery: the pathologist as medical information specialist. *Arch Pathol Lab Med.* 1987;111(7):637-645.

8. Friedman BA. The laboratory information system as a tool for implementing a strategic plan. *Am J Clin Pathol.* 1989;92(4 Suppl 1):S38-43.

9. Friedman BA. Informatics as a separate section within a department of pathology. *Am J Clin Pathol.* 1990;94(4 Suppl 1):S2-6.

10. Buffone GJ, Beck JR. Informatics: a subspecialty in pathology. *Am J Clin Pathol.* 1993;100(1):75-81.

11. Cornet R, de Keizer N. Forty years of SNOMED: a literature review. *BMC Med Inform Decis Mak.* 2008;8(Suppl 1):S2.

12. McDonald CJ, Huff SM, Suico JG, et al. LOINC, a universal standard for identifying laboratory observations: a 5-year update. *Clin Chem.* 2003;49(4): 624–633.

13. Valenstein PN. Formatting pathology reports: applying four design principles to improve communication and patient safety. *Arch Pathol Lab Med.* 2008; 132(1):84-94.

14. Dunn BE, Choi H, Recla DL, Kerr SE, Wagenman BL. Robotic surgical telepathology between the Iron Mountain and Milwaukee Department of Veterans Affairs Medical Centers: a 12-year experience. *Hum Pathol.* 2009;40(8):1092-1099.

15. Horbinski C, Wiley CA. Comparison of telepathology systems in neuropathological intraoperative consultations. *Neuropathology.* 2009;29(6):655-663.

16. College of American Pathologists. Cancer protocols and checklists. Available at: www.cap.org/cancerprotocols. Accessed Sept 11, 2010.

17 Regenstrief Institute. LOINC: Logical Observation Identifiers Names and Codes. Available at: http://loinc.org/. Accessed Aug 15, 2010.

18. SNOMED CT. Available at: http://www.ihtsdo.org/snomed-ct/. Accessed Aug 15, 2010.

19. Le Bozec C, Henin D, Fabiani B, et al. Refining DICOM for pathology: progress from the IHE and DICOM pathology working groups. *Stud Health Technol Inform.* 2007;129(Pt 1):434-438.

20. Lyman JA, Scully K, Harrison JH Jr. The development of health care data warehouses to support data mining. *Clin Lab Med.* 2008;28(1):55-71.

21. Brown DE. Introduction to data mining for medical informatics. *Clin Lab Med.* 2008;28(1):9-35.

22 Aller RD. The clinical laboratory data warehouse: an overlooked diamond mine. *Am J Clin Pathol.* 2003; 120:817–819.

23. Brossette SE, Hymel PA Jr. Data mining and infection control. *Clin Lab Med.* 2008;28(1):119-126.

24. McDonald JM, Brossette S, Moser SA. Pathology information systems: data mining leads to knowledge discovery. *Arch Pathol Lab Med.* 1998;122(5):409-411.

25. W3C. XML Technology. Available at: http://www.w3.org/standards/xml/. Accessed Sept 11, 2010.

26. Dolin RH, Alschuler L, Boyer S, et al. HL7 Clinical Document Architecture, Release 2. *J Am Med Inform Assoc.* 2006;13(1):30-39.

27. Ferranti JM, Musser RC, Kawamoto K, Hammond WE. The clinical document architecture and the continuity of care record: a critical analysis. *J Am Med Inform Assoc.* 2006;13(3):245-252.

28. HL7. Product Brief - CCD - Continuity of Care Document. Available at: http://wiki.hl7.org/index.php?title=Product_CCD. Accessed Aug 22, 2010.

29. Harthun K. What's your system's survival time? Available at: http://itknowledgeexchange.techtarget.com/security-corner/whats-your-systems-survival-time/. Accessed Aug 18, 2010.

30. Burr WE, Dodson DF, Polk WT. Electronic authentication guideline. NIST Special Publication 800-63 [online]. 2006. Available at: http://www.csrc.nist.gov/publications/nistpubs/800-63/SP800-63V1_0_2.pdf. Accessed Sept 11, 2010.

31. CLIA. Records and reports. 21 CFR Part 606, Subpart I (606.160). December 2005.

32. CLIA. Standard: Retention requirements. 42 CFR Part 493, Subpart J (493.1105). October 2007.

33. ROC.KIT. Available at: http://www.formatio-reticularis.de/roc/. Published 2006. Accessed Aug 22, 2010.

34. Theodorsson E. Advanced statistics and data analysis in laboratory medicine: steep learning curve but substantial rewards. *Scand J Clin Lab Invest.* 2008;68(6):434–436.

35. Analyze-it Software L. Analyze-it Method Evaluation Edition. Available at: http://www.analyse-it.com/products/method%5Fevaluation/. Accessed Aug 22, 2010.

36. Data Innovations, Inc. EP Evaluator. Available at: http://www.dgrhoads.com/. Accessed Aug 22, 2010.

37. Microsoft Corp. Visual Basic developer center. Available at: http://msdn.microsoft.com/en-us/vbasic/default.aspx. Updated 2010. Accessed Aug 22, 2010.

38. Berman JJ. *Methods in Medical Informatics. Fundamentals of Healthcare Programming in Perl, Python, and Ruby.* New York: CRC Press/Taylor and Francis Group; 2010.

39. Unified Modeling Language. UML Resource Page. Available at: www.uml.org. Accessed Jan 3, 2011.

40. Cowan DF. *Informatics for the Clinical Laboratory. A Practical Guide.* New York, NY: Springer; 2003.

41. Pantanowitz L, Henricks WH, Beckwith BA. Medical laboratory informatics. *Clin Lab Med.* 2007; 27(4):823-843.

42. Sinard JH. *Practical Pathology Informatics. Demystifying Informatics for the Practicing Anatomic Pathologist.* New York, NY: Springer Science+ Business Media; 2006.

43. Daniel C, García Rojo M, Bourquard K, et al. Standards to support information systems integration in anatomic pathology. *Arch Pathol Lab Med.* 2009;133(11):1841-1849.

44. HL7 Pathology Special Interest Group. Anatomic pathology CDA project description. Available at: http://wiki.hl7.org/index.php?title=Anatomic_Pathology_CDA_Project_Discription. Published 2006. Accessed Aug 23, 2010.

The author thanks James C. Boyd, MD; Alexis B. Carter, MD; Carol Beth Casto, MT; Paul G. Catrou, MD; and Walter H. Henricks, MD, for helpful reference materials and comments.

Appendix 6-1.
Site Visit Questions
for LIS Acquisition

A site visit is crucial to making a good decision on an LIS and is part of standard due diligence prior to selecting a system for installation. An LIS is a complex, engineered system and, like other engineered systems such as buildings and bridges, the quality of its engineering is better indicated by performance over time than feature lists and superficial appearance. Ideally, a site that is similar in complexity and other characteristics to the planned install site should be visited. Vendors generally recommend sites for visiting that are having good experiences with the product. It may be beneficial to visit or at least call an additional site "off the list" if one is available. A site visit team should include representatives from all major laboratory areas and administration, and team members should visit each of these areas and watch the system in operation. It is important to speak with the people in the laboratory who are actually using the system on a daily basis, as well as the pathologist, administrators, or hospital CIO who were involved in the acquisition.

Questions to Consider

- Was the vendor forthright in presenting the system's capabilities and its ability to meet the goals established in the site's RFI/RFP? Does the system operate as expected?
- Were there any unexpected outcomes or "gotchas" related to installation or use?
- Did the vendor's system installation and training plan and support services meet the needs of the site?
- How much time did the installation process require?
- How well was go-live handled, and how long after go-live did it take to get comfortable with the system?
- What is the extent of connectivity to other systems (instruments and instrument managers, EMR/HIS/billing, remote locations, reference laboratories), and have there been any problems in developing and maintaining interfaces or interface performance?

- Is the overall responsiveness of the system adequate (user interface responsiveness, query time, printing time)?
- Is the system reasonably efficient to learn and use on a daily basis? Do technologists, supervisors, pathologists, and laboratory administrators like it (review each subsystem)?
- If appropriate, how well does the system support laboratory automation, including specimen transport tracks and storage repositories?
- If appropriate, how well does the system handle multiple laboratories, hospitals, and clinics that may have differing patient identification, ordering, sample handling, and reporting requirements?
- What are the downtime requirements, and how much unscheduled downtime has occurred? How long does recovery from downtime take?
- What are the strategies for high-availability operation, backup, and disaster recovery, and are they compatible with the needs of the visiting team?
- Does the vendor's ongoing technical support meet the needs of the laboratory? Is the response to contacts timely? How quickly are issues resolved? Are there any unresolved issues or bugs?
- Does the vendor provide good quality technical and user training materials for ongoing use, such as printed material, online learning modules, or webinars?
- Is there a user group for the software, and is it active and useful?
- What are the strongest and weakest points of the system?
- Are operating costs as projected?
- Does anything at the site suggest that the system will not be able to support the requirements listed in the RFI/RFP of the visiting team?
- Would the site buy or lease the software again? Why or why not?

See also Chapter 5, "Equipment, Supplies, and Space," pages 75 to 79.

CHAPTER 7

Quality Management in Laboratory Medicine

David S. Wilkinson, MD, PhD
Elizabeth A. Wagar, MD

Contents

History of Quality Management

When the Clinical Laboratory Improvement Act (CLIA) was first passed in 1967, quality was an intrinsic expectation in clinical laboratories. As CLIA evolved in newer versions in 1988 and 2003, it addressed quality activities for the various levels of test complexity in the laboratory. Most recently, CLIA discussed the frequency of quality control (QC) and the verification of test performance as prescriptive activities. Quality practices and quality management are continuously discussed in the clinical laboratory; someone listening casually to conversations among laboratory staff and leaders quickly comes to understand that quality services are critical to pathology and laboratory medicine. However, before applying a microscope to the notion of "quality" in the laboratory, examining the origins of total quality management at a global level and analyzing its evolution over the past 100 years may offer some insight.[1]

The concept of total quality management developed rapidly during the twentieth century in Japan and the United States. Total quality management refers to a philosophy of excellence for quality work and products throughout a production or service system. One of the first advocates of quality management was Walter Shewhart (1891–1967). After completing his doctorate in physics in 1917, Shewhart joined the Western Electric Company and was responsible for building quality equipment for the nation's first telephone system, whose products were manufactured in Illinois at the Hawthorne Works, a large operation employing 40,000 people.

Shewhart developed the concept of statistical control of quality. He defined the causes of quality variance in production as chance-cause (or common-cause) variation and assignable-cause (or special-cause) variation. Chance-cause variation results from the inescapable vagaries with no identified cause that statistically occur in a process.

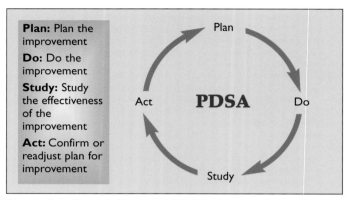

Plan: Plan the improvement

Do: Do the improvement

Study: Study the effectiveness of the improvement

Act: Confirm or readjust plan for improvement

Figure 7-1. Plan-Do-Study-Act (PDSA). Diagram of the Shewhart quality review process.

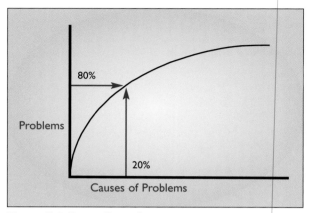

Figure 7-2. Pareto Principle.

Assignable-cause variation results from specific circumstances that can be identified and corrected. Focusing on assignable-cause variation, Shewhart challenged correctable variation with statistical controls to show quality improvement in a given product. He also created the control chart, the precursor of charts such as the Levey-Jennings chart, which is a familiar statistical quality tool in the laboratory. Shewhart's theory of statistical control of quality was adopted by the American Society for Testing and Materials (ASTM) and contributed to World War II–related production in the United States and US-led economic industrial development in Japan after World War II.

Another aspect of Shewhart's theory of statistical quality control is the Plan-Do-Study-Act (PDSA) model (sometimes referred to as the Plan-Do-Check-Act [PDCA] model), which is used to thoroughly analyze quality improvement efforts. The PDSA model logically guides an investigation of assignable-cause variation by creating an action plan, proceeding with defined corrective actions, studying or checking metrics, and acting on any findings that occur as a result of the process (Figure 7-1).

W. Edwards Deming (1900–1993), who worked in Japan for the Supreme Command of the Allied Powers and advised the Japanese Union of Scientists and Engineers, studied and adopted statistical process control and the PDSA model from Shewhart and extended Shewhart's principles to encompass the concept of total quality management. Deming's model of total quality management suggests that leaders and managers in laboratories should espouse the elements of total quality management with the belief that all staff and leadership are part of the quality management plan and that all staff and managers participate in continuous process improvement.

Any history of quality management must include Joseph M. Juran (1904–2008). Juran, at one time an engineer at the Hawthorne Works, was eventually appointed to the Inspection Statistical Department, where he introduced the now widely recognized Pareto diagram (Figure 7-2). The Pareto diagram provides a means for identifying and emphasizing the most important events for improving a process while avoiding distractions from trivial events. As a general concept, 20% of causes lead to 80% of the problems. As another example, 80% of revenue may come from 20% of a laboratory's test menu.

After World War II, quality became a defining feature in Japanese industry. The Toyota Production System was the first to apply Lean production. This system became widely popular in the US, with many business-consulting firms entering the market to develop Lean systems. Recently, the laboratory industry has had similar exposure to Lean, with consultants and publications offering advice and system approaches for clinical laboratories. Lean began in Japan with the Toyoda family, who developed an automobile manufacturing operation before World War II. As part of the post-war renewal process, Toyota investigated Ford Motor Company and other assembly line models. An employee, Taiichi Ohno, extrapolated from these systems to develop the Kanban system of just-in-time production and inventory management. Toyota recognized that such planning reduced waste and managed production-timing problems by strictly defining work methods, which reduced variability in work; defining hand-offs and connections with customers and suppliers; defining just-in-time activities based on quantitative management of work stations; instituting "hard" QC systems (eg, electronic recognition of defective parts); and emphasizing continuous improvement. Lean thinking clearly revolutionized US industries and is being pursued in many laboratories.[2]

Other recent trends reflect the modifications and adaptations of many of the historical developments described above.[3] Six Sigma, for example, is an adaptation of the statistical models first proposed by Shewhart and Deming. An understanding of the history of quality should help pathologists and laboratory directors understand management proposals and the variety of consultant and educational programs offered to improve laboratory quality.

Elements of a Quality Management Plan

The quality management plan is a document describing all aspects of a clinical laboratory's activities related to quality and patient safety. A quality management plan is required in College of American Pathologists (CAP)–accredited laboratories and is a critical policy or procedure for other accreditation agencies. Laboratory directors and pathologists are required to develop and authorize a quality management plan for laboratory services. CAP accreditation also requires an annual review of the quality management plan, including reviews of any performance-improvement projects, benchmarks, or monitors. In 2004, 2.2% of laboratories inspected by the CAP were cited for a Phase II deficiency because the quality management plan had not been reviewed for effectiveness in the prior year.[1]

The CAP and standards-forming organizations such as the Clinical and Laboratory Standards Institute (CLSI) and the International Organization for Standardization (ISO) describe 13 elements that are essential to a quality management plan.[4] The following sections should be listed in the introduction of one's quality management standard operating procedure (SOP)[5]:

- Organization
- Personnel Resources
- Equipment
- Supplies and Suppliers
- Customer Issues
- Process and Performance Control
- Documents and Records
- Occurrence Management
- Assessments and Audits
- Process and Performance Improvement

**Introduction:
ABC Laboratory Quality Management Plan**

This quality management plan provides for continuous monitoring and evaluation of patient care activities within the ABC Clinical Laboratory. Monitoring includes preanalytic, analytic, and postanalytic phases of testing. The plan describes a standardized quality control system that maximizes the quality of laboratory testing to produce the accurate and timely results needed in support of quality patient care. The plan includes provisions for employee training and competency assessment, document control requirements, procedures for monitoring quality control, quality indicators, internal and external customer satisfaction, a process for systematic approach to occurrence management, processes for data access security and transfer integrity, and a formal departmental committee structure for the documentation and reporting of internal quality improvement activities. The plan was designed to maintain compliance with federal, state, and local laws and regulations, as well as organizational policies and ethical standards. Elements of this plan were developed after a careful risk assessment conducted by the laboratory and hospital leadership.

Figure 7-3. Quality Management Plan Introduction.

- Facilities and Safety
- Information Management
- Customer Service and Satisfaction Surveys

Some of these sections are covered in detail in the quality management plan. Other sections of the plan may be deferred to specific SOPs in operational laboratory sections.

The introduction of a quality management plan should outline the approach to quality management as prescribed by accrediting and regulatory agencies. The plan should communicate the means for directing and controlling the organization with regard to quality. It should also include the scope of the plan. An example quality management plan introduction is shown in Figure 7-3. A review of each of the elements indicates how to make the concept of a quality management plan manageable.

Organization

The first element of the quality management plan should indicate the geographical scope of the organization (eg, whether the organization includes one laboratory section or several laboratories). One way to briefly describe the organization is to insert an organizational chart (see Chapter 1, "Management Principles," and Chapter 3, "Laboratory Operations"). This chart should indicate the medical and administrative directors and the laboratory managers and supervisors; it should

> ### Equipment:
> ### ABC Laboratory Quality Management Plan
>
> The laboratory has policies, processes, and procedures for the selection, acquisition, installation, validation, periodic maintenance, and quality assessment of equipment critical to the provision of services in the Department in the respective laboratory sections. Each piece of equipment is uniquely identified; calibration, maintenance, and monitoring conform to specified requirements. In addition, the laboratory maintains a process to investigate and follow-up equipment malfunctions, failures, and adverse events. Prior to disposal or release to surplus inventory, equipment that may have been in contact with chemical, biohazardous, or radioactive substances is decontaminated and decommissioned.

Figure 7-4. Quality Management Plan Equipment Paragraph.

also be dated and reviewed annually for updates. This annual review has the additional advantage of keeping a laboratory "inspection-ready" since organizational charts are reviewed in all types of governmental and accreditation inspections.

Personnel Resources

Personnel resources are the second element of the quality management plan. A good way to introduce this element is to list the CLIA personnel and definitions required for the described laboratory. A cross-reference chart indicating local job titles versus CLIA personnel titles may also be helpful. The personnel resources section should also describe new employee orientation, including new employee training and annual competency assessment (including age-specific training as appropriate). A summary of educational resources as well as the location of the documentation for employee performance reviews and competency assessments should be provided. (Some aspects of performance review may also be included in more detailed SOPs.) Some aspects of the personnel resources section will incorporate regulations required by human resources departments,[6] for example, an institution may require that newly hired staff complete hospital orientation within 45 days of hire and a department-specific orientation within 30 days of hire. Further information regarding personnel management is provided in Chapter 4, "Personnel Management."

Equipment

Equipment is the third element of the quality management plan. In many laboratories, this section is deferred to individual laboratory sections. Policies outlining the selection, acquisition, installation,

validation, maintenance, and disposal or release of laboratory equipment, as well as policies describing the investigation of adverse events related to equipment use, should be briefly described in one paragraph (Figure 7-4). Equipment management is described in further detail in Chapter 5, "Equipment, Supplies, and Space."

Supplies and Suppliers

The fourth element of a quality management plan includes supplies and suppliers. While the details of supply management for a given laboratory section may be provided in another SOP, the person(s) responsible for supporting laboratory operations to ensure an uninterrupted flow of materials and services should be provided in the quality management plan. Laboratory supplies should arrive in the right quantity, with the right quality, at the right time, from the right supplier for the right price. The procedure for supply recall must also be noted. Supplies are also discussed in greater detail in Chapter 5, "Equipment, Supplies, and Space."

Customer Issues

The fifth element of a quality management plan is customer issues. Two important aspects of customer issues are referral (send-out) laboratories and customer service and satisfaction surveys. The authority for selecting referral laboratories rests with the laboratory director, who consults with the facility and medical staff. The laboratory director is ultimately responsible for ensuring the quality of testing at a referral laboratory. The list of referral laboratories should be reviewed and approved annually at an institutional level. In addition, results should be audited to ensure that the referral laboratory is meeting quality and service standards. The contracts for referral laboratories must also be reviewed annually to ensure that the institution is in compliance with federal requirements for referral laboratory contracting.

Process and Performance Control

The sixth element of a quality management plan is process control. This includes quality control (QC) and proficiency testing (PT). QC is one of the oldest quality procedures in clinical laboratories.[7] Quality control is the analyzing of materials of known composition or reactivity in conjunction with testing patient samples to verify the performance of a certain test. QC is an ongoing measure of precision and confirms the maintenance of an instrument by calibration. Precision is best measured statistically by the coefficient of variation as applied to repeat QC results from a given lot of QC reagents. When entered on a Levey-Jennings control chart, QC quickly indicates whether an instrument is meeting precision specifications per sets of statistical rules known as Westgard rules. The CAP requires that externally acquired or purchased QC reagents be used in addition to vendor-supplied QC reagents in instrument QC analysis. For QC frequency, pathologists can refer to the vendor's recommendations; however, accreditation agencies such as the CAP may require more frequent QC checks. The duration of retention of QC records should also be part of the process control description.

A second important element of process control is proficiency testing. PT is "the testing of unknown samples sent to a laboratory by a CMS [Centers for Medicare and Medicaid Services]–approved PT program."[8] PT suppliers usually send unknown challenge samples to participating laboratories three times per year. PT is a very important tool for assessing the accuracy of testing, since it represents a standardized "blind" sample and compares one laboratory's results to those of multiple laboratories. The CAP is among several suppliers of PT samples (list of providers available at www.cms.hhs.gov/CLIA). CLIA designates a list of regulated analytes that must be scored by the PT provider and reported to CMS if the results are outside acceptable performance. CAP laboratory accreditation additionally requires PT for all tested analytes. If no graded PT is available, alternate performance assessment must be performed semiannually. Howanitz and Howanitz provide detailed information regarding the proper statistical management of PT.[7] Most standard quantifiable PT analytes are evaluated using the coefficient of variation and standard deviation index. (PT and its impact on laboratory performance and operations are discussed in Chapter 12, "Laboratory Laws and Regulations.")

Documents and Records

The seventh element of a quality management plan is a discussion of documents and records, referred to as document control. Document control is the management of documents (policies, procedures, QC records, PT records, etc) for appropriateness (current version), availability, security, privacy, visibility, safety, and auditing purposes. Document control consists of a master list of documents followed by a description of document management, review, and signature responsibilities. An SOP format may also be provided in the

quality management plan. Tools for developing SOP formats for documents are available from the CLSI, ISO, and other standards-generating organizations.[5] This section of the quality management plan may also include a table showing the periods for which documents must be retained and recording the disposition of discontinued documents (Table 7-1).[1] Local, state, and accrediting agencies require differing, and usually longer, retention times than federal agencies.

Occurrence Management

Occurrence management is the systematic analysis of events that affect laboratory services, quality, and patient safety. The quality management plan should include a section describing occurrence management. To identify systematic laboratory problems, laboratory staff should be actively involved in capturing and analyzing information about nonconforming events. There are three methods for documenting and reviewing occurrence management: (1) random review (predetermined internal review), (2) laboratory detection (detection by a technologist), and (3) external detection (detection by a physician, nurse, patient, or other customer). Since documentation of occurrences alone is insufficient to elicit corrective action, occurrences should be documented and analyzed for opportunities to take corrective action. A number of formats for occurrence management recording are available, from paper-based and electronic event-reporting for infrequent occurrences to trend analysis for more frequent events. Isolated and repeat serious events should be analyzed and referred for root cause analysis and failure mode and effects analysis.

Assessments and Audits

This element of the quality management plan describes the participation of the laboratory in audits and assessments. This section of the quality management plan describes external assessments by the CAP, the Food and Drug Administration, the AABB (formerly American Association of Blood Banks), the Centers for Disease Control and Prevention (CDC), state agencies, and the Joint Commission, as well as internal assessments (eg, CAP interim inspection, annual environment of care audit [for safety], and personnel competency reviews), and defines the parties responsible for completing these assessments. These numerous activities should be briefly defined, and readers should be referred to a more detailed SOP for further information.

Table 7-1. Document Retention

Document or Material	Retention Time
General Laboratory	
Accession log records	2 years
Instruments/temperature/other maintenance records	2 years
Quality control/management records	2 years
Surgical Pathology / Bone Marrow	
Wet tissue	2 weeks after final report
Paraffin blocks	10 years
Slides	10 years
Reports	10 years
Cytology	
Slides (all gynecologic diagnoses)	5 years
Fine-needle aspiration slides	10 years
Reports	10 years
Autopsy (Non-Forensic)	
Wet tissue	3 months after final report
Paraffin blocks	10 years
Slides	10 years
Reports	10 years
Autopsy (Forensic)	
Wet tissue	3 years after final report
Paraffin blocks	Indefinitely
Slides	Indefinitely
Reports	Indefinitely
Gross images	Indefinitely
Accession log records	Indefinitely
Dried blood stains or frozen tissue for DNA	Indefinitely
Body fluids/tissue for toxicology	1 year

Document or Material	Retention Time
Clinical Pathology Records	
Patient test records	2 years
Serum/plasma/cerebrospinal fluid/body fluids other than urine	48 hours
Urine	24 hours
Peripheral blood and body fluid smears	7 days
Permanently stained slides (eg, Gram, trichrome)	7 days
Cytogenics	
Permanently stained slides	3 years
Fluorochrome stained slides	Director's discretion
Fixed cell pellet	2 weeks after final report
Final report	20 years
Diagnostic images (digitized or negatives)	20 years
Wet specimen/tissue	When adequate metaphase cells obtained
Transfusion Medicine	
Donor records	10 years
Patient records	10 years
Quality control records	5 years
Specimens from transfused donor units	7 days after transfusion
Specimens from blood donor recipients	7 days after transfusion
Records of employee signatures, initials, identification codes	10 years
Records of indefinitely deferred donors, permanently deferred donors, donors placed under surveillance for recipient's protection	Indefinitely

Adapted from Valenstein P, ed. *Quality Management in Clinical Laboratories. Promoting Patient Safety Through Risk Reduction and Continuous Improvement.* Northfield, IL: College of American Pathologists; 2005:132-133.

Process and Performance Improvement

This element of the quality management plan should define the authority, including the laboratory director and the quality management team.

The basis for review, including the establishment of a quality committee, should also be described, as well as the mechanism for organizing a performance improvement project. The process and performance improvement element ensures that all laboratory sections participate in a performance improvement project and that the laboratory as a whole adequately covers preanalytical, analytical, and postanalytical processes.

The FOCUS-PDCA model for performance improvement projects, which is based on Shewhart's and Deming's PDSA approach, is an example of a template for performance improvement. The steps for undertaking a performance improvement project using FOCUS-PDCA are shown in Figure 7-5. In some institutions, the performance improvement process is described differently.

Interdisciplinary activities for process improvement should also be described in this element. A list of hospital or medical staff committees in which pathologists or laboratory staff participate—for example, infection control, transfusion medicine, emergency medicine, and safety and quality committees—should be provided. The quality management plan should also note that interdisciplinary activities are a means for demonstrating the integration of the laboratory and the hospital or administration in quality management programs.

Facilities and Safety

The quality management plan should include an element describing participation in facilities and safety activities. In most institutions, the safety manual is a large, stand-alone document; thus, referencing the safety manual in the quality management plan suffices in terms of documentation. A safety committee for the laboratory is the primary resource for managing safety and facilities initiatives. The safety committee should be charged with the following:

- Keeping all sections of the laboratory current with safety-related information
- Ensuring safety-related tasks are occurring on schedule
- Reviewing revised safety regulations, policies, and training materials
- Conducting safety-related performance improvement initiatives
- Addressing safety concerns
- Clarifying safety policies
- Evaluating incident and accident reports
- Reviewing and evaluating the effectiveness of the chemical hygiene plan
- Making recommendations to executive management related to safety policies

FOCUS — PDCA

FOCUS
- **F**ind a process to improve
- **O**rganize a team
- **C**larify current knowledge
- **U**nderstand sources of variation
- **S**elect process to improve

PDCA
- **P**lan the improvement action
- **D**o/test the action
- **C**heck to determine effects of the action
- **A**ct to implement or change approach, solidify

Figure 7-5. An Example of a Quality Improvement Program.

Information Management

Information management, an increasingly important aspect of QC, is an essential element of any quality management plan. The information management element indicates who can authorize the use of an institution's computerized information systems. It also states that policies and procedures exist to ensure data access security and transfer integrity. Representative security measures that should be described include:

- Computer menus to which users are assigned on the basis of their responsibilities
- Access level groups
- User profiles
- Operator codes
- User identification codes
- Passwords

All computer network connectivity should be maintained in a secure environment that follows policies for antivirus protection, antispyware protection, and operating system critical patch updates. The quality management plan should ensure that audits are performed to ensure the integrity of stored data, and that access criteria remain intact and security continues to function as required. Requesting an annual summary report of new validations and audits of the information system is recommended.

The importance of the Health Insurance Portability and Accountability Act of 1996 (HIPAA) should also be discussed in this section of the quality management plan (see also Chapter 12, "Laboratory Laws and Regulations"). HIPAA was passed by Congress to make it easier to detect and prosecute fraud and abuse and enable workers to change jobs without losing their health insurance. As part of this legislation, safeguarding patient privacy with respect to health-related information was incorporated. The HIPAA Privacy Rule, which went into effect in 2003, is particularly important to laboratories because the transmission of patients' laboratory results is considered protected health care information. All electronic transmission and record storage must be HIPAA compliant. Most large institutions have a HIPAA privacy officer to help guarantee patients' privacy and the confidentiality of patients' medical records. Thus, all aspects of quality information management must be performed in accordance with this important legislation. Information about HIPAA can be found at www.cms.hhs.gov/HIPAAGenInfo/.

Customer Service and Satisfaction Surveys

The quality management plan should include a discussion of managing customer issues in the clinical laboratory. Referring physicians, nursing staff, and other customers should be surveyed regularly for satisfaction and improvement opportunities. Patients (as customers) are frequently surveyed for satisfaction in phlebotomy and specimen collection areas. Examples of improvements to survey for include stat/routine test turnaround times, reliability of results, critical value notification, phlebotomy patient courtesy and care, and test menus. CAP-accredited laboratories are required to perform such surveys at least once every 2 years. Institutions may have additional customer and employee satisfaction surveys. Employee concerns may involve communicating, balancing work and life responsibilities, having access to support systems and education, being rewarded or recognized for their contributions to the institution, and creating a culture of excellence. Many hospitals also have a patient relations department to oversee customer complaints and participate in the occurrence management process. Some simple surveys can be generated electronically, and a department website and hyperlink can be used to encourage participation. (A sample customer satisfaction survey for physicians is shown in Appendix 7-1.)

In summary, a quality management plan provides a real-time review of all of the activities essential to ensuring quality in a laboratory. Total quality management is defined in terms of services that meet customers' needs. Laboratories have many customers, including patients, nurses, and physicians. Quality management may not in and of itself be "marketable"; however, it will determine the success of a clinical laboratory in the eyes of its customers. The elements of a quality management plan provide an overview of all quality operations and educate the laboratory staff and pathologists about the kinds of activities that are essential for a great laboratory.

Responsibilities of Laboratory Directors and Pathologists

CLIA explicitly describes laboratory directors' responsibilities for ensuring quality in the laboratory: It is the responsibility of the laboratory director to "…ensure that [the] laboratory develops and uses a quality system approach to laboratory testing that provides accurate and reliable patient test results."[9] Integral to the quality systems or quality management approach is continually monitoring each testing process (eg, QC, PT), taking corrective action, and evaluating the corrective actions taken to make sure that they were effective and will prevent recurrence. These steps are very similar to those described in Shewhart's and Deming's PDSA model. It pays to know the basic elements and history of quality because similar approaches appear throughout clinical laboratory services.

The laboratory director should not work alone. Quality is only effective if the pathology group, entire laboratory staff, and all steps of laboratory testing are included in the quality management plan. Quality often intersects with compliance, education, and safety management; a template for organizationally managing these important activities is provided in Figure 7-6.

Making the Quality Management Plan Operational

Maintaining quality is a major challenge for clinical laboratories of all sizes. Several areas, including quality management, regulatory compliance, safety, and education, intersect with and affect quality. Much regulatory compliance is designed to ensure quality and safety. Education is a key activity for keeping all laboratory personnel informed about quality, regulations, and safety. Safety is core to meeting the expectations of many regulations. These four areas are intertwined and often best managed by a core quality and regulatory affairs group within the laboratory. Sample organizational charts for a moderately sized laboratory are shown in Figure 7-6.

Although laboratory quality management personnel typically perform quality and regulatory affairs activities, it is equally important that test-

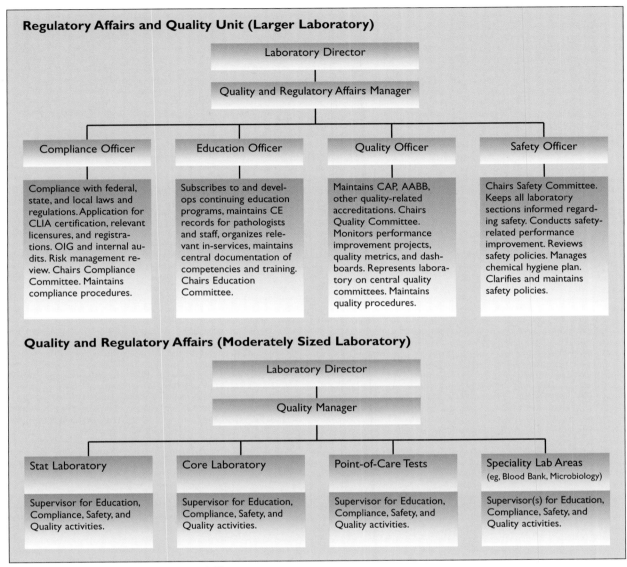

Figure 7-6. Quality Unit Organizational Charts.

ing and support personnel be involved in all types of quality, compliance, regulatory, and education activities. Small laboratories may not have enough staff to support quality activities; in these circumstances, the laboratory director must be a true leader for these complex requirements and find talent in each laboratory section to support quality activities and other related requirements. Quality efforts should be integrated throughout the laboratory, regardless of its organization.

Tools, Metrics, and Outcomes

Knowledge of the definitions of the following tools and their applications is essential for understanding the language of quality in the clinical laboratory.

Statistical Control Charts

Deming and others were strong advocates of the statistical control chart. Such charts provide a chronology of performance.[1] There are two types of statistical control charts: the X-bar control chart and the p-chart. X-bar control charts are used to measure continuous variables such as an analyte quantitative result or the turnaround times for stat potassium measurements. The p-chart is used for "yes/no" responses, for example, to determine the percentage of critical values that resulted in notification (yes) or non-notification (no).

The most widely used statistical tool for managing statistical control charts is the standard deviation. Standard deviation (SD) is a measure of vari-

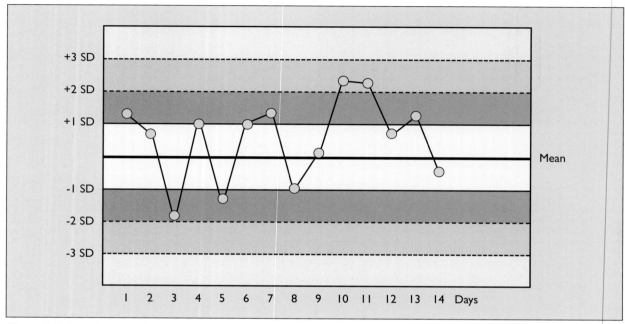

Figure 7-7. Levey-Jennings Control Chart.

ability. It shows the amount of variation from the mean. A low standard deviation indicates the data points are close to the mean. A bell curve indicating result distribution can be used to show the width of 1, 2, and 3 SD. Single results within 2 SD are within a 95% confidence interval and presumed a component of normal variability. Results that are occurring repeatedly at greater than 2 SD or single results greater than 3 SD are the basis for applying rules such as Westgard rules to statistical control charts. When only a sample of data is available, the standard deviation can be estimated by using a modified quantity called the sample standard deviation.

As an example, the turnaround time for routine potassium measurements at a given laboratory varies between 45 minutes and 70 minutes. After measuring the turnaround times in minutes in each shift over a 1-week period, the laboratory supervisor decides to use an X-bar chart to determine the lower and upper control limits for these varying turnaround times.

The control limit for an X-bar chart is calculated as:

Lower Control Limit = $m - 3\,SD/$ square root of n

Upper Control Limit = $m + 3\,SD/$ square root of n

where m is the mean of the turnaround time values for potassium for 1 week, and n is the number of measurements per day.

Similarly, to determine whether critical value notifications occur, a p-chart can be created based on the percentage of calls with completed notification over a 1-month period. The control limit for a p-chart is calculated as:

Lower Control Limit = $p - 3 \times$ square root of $p(1-p)/n$

Upper Control Limit = $p + 3 \times$ square root of $p(1-p)/n$

where p is the average fraction of successful calls made during the previous 20 days, and n is the size of each sample—in this case, the number of calls.

A laboratory can also set thresholds for desired turnaround times that are different from the statistical control limits to set qualitative goals desired by the customers.

A common laboratory statistical control chart is the Levey-Jennings chart, which is frequently used for analytes in chemistry and is often calculated as part of QC and precision review (Figure 7-7). In the current example, if the QC results for potassium measurements over 14 days are compared to the standard deviation, major variations in precision can be quickly observed, and the acceptability of a run can be established. Levey-Jennings control charts are often used according to Westgard rules. (Two examples of the rules used when using one control or two controls are shown in Figure 7-8.) An extensive review of Westgard's multiple rules and algorithms can be found at www.westgard.com.

Process Design Charts and Workflow

Process design charts (also known as workflow or process maps) are diagrammatic representations

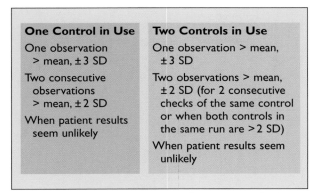

Figure 7-8. CAP Modified Quality Control Rules for Levey-Jennings Plots: One Control and Two Controls.

One Control in Use	Two Controls in Use
One observation > mean, ±3 SD	One observation > mean, ±3 SD
Two consecutive observations > mean, ±2 SD	Two observations > mean, ±2 SD (for 2 consecutive checks of the same control or when both controls in the same run are >2 SD)
When patient results seem unlikely	When patient results seem unlikely

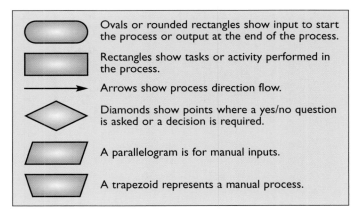

Figure 7-9. Process Chart Symbols.

Ovals or rounded rectangles show input to start the process or output at the end of the process.

Rectangles show tasks or activity performed in the process.

Arrows show process direction flow.

Diamonds show points where a yes/no question is asked or a decision is required.

A parallelogram is for manual inputs.

A trapezoid represents a manual process.

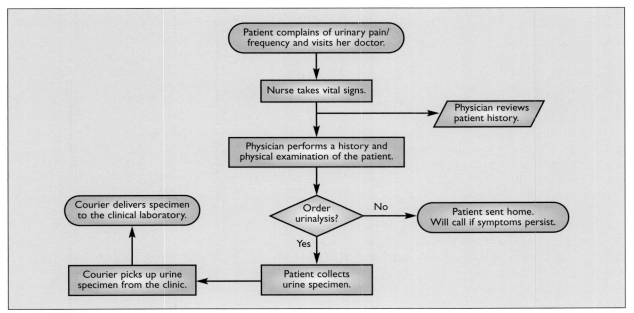

Figure 7-10. Process Chart Example.

of a dynamic work process that use symbols to indicate the steps in a process or production model. Examining a process design chart helps to identify steps in the sequence that are prone to errors and provides a diagram that testing and support personnel can use to identify points of inefficiency and error. Process design charts are also basic tools used in root cause analysis and failure mode and effects analysis. Process charts provide a valuable tool in analyzing how work flows inside and outside the clinical laboratory. A basic knowledge of process charts is invaluable when discussing workflow with laboratory staff and administration.

The first step in constructing a process design chart is to determine the boundaries of the process to be examined. Next, the steps are listed, typical-

ly using a verb to describe the step. The sequence of the steps is then established. (Post-It notes can be used to sequence the steps until every step has been located and established as a true process step.) Next, appropriate symbols are drawn to represent activity boxes (Figure 7-9). Additional symbols are available for more complex process design charts. A process chart can thus be used to examine the steps related to ordering a test and receiving a specimen in the laboratory. An example of a simple process map is shown in Figure 7-10.

Looking carefully at the process chart, one can probably think of other steps that may be inserted. For example, did the physician have the nurse complete a requisition for the urinalysis? Did the courier complete a manifest or fill out a log when he picked up the specimen? A more detailed process map may be required for evaluating major changes in the way a given laboratory operation is performed.

Root Cause Analysis and Failure Mode and Effects Analysis

The basic process chart model described above can be applied to some important activities related to identifying errors and taking corrective action. Root cause analysis (RCA) is the retrospective analysis of a sentinel event. A sentinel event is an event that threatens a patient's life, causes a patient significant morbidity, or leads to a patient's death. An example of a sentinel event is a hemolytic transfusion reaction in the operating room. The RCA is a multidisciplinary process by which the workflow is examined by all participants for the point at which human error is considered a cause of the event.[10]

The root cause of a sentinel event is usually not a conscious error but instead relates to fatigue, non-use of a checklist, or other aspects of the work environment. RCA proposes that every sentinel event has at least one preceding or underlying cause. In addition to the root cause, RCA identifies other contributing factors that contributed to an adverse event. To be credible, the RCA should involve the laboratory director and/or administrative director. The RCA should also review the literature relevant to the facts surrounding the event. Positioning the RCA in patient safety programs is further discussed below.

Failure mode and effects analysis (FMEA), which has been used in the aerospace engineering industry for many years, is different from RCA in that it is a prospective analysis that identifies failure-prone steps in a system. A thorough FMEA relies on a process chart that identifies steps where errors are likely to occur. The error-prone steps are then graded on a one to five scale according to three features: their detectability, likelihood of occurrence, and severity of error (in terms of potential harm to patients). The scoring for these three features creates a risk priority number. Steps with high-risk priority numbers are deemed to be likely critical error points, and the process can then be reworked to increase the detectability, reduce the severity, and/or reduce the likelihood of the error. The Joint Commission requires that each institution perform at least one FMEA per year. Since the clinical laboratory is often involved in process review, laboratory representatives are frequent members of FMEA teams. As laboratory leaders, pathologists and laboratory directors are frequently asked to participate in FMEA-related activities.

Lean and Six Sigma

Lean is an example of total quality management as it applies to process analysis. Based on the Toyota Production System, Lean is a practice in which each step of a process chart is examined for ways to standardize and create a more efficient and less error-prone process.[2] The ancestor of Lean is probably the engineering time-motion study. To incorporate Lean analysis, the team members analyzing the process should be employees who actually work in the areas being analyzed. Such a team is best able to define the points at which standardizing the work can bring the most comprehensive results. Improving efficiency is one reason for performing Lean analysis. Since variation in work is also a primary contributor to adverse events, Lean is also very valuable in improving the quality of the work performed and decreasing human errors. An example is standardizing phlebotomy carts or trays by regularly stocking supplies in a uniform manner to increase the likelihood that adequate supplies are available and quickly visible to the phlebotomists collecting blood in patient wards. Lean is another example of a quality activity that is highly dependent on the process chart.

In contrast to Lean, which is work process oriented, Six Sigma is a derivative of the statistical control chart and PDSA model of Plan, Do, Study, Act.[3] Six Sigma is a quality management tool that uses statistical evaluation to reduce variation, eliminate defects, and reduce errors in a production system. Six Sigma creates a personnel infrastructure (green belts, black belts) based on employee expertise and leadership roles in the Six Sigma processes for their institution.

Sigma (σ) represents the standard deviation or a measure of variation in a population. The concept of the Six Sigma process implies that if one has 6 SD between the process mean and the nearest specification limit, rare items fail to meet the specifications. The widely accepted definition of a Six Sigma process is one that has 3.4 defects per million opportunities (DPMOs).

When compared to the number of total opportunities for defects (eg, all specimens), most laboratory defects (eg, unlabeled specimens) are in the range of 3 to 4 sigma:

- 1 sigma = 690,000 DPMOs = 31% efficiency
- 2 sigma = 308,000 DPMOs = 69.2% efficiency
- 3 sigma = 66,800 DPMOs = 93.32% efficiency

- 4 sigma = 6,210 DPMOs = 99.379% efficiency
- 5 sigma = 230 DPMOs = 99.977% efficiency
- 6 sigma = 3.4 DPMOs = 99.9997% efficiency

Six Sigma also uses two evaluation models based on the PDSA model for existing and new processes. Although this text does not discuss these models in detail, other references are available to help pathologists incorporate Six Sigma into the operations of their clinical laboratories.[1,3]

External Quality Activities

Several types of external quality activities are also offered to clinical laboratories interested in benchmarks or comparison to other laboratories. These models range in type from single studies, annual evaluations, and personal (individual) performance comparisons.

Check Sample is an American Society for Clinical Pathology educational program that provides pathologists and senior technologists with case studies and teaching materials in surgical pathology, cytology, and clinical pathology. This self-directed learning tool fulfills the American Board of Pathology's requirements for certification maintenance.

The American Society for Clinical Pathology Board of Certification has a certification maintenance program specifically designed for laboratory professionals (medical technologists) that meets the recertification requirements.

Q-Probes is an external CAP peer-comparison program that addresses process-, outcome-, and structure-oriented quality assurance issues. Q-Probes establishes benchmarks through external database comparisons. Using short-term studies, Q-Probes provides a one-time comprehensive assessment of key processes in a laboratory. The studies focus on reducing medical errors and highlight processes that contribute to quality of care, patient safety, and outcomes. Examples of recent Q-Probes include Technical Staffing Ratios, Patient Safety Practices for Monitoring PT/INR, and Mammography Correlation with Pathology Reports.[11]

Q-Tracks is a CAP program that reaches beyond the testing phase to evaluate the quality of processes both within and beyond the laboratory that can impact test results and patient outcomes. Each Q-Tracks monitor provides a quarterly performance report package that helps identify improvement opportunities and monitors the effectiveness of changes implemented over time. Examples of current Q-Tracks include Patient Identification Accuracy, Blood Culture Contamination, and Turnaround Time of Troponin.[11]

In addition to the accreditation programs discussed in Chapter 12, "Laboratory Laws and Regulations" (CAP, AABB, American Society for Histocompatibility and Immunogenetics), an additional external international program, ISO (International Organization for Standardization), is also available. ISO standard 15189, titled "Medical Laboratories – Particular Requirements for Quality and Competence," is an internationally recognized laboratory accreditation standard that specifies the quality management system and competency requirements unique to medical laboratories. It is based on ISO standard 17025 and ISO standard 9001. Introduced in 2003 and developed with CAP input, 15189 has gained some standing abroad; however, in the United States, 15189 accreditation remains optional and does not have deemed status under CMS/CLIA.

ISO 15189 does not replace the longstanding CAP Laboratory Accreditation Program. The two programs are complementary. Whereas the CAP Laboratory Accreditation Program focuses on procedural excellence and good laboratory practice, fulfills CLIA requirements, uses discipline-specific checklists, and relies on unannounced inspections, the ISO standard uses announced inspections, is less prescriptive in nature, and emphasizes operational systems improvement, risk mitigation, and quality management. ISO 15189 includes provisions for the collection of patient samples, the interpretation of test results, acceptable turnaround times, testing in medical emergencies, and the laboratory's role in educating and training health care staff. Some laboratories are pursuing ISO 15189 accreditation both for quality improvement and marketing advantage.

Quality Dashboards

Dashboards are reporting formats that organize extensive data into single pages and a few succinct tables. Dashboards are frequently used in laboratories to consolidate performance improvement projects and report trend analyses over time (eg, monthly or quarterly). Dashboards are also frequently employed by hospital administration or the administration of an independent laboratory to report from multiple sectors of the operation. Sometimes color is used to demonstrate progress in a given dashboard line item (for example, turnaround times for emergency room stat testing). Dashboards may be compiled to show multiple units (nursing, laboratory, radiology, etc) to cross-compare success at management meetings. Pathologists and laboratory directors should be familiar with the dashboard concept and know which elements of the laboratory performance projects are being examined in the institution-wide format. Laboratory directors may also wish to maintain their own internal dashboards to quickly check on the progress of multiple laboratory initiatives.

Ensuring Patient Safety in the Laboratory

In 1998, the Institute of Medicine (IOM) initiated the Quality of Health Care in America project to review quality findings, articulate a policy framework, identify enablers for continuous improvement, develop a research agenda, and raise awareness among the public and stakeholders. In the first report, published in 2001,[12] the IOM extrapolated data from studies conducted in Colorado and Utah and found that between 44,000 and 98,000 patients die because of medical errors in hospitals, which would suggest that medical errors are the eighth leading cause of death.[13] A 1991 survey in New York indicated that adverse events were identified in 3% and negligence in 1% of all discharges.[14] The IOM also reported that adverse events are costly, with social costs alone ranging from $17 billion to $29 billion.

The commercial airline industry has the longest-standing safety program. Regardless of their experience, airline pilots rely on explicit checklists to confirm maintenance, personnel, electrical, and mechanical actions or reviews. Similarly, specific follow-up actions for any finding are prescribed prior to take off. No one is "too smart" or "too busy" to follow the safety rules. In contrast, the medical field has a culture of "doing it all," even when health professionals are too tired or too busy to perform tasks safely and efficiently. Historically, physicians were trained in an environment in which they were expected to perform patient-care activities late at night and while on call. In response to resident errors resulting in patient deaths, the Accreditation Council for Graduate Medical Education has since limited the number of continuous hours a resident is allowed to provide patient care.

The IOM entered the arena of patient safety expecting that culture change would become part of patient safety initiatives. They began by providing some basic definitions:

- Safety: Freedom from accidental injury
- Error: Failure of a planned action to be completed as intended or the use of a wrong plan to achieve an aim
- Adverse Event: An injury resulting from medical intervention, not due to an underlying condition

A more extensive classification of errors is provided by Reason and Rasmussen.[15,16] Cognitive errors are classified into two types: (1) errors of automatic action (commonly referred to as slips and lapses) and (2) errors of judgment (commonly referred to as mistakes). Much human action is automatic action, that is, repeat actions that proceed without much thought because of familiarity. Errors of judgment occur when a wrong rule is chosen or a rule is defective. Bias, overconfidence, or lack of knowledge cause knowledge-based errors.

Errors can also be categorized as active or latent errors. The effects of an active error are immediately felt. They occur at what is sometimes referred to as the "sharp end" of an error process. An example is a failure to clamp an artery in a surgical field, which results in immediate, and immediately-recognized, blood loss. Latent errors are errors that are embedded in the process or the system. They are typically distant or obscured and thus not immediately recognized, and are sometimes referred to as "blunt-end" errors. For example, a laboratory technologist may forget to forward a specimen from the chemistry area to the serology section for further testing; 2 days later, the ordering physician wants to know the results for hepatitis B antibodies. The error is finally traced when the specimen is located in the refrigerator in the chemistry laboratory.

Some of the approaches for improving patient safety employ techniques that are discussed above. RCA and FMEA, so-called system approaches to patient safety, are now common processes in health care. Other corrections are "hard" corrections, or human engineering approaches to patient safety, which include engineering or ergonomic improvements that are either more user-friendly or do not permit errors through new instrumentation or technology. An example is the use of a volume detector on an automated line that will not allow testing if the volume in the tube is insufficient. Also, improved instrument switches and knobs may be made to be more ergonomically acceptable, thus enhancing their usability and preventing errors.

It is unlikely that patient safety will "go away" as a topic of discussion in the medical community.

Since the first publication of *To Err is Human: Building a Safer Healthcare System*, the IOM has published a second report, *Crossing the Quality Chasm: A New Health System for the 21st Century*.[17] Some laboratory professionals perceive quality management as operational at an internal level and patient safety as the "public face" of quality. Regardless, many of the issues and research tools are similar or the same.[18] It is essential that pathologists and laboratory directors have an understanding of both quality and patient safety.

Disaster Preparedness in the Laboratory

The ultimate test of laboratory quality is planning for essential functions in the presence of an acknowledged disaster. The CDC has multiple resources on their website for the various types of disasters that health care institutions and clinical laboratories may encounter (see the Preparation and Planning section of the CDC Emergency Preparedness and Response website at www.bt.cdc.gov/planning). External disasters may present as bioterrorism emergencies, chemical emergencies, mass casualties, natural disasters, or radiation emergencies. In addition, each institution should identify internal disasters which may not affect the outside community. Examples are the loss of the hospital water supply when a water line to the hospital is disrupted or an internal chemical spill.

Disaster planning for the clinical laboratory should be coordinated with the disaster planning for the entire institution. Hospital administration will be in contact with local and regional public safety services, and hospital administration will typically coordinate disaster management. The laboratory disaster team, including the laboratory director, laboratory administrative leadership, and blood bank leadership, should be identified and their contact information added to the institution-wide disaster contact list.

A first disaster notification will indicate whether an internal or external disaster has been encountered and who should assemble on-site for the disaster management. The laboratory disaster team is critical for this preliminary evaluation and should be a part of the first response team. The laboratory disaster team should assess the following:

- Personnel safety
- Personnel availability
- Facilities function
- On-hand blood and blood products
- On-hand supplies

The institutional disaster leadership may create a command center or response center. The laboratory disaster team will then provide a first and subsequent periodic status reports to institutional leadership. Of first import in any disaster is a report and management of the well being of personnel and patients in any laboratory areas, including phlebotomy draw stations. A casualty list may be created in severe disasters such as floods and earthquakes.

The laboratory disaster team should next evaluate laboratory facilities for safety and function. Those instruments required for critical testing should be on institutional emergency (generator) power. Clinical microbiology areas should assess the function of incubators, and refrigerators and freezers should be checked in all areas. Any electrical, fire, or structural hazards should be cleared of personnel and reported to the institutional command center. In addition, the laboratory disaster team should decide which instruments should be available for testing. This usually includes critical testing, such as blood gases, electrolytes, hemoglobin, some additional chemistry analytes, and transfusion medicine emergency testing. All other ancillary testing may be discontinued at the judgment of the laboratory disaster team and the institution. All hospital personnel should be informed that only stat specimens will be tested during the emergency.

Thirdly, the laboratory needs to assess personnel availability. Are phlebotomists available to assist in the emergency room for mass casualties? Are laboratory technologists available for critical testing and blood distribution? It is important to also make a judgment call regarding whether employees should be held beyond the duration of their normal shift, taking into consideration, of course, employee family needs.

Should mass casualties be anticipated, blood bank personnel will simultaneously assess the above and immediately audit their blood and blood product availability. The institutional command center will request the availability of all blood products, with particular attention to O-negative units. Blood bank personnel will also contact local blood banks and other hospitals to assist in regionally managing the blood supply.

Finally, any supplies that may limit essential laboratory services should be assessed. As part of the refrigerator and freezer review, any essential

Case Example of Health Care Error: The Swiss Cheese Model

A 43-year-old man, James T. Smith, presents to the renal transplant clinic for evaluation. He has renal failure, is on dialysis, and is awaiting a kidney transplantation. On the same day, a second man, 56-year-old James A. Smith, goes to the renal transplant clinic for the first time for a preliminary evaluation of renal function. He is doing quite well—he is not yet on dialysis—but he wants to start the evaluation process for transplantation. The clinic nurse prints out labels for both patients ahead of time; as part of the workup, the nurse draws blood from each patient for creatinine levels and glomeruler filtration rates. The nurse fails to see the similarity of the names and accidentally marks the blood sample from the healthier 56-year-old patient with a label for the 43-year-old patient awaiting a transplant. As a consequence, the healthier 56-year-old patient's creatinine level comes back markedly elevated. The nephrologist is quite concerned and schedules a renal biopsy. Prior to biopsy, the renal biopsy nurse also fails to double-check the medical record numbers or birth dates for the two patients. A biopsy is performed on the 56-year-old patient unnecessarily. What went wrong?

This scenario is a classic case of the "Swiss cheese model" (figure). In the Swiss cheese model, each hole in a slice of Swiss cheese represents a procedure or function in which an error can occur. When looking at an entire block of Swiss cheese, no holes are evident; however, when the holes align, with multiple errors overlapping, a hole traversing the entire block of cheese can be seen. This is when an error can occur and when patient safety may be threatened.

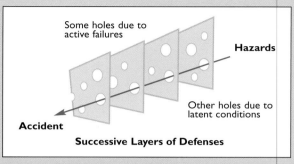

Successive Layers of Defenses

In this case, the renal transplant clinic mislabeled specimens from two patients who had similar names. The renal biopsy clinic personnel failed to note the mismatches in the patients' names, birth dates, or medical record numbers. The immediate reaction might be to blame the clinic nurse. However, the principles described in the concept of root cause analysis require that all the other slices of cheese be examined. Are there other causes? Did the hospital information system have a "similar names alert" feature so that the nurse would have been alerted when she printed the labels? Did the laboratory information system likewise have a "similar names alert" that could have alerted the technologist? Was a "delta check" available in the laboratory that might have shown that the first patient had an unusual change in his test results?

Going even further, looking for more "slices" with holes: Was the nurse tired? Had she been asked to work a double shift? Was staffing in the clinic adequate? Did the nephrologist not recognize the discrepancy between the second patient's clinical appearance and his creatinine? There are likely several other slices with holes. A good RCA process will identify as many weaknesses in a process as possible.

supplies should be stored in units with access to emergency power. Phlebotomy supplies should be well organized and ready to mobilize to the emergency room or other sites.

Some types of disasters require specific laboratory expertise. An example is a bioterrorism threat as occurred in the anthrax outbreak of 2001. Under this scenario, the Laboratory Response Network managed by the CDC and the Association of Public Health Laboratories will go into operation. The Laboratory Response Network is a schematic that identifies sentinel laboratories ("first respon-

der" microbiology laboratories), reference laboratories (public health laboratories), and national laboratories (eg, CDC). Clinical laboratories should determine in advance whether their microbiology laboratories have sentinel or advanced sentinel laboratory status. A laboratory with advanced sentinel laboratory status will have Biosafety Level 2 facilities and a biosafety cabinet for management of potential bioterrorism specimens. Explicit guidelines are provided by the CDC for management of potential bioterrorism attacks.

References

1. Valenstein P. ed. *Quality Management in Clinical Laboratories. Promoting Patient Safety Through Risk Reduction and Continuous Improvement.* Northfield, IL: College of American Pathologists; 2005.

2. Shinkle G, Gooding R, Smith M. *Transforming Strategy into Success. How to Implement a Lean Management System.* New York, NY: Productivity Press; 2004.

3. Brussee, W. *Statistics for Six Sigma Made Easy.* New York, NY: McGraw Hill; 2004.

4. Berte LM, Boone DJ, Cooper C, et al. *Application of a Quality Management System Model for Laboratory Services. Approved Guideline.* 3rd ed. Wayne, PA: Clinical and Laboratory Standards Institute; 2004. Document GP26-A3.

5. Berte LM, Callihan DR, Carlson J. *Laboratory Documents. Development and Control. Approved Guideline.* 5th ed. Wayne, PA: Clinical and Laboratory Standards Institute; 2006. Document GP2-A5.

6. *The American Bar Association's Guide to Workplace Law.* 2nd ed. New York, NY: Random House Reference; 2006.

7. Howanitz PJ, Howanitz JH. *Laboratory Quality Assurance.* New York, NY: McGraw-Hill; 1987.

8. Department of Health and Human Services. Centers for Medicare and Medicaid Services. Clinical Laboratory Improvement Amendments (CLIA) Proficiency Testing Dos and Don'ts. April 24, 2003. Available at: https://www.cms.gov/CLIA/ downloads/CLIAbrochure8.pdf. Accessed Nov 17, 2010.

9. Department of Health and Human Services. Centers for Medicare and Medicaid Services. Clinical Laboratory Improvement Amendments (CLIA) Laboratory Director Responsibilities: What Are My Responsibilities as a Laboratory Director? August 2006. Available at: http://www.cms.hhs.gov/CLIA/ downloads/brochure7.pdf. Accessed Nov 10, 2010.

10. Ammerman M. *The Root Cause Analysis Handbook.* New York, NY: Productivity Publications; 1998.

11. College of American Pathologists. Past Q-Probes studies. Available at: www.cap.org. Accessed Jan 7, 2011.

12. Institute of Medicine. *To Err is Human. Building a Safer Health System.* Washington, DC: National Academies Press; 2000.

13. Orentlicher D. Medical malpractice: treating the causes instead of the symptoms. *Med Care.* 2000;38:261-271.

14. Brennan TA, Leape LL, Laird, et al. Incidence of adverse events and negligence in hospitalized patients — results of the Harvard Medical Practice Study I. *New Engl J Med.* 1991;324:370-376.

15. Rasmussen J. Skills, rules, knowledge: signals, sign and symbols and other distinctions in human performance models. *IEEE Transactions on Systems, Man and Cybernetics.* 1983;SMV-13:257-266.

16. Reason J. *Human Error.* Cambridge, England/New York: Cambridge University Press; 1990.

17. Institute of Medicine. *Crossing the Quality Chasm: A New Health System for the 21st Century.* Washington, DC: National Academies Press; 2001.

18. Wagar EA, Yuan S. The laboratory and patient safety. *Clin Lab Med.* 2007;27:909-930.

Challenge Questions

What is the best statistical measure of precision ?
A. Chi square test
B. Coefficient of variation
C. Pareto diagram
D. Levey-Jennings chart
E. None of the above
Answer: B; see pages 122 to 123.

What does the diamond symbol in a process chart represent?
A. An input or output
B. A manual process
C. A decision point
D. A process step
E. A feedback loop
Answer: C; see page 129 and Figure 7-9.

Describe the role of the laboratory director in proficiency testing, in laboratory accreditation, and in laboratory licensing.
Answer: See page 126 and Chapter 12.

Appendix 7-1.
Physician Satisfaction Survey

Annual Survey for Physicians

The following items refer to routine hematology and chemistry testing. Physicians were asked to rate the acceptability of the following laboratory service definitions on a scale of 1 to 5, with 1 being unacceptable and 5 being very acceptable.

1. Phlebotomy response time for an inpatient stat chemistry or hematology test request is 30 minutes.

2. Phlebotomy response for routine chemistry and hematology tests is 60 minutes.

3. Routine chemistry and hematology testing is completed in 180 minutes.

4. Routine chemistry and hematology outpatient testing performed in the ABC Laboratory is completed within 8 hours.

5. Stat chemistry and hematology testing is completed in 120 minutes.

6. Stat chemistry and hematology outpatient testing performed in the ABC Laboratory is completed within 60 minutes of phlebotomy.

Appendix 7-2.
Event Reporting Form

1. General Questions

Incident Type: (Patient, Visitor, Staff Member)

Patient Name:

Medical Record Number:

Date of Birth:

Gender:

Department:

Division:

Location: (Nursing Units, Clinical Laboratory, OR, ER, Ambulatory Care)

Unit:

Event Date:

Your Home Department:

Is this event related to one of the National Patient Safety Goals?

If so, please indicate which one:
1. Ambulatory Care
2. Behavioral Health Care
3. Critical Access Hospital
4. Home Care
5. Hospital
6. Laboratory
7. Long-Term Care
8. Office-Based Surgery

Is this patient on a research protocol that is related to this event?

Was there harm to the patient/visitor/staff member?

Were there any interventions or treatments that occurred as a result of this event? If so, please indicate:

Were there any changes in the level of care resulting from this event? If so, please indicate:

2. Category/Subcategory:

Category: (Pathology and Laboratory Medicine: Specimen Collection, Lab Processing, Lab Results, Pathology Specimen Collection, Pathology Processing, Pathology Reporting, Staff Professionalism, Physician Professionalism)

Subcategory: (Pathology and Laboratory Medicine: Specimen Not Collected, Specimen Not Received, Specimen Not Adequate, Specimen Processed Incorrectly, Specimen Unlabeled, Specimen/Requisition Mismatch, Specimen Mislabeled, Incorrect Result)

3. Event Description:

(Please describe this event.)

4. Witnesses:

(Please list witnesses.)

5. Reporter Details:

Name:

E-mail

Phone:

Pager:

Other Title:

Department:

Form Start Entry Date/Time:

Form Complete Entry Date/Time:

6. Severity Ranking:

(Please select from the list.)
1. No harm: Did not reach patient
2. No harm: Reached patient
3. Minimal harm or impact
4. Moderate harm or impact
5. Serious harm or impact
6. Patient death
7. Unable to determine

7. Type of Harm:

(Please describe.)

8. System Messages:

Report date/time:

E-mail notification:

E-mail viewed by (date/time):

CHAPTER 8

Quality Assurance in Anatomic Pathology

Michael O. Idowu, MD, MPH
Raouf E. Nakhleh, MD

Contents

Early Quality Assurance Efforts in Anatomic Pathology

Because pathology is intertwined with nearly every medical specialty, pathologists are in a position to contribute significantly to quality patient care. The basic statistical processes for clinical chemistry tests that Levey and Jennings proposed in 1950[1] were already being applied in clinical laboratories by 1967 when the Clinical Laboratory Improvement Act (CLIA) was first passed. Quality control in the clin-ical laboratory was probably the first form of quality management in health care as a whole.

Although clinical laboratories, with a focus on test accuracy and precision, developed and implemented quality control measures much earlier than anatomic pathology laboratories, the issues of error reduction, quality assurance, and quality control are not new in anatomic pathology. Articles addressing these issues as they related to anatomic pathology were first published in the 1950s and 1960s and dealt with process, reproducibility, diagnostic accuracy, standardization, and turnaround time.[2-6] In 1967, Nakazawa et al, commenting on frozen section diagnoses, asserted that "if high standards of accuracy are not established and met, the pathologist cannot reliably fulfill an often vital role in diagnosis and subsequent therapy."[3] Wilson and Burke, observing that different pathologists were using different criteria for the interpretation of pulmonary specimens, also recognized a need for standardization.[4-6]

Despite the early recognition of the need to improve quality in anatomic pathology, there was a long delay before formal quality assurance programs were developed and implemented in anatomic pathology laboratories. This delay may have been caused in part by a widespread belief that the "test result" in anatomic pathology was not a quantitative value generated by some sophisticated analytic instrument but was instead based on clinical correlation and cognitive interpretations of specimens (an art rather than science), which introduced subjectivity.

Studies in the 1980s and 1990s that assessed errors in anatomic pathology[7-12] received relatively little attention. In 1999, the Institute of Medicine published a report, *To Err is Human: Building a Safer Health System,* which estimated that between 44,000 and 98,000 patients die each year as a result of medical error, with many more suffering as a result of ailments associated with medical error.[13] The report's findings resonated with the public

Table 8-1. Items that Should be Included in a Quality Management Plan

A quality assurance team with a clear charge
The scope of the quality assurance program
An assessment of the risk to the laboratory
A list of monitors that address laboratory risk
The time frames of data collection
Method of data evaluation
The individual responsibility for the various monitors that are part of the quality assurance plan, including collection and maintenance of the quality assurance data (duties may be divided among a number of individuals in the laboratory)
A plan for distribution of *relevant* quality assurance data to appropriate institutional bodies
Annual evaluation of the program's effectiveness and annual review of the plan

and legislators. Although the majority of reported errors were medication related, the report shone a spotlight on errors across the entire health care industry, including errors in anatomic pathology. Reported error rates in anatomic pathology are widely variable, ranging from less than 1% to 43%.[14] The processes involved in arriving at a finished, quality product in surgical pathology are complex and require a solid quality assurance program. This chapter highlights the principles of quality assurance and the development and implementation of quality assurance programs in anatomic pathology.

Principles of Quality Assurance

Quality in any industry can be defined as the production of a product or service that meets customers' expectations or requirements. All industries' quality assurance principles are similar and emphasize continuously improving their products. Anatomic pathology provides diagnostic and prognostic information that frequently guides the type of treatment the patient receives. Therefore, quality is essential in anatomic pathology, and it relates to three elements: diagnostic accuracy, report completeness and clarity, and report timeliness. All these elements should be addressed to improve the quality of anatomic or surgical pathology.

A systems approach is an ideal approach to quality management. The basic principles of a sys-

tems approach derive from the fact that humans make mistakes and that mistakes are unavoidable. This intrinsic human shortcoming may be mitigated, but cannot be eliminated, by education and/or training. Therefore, quality management systems must be designed (and redesigned continuously) to prevent errors and quickly detect errors should they occur. The system must be addressed as a whole, but individual performance cannot be ignored. Quality management systems should continuously monitor individual performance and cognitive learning in addition to a system relying only on individual accountability.

It is almost impossible to have "zero error," and there is a point at which increased expenditure leads to diminishing returns with respect to benefits.[15] However, it is possible to have continuous improvement with persistent efforts and continuous redesign of the system. Different methods of continuous quality improvement include Six Sigma, Lean (the Toyota Production System), and total quality management, any of which can be adapted to anatomic pathology.

Improving patient care is the primary reason for developing and implementing quality management plans in anatomic pathology; additional reasons include meeting regulatory compliance and engendering the public's trust. The College of American Pathologists (CAP) Laboratory Accreditation Program (LAP) mandates the existence of a quality assurance program. LAP checklist item ANP.10000 states, "The quality management program is defined and documented for surgical pathology," and GEN.13806 states, "The laboratory has a documented quality management (QM) program." All quality assurance programs in anatomic pathology should be clearly described in a written document, which should be reviewed annually and revised as necessary. The document should include details on the items in Table 8-1.[16,17]

Significant resources and efforts are likely to be expended in developing and implementing a successful quality management plan. At a minimum, the quality management plan should focus on metrics that will satisfy regulatory compliance, address observed laboratory quality issues, and improve laboratory performance.

Metrics for Anatomic Pathology

The cycle of any laboratory test includes three phases: the preanalytic phase (specimen collection, delivery, and accessioning), the analytic phase (actual testing), and the postanalytic phase

Table 8-2. Test Cycle Phases, Processes, and Potential Quality Management Monitors

Process	Possible Quality Assurance Monitors
Preanalytic	
Patient registration	—
Requisition sheet with adequate patient identifiers on the requisition form (at least 2 unique identifiers) and history	Rates of cases with improperly filled requisition; rates of cases with no patient history
Specimen procurement and adequacy	Rates of cases requiring re-biopsy for a definite diagnosis (specimen insufficient for diagnosis)
Specimen identification	Rates of mislabeled specimens
Specimen integrity and appropriate fixation	Rates of specimens in wrong fixatives; rates of specimens with prolonged nonfixation
Specimen transportation	Rates of specimens with delayed transportation
Accessioning	Rates of specimens with accessioning problems
Analytic	
Gross examination/adequate sampling/appropriate sections/specimen fixation	Rates of specimens needing additional sections; rates of gross sections needing reprocessing (rates of mislabeled cases, specimen, slides and blocks)
Specimen processing/processor	Rates of instrument failure
Specimen embedding/sectioning	Rates of "floaters" or extraneous tissues; rates of specimen lost in processing; rates of slides requiring recuts due to cracked/torn sections, poor staining quality, etc
Special stains (histochemical and immunohistochemical)	Rates of repeat special stains; correlation of ancillary studies with histopathologic findings (ANP.22200-22900)
Frozen sections	Correlation of frozen and final diagnosis (ANP.12000, 12075 [see also Table 8-5])
Microscopic examination	Rates of amended reports; rates of intradepartment peer review (ANP.10150, 30050); error rates detected by targeted review of cases; error rates detected by review of fixed percentage of cases; rates of cervical cytology–histology correlation; proficiency testing performance; internal quality assessment performance
Diagnosis verification	—
Postanalytic	
Electronic report transmission/delivery: accuracy of report integrity	Periodic review and comparison of the original and electronic reports for errors in data transmission, storage, and processing (GEN.48500)
Report completeness	Rates of cancer report completeness
Transcription	Rates of transcription errors
Timeliness of report	Rates of reports exceeding the expected turnaround time
Customer satisfaction	Survey of the clinical staff satisfaction with laboratory services

(report generation and delivery). Actions in one part of the test cycle may affect the other phases of the cycle. For example, providing the clinical information that accompanies a specimen is clearly a preanalytic process; however, improper, inadequate, or no clinical history may lead to important aspects of testing being omitted or performed incorrectly. If a kidney biopsy sample comes with the history "rule out malignancy," the sample will likely be placed in formalin and processed routinely; however, if the kidney biopsy sample is accompanied with the history "hematuria, rule out glomerulonephritis," the sample will be divided, placed in different fixatives, and processed for light microscopy, immunofluorescence, and electron microscopy. Similarly, incorrect patient identification or a specimen mix-up may result in one patient's diagnosis being accidentally provided to another patient, with potentially serious consequences. Thus, shortcomings in the preanalytic phase may result in improper processing and examination in the analytic phase or even inadequate or incorrect reports in the postanalytic phase of the test cycle. Therefore, all aspects of the test cycle must be examined within the quality assurance program.

In addition to the phases of the test cycle, other important aspects of quality that should be addressed in the quality management plan include report timeliness and customer or clinician satisfaction.

Determining whether a measured performance is satisfactory requires a standard to which the performance can be compared. Benchmarks are accepted performance standards that may be available within an industry or profession. In pathology, most benchmarks can be obtained through a diligent review of the literature on a specific topic or measure. However, one must be cautious when evaluating the literature because benchmarks are heavily dependent on the method of data collection and the specifics of the quality monitor. In addition, benchmarks may change over time or as new technologies become available. In some cases, there may not be a generally accepted benchmark, and pathologists may need to work with clinicians to determine acceptable benchmarks for a specific metric within their institution.

Preanalytic Phase

Assuring quality in the preanalytic phase may be challenging because some of the processes are not under the control of the laboratory. Specimens are obtained from many sources, including doctors' offices, operating rooms, endoscopy suites, and outpatient and inpatient facilities. Many individuals involved in this process are not employed or trained by the laboratory but are nevertheless responsible for obtaining specimens, appropriately labeling specimen containers, and completing the accompanying requisitions. The submitting physicians are responsible for providing the appropri-

ate clinical information and ensuring that specimens are properly procured, labeled, handled, and delivered to the laboratory. The laboratory has a shared responsibility in the process to ensure quality care; errors can easily occur if all of the processes are not clearly defined, accepted, and monitored. Close cooperation and communication between the pathology and clinical services are necessary to ensure that specimens are properly procured and delivered to the anatomic pathology laboratory. Multiple aspects of the preanalytic phase of the test cycle that can be monitored are listed in Table 8-2.

Specimen identification is perhaps the most important process in the preanalytic phase of the test cycle. Potential problems in specimen identification are listed in Table 8-3.

Errors in patient information, identification, history, or laterality may lead to an incorrect diagnosis or a correct diagnosis for the wrong patient or body site. In some cases, the impact such an error may have on the patient may not be serious and may just be embarrassing to the laboratory—for example, reporting a pap smear (cervical cytology) for a male patient or a prostate biopsy for a female patient. But in others cases, identification errors may compromise patient safety and lead to significant morbidity or even death. The Joint Commission's National Patient Safety Goals focus on patient identification, which encompasses specimen identification. Specimens that have deficiencies or errors related to identification should not be accessioned until the deficiency has been corrected. Most of these deficiencies should be resolved according to institutional policy, but typically errors must be corrected by the individual who was responsible for the particular specimen. Since most surgical specimens are irreplaceable or unique, specimen rejection should be the last recourse, and this recourse should be taken only if exhaustive attempts to correct the deficiencies have proven ineffective.

Organizations should consider making specimen identification quality an institutional quality assurance goal rather than just a laboratory goal. This may be achieved by sharing the quality assurance data of specimen identification deficiencies with the clinical departments in a nonconfrontational manner. In some cases, there may be a need to educate "repeat offenders."

Monitors

Most laboratories have specimen identification logs (Table 8-4) for documenting cases with deficiencies such as improper labeling, incomplete la-

Table 8-3. Possible Deficient Elements in Specimen Identification

Incomplete or absent specimen identification	No label on container No requisition sheet or requisition sheet not received with specimen No unique patient identifier (UPI) on specimen container No UPI on the requisition sheet Patient name or UPI on the specimen container and requisition sheet do not match Wrong patient name or UPI on either specimen container or requisition sheet Illegible information on specimen container or requisition sheet
Incomplete history or description of procedure	No tissue source indicated on the container or requisition sheet No clinical history No date or time of the procedure No name of the submitting physician Incorrect patient information at patient registration
Incorrect handling of specimen	Specimen lost in transportation Delayed delivery of specimen to the laboratory Delivery of specimen to the wrong location Inadequate or improper fixative in specimen container Damaged containers

Table 8-4. Example of a Specimen Deficiency Log

Date	Deficiency	Location	Action Taken by Laboratory Personnel	Corrective Action Taken by Initiating Location	Specimen Disposition
11/1/09	Patient registered as a male; cervical specimen	Obstetrics and gynecology clinic	Clinician notified	New requisition with proper designation submitted	Accept specimen
11/8/09	Specimen container information does not match requisition sheet	Breast imaging clinic	Radiologist notified	Correct matching requisition sheet received	Accept specimen

beling, absence of a requisition sheet, or requisition sheet labeling that does not match specimen container labeling. This information is vital to addressing problems of specimen identification.

Benchmarks

A CAP Q-Probes study of clinical and anatomic pathology laboratories[11] reported an aggregate preverification identification error rate of 324 per 1,000,000 billable tests and an aggregate postverification error rate of 55 per 1,000,000 billable tests. Approximately 1 in 18 identification errors resulted in an adverse event. Block or slide labeling errors accounted for 3.8% of these errors.[11] Noting that ongoing monitoring was associated with a lower error rate, the authors recommended monitoring identification errors. Ideally, the institutional quality assurance plan's goal should target "zero" specimen identification deficiencies. At the very least, individual laboratories should work toward incremental improvement.

Other preanalytic monitors to consider include specimen adequacy, specimen integrity, appropri-

ate fixation, appropriate containers, delay before formalin fixation of surgical specimen, and specimen transportation. Prolonged delay before formalin fixation may have adverse effects on the histologic interpretation and possible ancillary testing of the specimen. As a general policy, most laboratories provide appropriate fixatives to specimen collection areas and encourage open communication if questions arise. Specimen transport is another potentially problematic area. Monitoring the time between obtaining the specimen and delivery to the laboratory may offer clues to problems.

Analytic Phase

The analytic phase of the test cycle represents all of the steps involved in processing and evaluating the specimen until a diagnosis is rendered and a report issued. Table 8-2 lists some of the analytic processes and some commonly used quality assurance monitors. Diagnostic accuracy, one of the main elements of quality, is perhaps the most monitored element of the analytic phase and probably the most difficult to measure. Measuring diagnostic accuracy comes with some caveats. Because it is impractical to wait for an outcome to determine the correctness of a diagnosis, pathologists do not really measure accuracy, but rather diagnostic reproducibility or precision. Typically, diagnostic concordance between one or more reviewers is used as a surrogate marker for diagnostic accuracy.

Rates of Correlation Between Intraoperative Consultation and Final Diagnosis

Intraoperative consultation provides pathologists with an opportunity to have real-time influence on patients' surgical care and constitutes a prime example of pathologists working within a team for the benefit of patients. Intraoperative consultation is very useful in certain types of surgeries and is most often used to determine margin status, evaluate tumor extent, determine tissue adequacy, and diagnose tumor types to help determine the extent of surgery required for staging (for example, by distinguishing ovarian cystadenoma from borderline tumor or carcinoma, or by evaluating axillary sentinel lymph nodes in breast cancer patients). Frozen section evaluation, which is used for intraoperative consultation, is a rapid process with multiple potential pitfalls that may lead to erroneous interpretations and outcomes. The limitations of frozen section analysis may lead to an irreducible error rate; however, while errors may inevitably occur, their impact must be minimized. Monitoring for these errors helps pathologists understand the potential pitfalls of frozen section examination and helps them to not only avoid the same mistakes, but also to engender trust by communicating limitations to the clinicians and reconciling these limitations with the clinicians' expectations. Long-term monitoring may improve performance[18]; the reasons for this are not entirely clear but may be related to continuously focusing on and addressing repeated difficult-to-interpret frozen sections. Lastly, intraoperative consultation errors must be monitored for regulatory compliance. For example, CAP LAP checklist item ANP.10100 states, "When significant disparity exists between initial intraoperative consultation (eg, frozen section, cytology, gross evaluation) and final pathology diagnosis, it is reconciled and documented either in the surgical pathology report or in the departmental quality management file," and checklist item ANP.12075 states, "Following frozen section examination, the residual frozen tissue is routinely processed into paraffin, and a histologic section prepared and examined for comparison with the frozen section interpretation."

Monitors

Laboratories typically keep a log of all correlations between the frozen section diagnosis and the final diagnosis (Table 8-5). Frozen section–final diagnosis correlations should be divided into the following categories: agreement, appropriate deferral, inappropriate deferral, minor disagreement, and major disagreement. In cases of major disagreement or inappropriate deferral, the source of the discordance should be categorized as one of the following: interpretation, block sampling, specimen sampling, technical inadequacy, or lack of essential clinical or pathologic data. These classifications are useful for evaluating data and identifying specific areas for improvement. For example, if the majority of the reasons for the discordance relate to interpretation errors, education or remediation may be warranted. Similarly, if the data point to specimen sampling or technical inadequacy as the major reason for the discordance, this issue may need to be addressed by the staff who process the frozen sections.

Benchmarks

Single-institution and CAP Q-Probes studies[19-22] have suggested that an acceptable diagnostic discordance rate is about 2%. A recent Q-Tracks study suggested that continuous monitoring can lower this rate to 1.1%, with a 1.8% deferral rate.[18] However, a discordance rate of even 1% means that 1 of every 100 frozen sections may be inaccurate and lead to potentially harmful effects on the patient. From this perspective, there is a clear need for continuous monitoring.

Gynecologic Cytology–Histology Correlation

Certain gynecologic screening cytology diagnoses often lead to colposcopy and directed biopsy or endocervical or endometrial biopsy or curettage. Correlation of the gynecologic cytology diagnosis with subsequent or corresponding histologic diagnosis is essential to determining and improving diagnostic accuracy and is necessary for regulatory compliance. Clinical Laboratory Improvement Amendment 88 493.1274(c)(2) states, "The laboratory must compare all gynecological cytology reports with an interpretation of [high-grade squamous intraepithelial lesion] or carcinoma with the histology report, if available, in the laboratory (either on site or in storage) and determine the cause of any discrepancy." Following this guideline may lead pathologists to understand the potential pitfalls of unnecessary procedures, patients' anxiety associated with unnecessary procedures, and the ways in which such procedures can be prevented.

Table 8-5. Example of Frozen Section Turnaround Time and Frozen Section–Final Diagnosis Correlation

Date	Specimen #	Patient Name/ MRN	Specimen	Log In Time	Call Back Time	TAT	Res/ Staff	Frozen Diagnosis	Final Diagnosis	Concordance/ Discordance/ Deferred
01/01/08	SP-08-00001	ABC	Ovary	11:00	11:25	0:25	AB/ CED	Serous cystadenoma	Serous borderline tumor	
01/01/08	SP-08-00024	CED	Right axillary sentinel lymph node	12:20	12:30	0:10	AB/ CED	Negative for carcinoma	Metastatic carcinoma, size 0.4 cm	
01/04/08	SP-08-00090	FGH	Bone mass	9:30	9:45	0:15	CD/ GGF	Aneurysmal bone	Telangiectatic osteosarcoma	
02/04/08	SP-08-00101	XYZ	Soft tissue mass	11:00	11:15	0:15	CG/ MO	High-grade sarcoma	Malignant peripheral nerve sheath tumor	
02/05/08	SP-08-00120	PQR	Lymph node	9:00	9:10	0:10	CR/ CP	Lympho-proliferative lesion	B-cell lymphoma	

The data may be shared with the departments that generate the gynecologic cytology specimens. The goal of the laboratory should be to minimize false-positive diagnoses and maximize true-positive diagnoses. However, it should be noted that gynecologic cytology is a screening test, and that false-negative cytology reports are potentially much more harmful to the patient than false-positive reports given the known sensitivity and specificity of gynecologic cytology for detecting cervical cancer and its precursor lesions.

Monitor

Pathologists should keep a log of all positive gynecologic cytology diagnoses and histologic follow-up biopsies. The log may be computer generated. A key laboratory technician or pathologist should work with a cytotechnologist to review the monthly data and determine the causes of any discordance. The reason for any discrepancy must be investigated. Although colposcopic biopsy is regarded as the "gold standard," the cause of the discrepancy may not always be identifiable because of sampling issues during the procurement of the biopsy specimen.

Benchmark

A CAP Q-Probes study of more than 22,000 paired gynecologic cytology and biopsy specimens revealed a discrepancy rate of 16.5%.[23] The majority of the discrepancies were nonlaboratory factors (eg, biopsy and cytology sampling errors) rather than analytic errors. If a discrepancy is due to biopsy sampling, the institution should determine the quality management pathway. Testing for human papillomavirus, a re-biopsy, or a repeat cytological sampling may be warranted.[24,25] Laboratories should work with clinicians to develop an institutional threshold at which the laboratory should investigate the reason for the discordance and attempt to address it.

Intradepartmental Peer Review

There is no standardized process of peer review for assessing the diagnostic accuracy of the interpretation of surgical pathology cases. Some of the methods that have been suggested include:

- Reviewing all new cancer cases
- Reviewing all cancer cases in specific organ systems
- Reviewing random cases
- Reviewing fixed percentages of all cases
- Reviewing difficult cases at consensus conference

Generally, retrospectively reviewing cases is used to determine error rates. However, the impact of this type of review is undetermined. Therefore, in the hope of reducing diagnostic errors, many laboratories have implemented prospective intradepartmental peer review of microscopic interpretation before cases are finalized.

Certain organ systems or diagnoses (eg, cancer) are targeted because they are deemed to be potentially difficult interpretations in some cases and may have profound impact on individual patients. Some of the organ systems that are frequently listed include esophageal biopsies for Barrett's dysplasia; brain, thyroid, breast, and prostate tissues; and melanocytic skin lesions. Some departments choose to document these reviews in the body of the reports, while other departments choose to document these consultations in peer review documents separate from the reports. Some laboratories also choose to monitor this practice for documentation that departmental policy is being followed. These data could be used as a part of a re-credentialing process. One potential pitfall of reviewing only cancer cases is that false-negative cases may not be identified. Although the emphasis in many laboratories is to identify false-positive cases, false-negative cases should also be identified because they may significantly impact patient care. If case review is done after the initial sign-out, the review should be performed shortly after case verification to minimize potential serious harm to patients should a major disagreement or error occur.

Monitors

In a recent Q-Probes study, Raab et al[26] suggested classifying diagnostic discrepancies into the following categories:

- Change in margin status
- Change in categorical interpretation (eg, benign to malignant)
- Change within the same category of interpretation (eg, squamous cell carcinoma to adenocarcinoma, carcinoma to sarcoma or lymphoma)
- Change in patient information
- Typographical error

Targeting a group of difficult diagnoses, the authors used a blinded quality assurance method within 48 hours of being signed out. If a disagreement in diagnosis occurred that might be clinically significant, the original pathologist submitted an amendment. Renshaw et al[27] proposed an alternative classification of peer review discrepancies. It has been suggested that blinded review is preferable because it is effective and is a relatively unbiased method for detecting disagreements and errors in surgical pathology.[28]

Benchmarks

A recent CAP Q-Probes[26] study revealed that the median discrepancy rate among surgical pathology cases was 5.1%. Almost half of the discrepancies were due to changes within the same category (ie, the benign or malignant category remained

unchanged), and about a fifth of all discrepancies involved a change in the other category (ie, benign to malignant and vice versa). The discrepancy rate was highest among cases in which a clinician requested a second opinion.[26] However, only 5.3% of the discrepancies had a moderate or marked effect on patient care. Therefore, an appropriate target of cases for peer review could be between 5% and 15%. A recent study observed that reviewing all breast, gynecologic, and nongynecologic cytology and endocrine material would involve 26.9% of all cases (this percentage varies depending on the case mix of a particular institution) and detect 88% of the amended reports. However, reviewing only nondiagnostic and atypical cases would involve only 4% of cases and detect 14% of the amended interpretations.[28] Therefore, targeted case review may be more effective than random case review. Regardless of the review method, each institution should determine the case mix and the most effective and efficient process for productive peer review.

Amended Report Review

Reviewing amended reports provides a wide net with which to examine errors occurring in a department. The term *amended* may be used in a broad sense to include all changed reports. However, some have defined "amended" or "revised" to indicate a change in the diagnosis. Reports with changes of information other than the diagnosis have been referred to as a *corrected* report. Also, "addendum reports" are those that add new information but do not alter any original information within the initial report.

Rates of amended reports are used as surrogate measurements of diagnostic error. The amended report rate is likely the best estimate of errors occurring in the laboratory, but it does not reflect the true diagnostic error rate. In many instances, the diagnostic error is due to typographical errors, errors in patient history, the incorrect laterality (as provided by the procuring clinicians), or a specimen mix-up prior to its arrival at the laboratory. Nevertheless, measuring the rates of amended reports also identifies cases of diagnostic errors.

Monitor

All amended reports should be monitored and categorized by error type and their potential for patient harm. It is essential that laboratories use a standardized amended report. At the very least, all changes in the diagnosis, regardless of their presumed clinical significance, must have an amended report.

Benchmarks

Renshaw et al[28] reported that specimens with the highest amendment rates were breast core biopsies and endometrial curettings. A Q-Probes study[29] reported an aggregate amended report rate of 1.9 per 1000 cases (0.19%; median, 0.15%). Of the amended cases, 38.7% involved change of the original diagnosis.

Postanalytic Phase

The postanalytic phase of the test cycle includes the production and dissemination of pathology reports. Report completeness and integrity are important aspects that require quality assurance monitoring.

Surgical Pathology Report Completeness

In oncologic care, complete and accurate cancer reports are necessary for accurately staging cancer and determining optimal therapy.[30,31] Surgical pathology cancer reports contain diagnostic, prognostic, and predictive information that is used to make therapeutic decisions. The American College of Surgeons (ACS) Commission on Cancer (CoC) requires that all scientifically validated elements such as those deemed essential by the CAP should be included in the cancer report.[32,33] Employing standardized reporting, using cancer checklists, monitoring the cancer reports for completeness, and giving feedback to the pathologists have been shown to improve the quality of reporting.[34-37] The CAP LAP has recently included a standard that requires a quality assurance monitor that evaluates the completeness of cancer reporting for laboratory accreditation.[38]

Monitor

All surgical pathology cancer reports should be reviewed for completeness; that is, the reports should include all scientifically validated elements as required by the ACS CoC.[32,33] Monitoring the use of cancer checklists may also be helpful. In high-volume services in which reviewing all the cancer reports would be daunting, randomized (eg, a fixed percentage of reports) or focused reviews (eg, reviews of breast cancer and colon cancer reports only) may be more practical.

Benchmarks

The CAP and the ACS CoC require at least 90% of the reports to include all the scientifically validated elements.[32] It is important to provide feedback to the pathologists and to monitor the improvement if the reports are incomplete.

Informatics and Report Integrity

The majority of laboratories currently use electronic reporting, and computer interface issues may affect report format or content. In fact, this is a regulatory compliance addressed by LAP checklist item GEN.41067, which states, "An individual meeting CAP laboratory director qualifications reviews and approves the content and format of paper and electronic patient reports at least every two years." (See also Chapter 3, pages 41 to 42.)

Monitor

Electronic reports should be periodically reviewed to detect errors in data transmission, storage, or processing and to ensure that the electronic reports correspond to the original reports. To ensure that all essential information in the original report is entirely and clearly communicated electronically, pathologists should review the entire report, including comments, addendum reports, and amended reports. In addition, pathologists must ensure that all reports are transmitted and available for the clinicians (ie, no "dropped" reports). Clinicians' complaints about being unable to access reports should also be investigated and may serve as a potential monitor for "dropped" reports.

Benchmarks

Currently, the literature provides no generally acceptable benchmarks for the integrity of electronically delivered reports. However, it is essential that the laboratory monitor report integrity to ensure that clinicians receive the intended information.

Turnaround Time

While report accuracy and completeness should not be sacrificed for speed, the timeliness of communication is a key quality indicator in anatomic pathology and complements diagnostic accuracy and report completeness. In anatomic pathology, turnaround time (TAT) is often measured from the time the specimen is received in pathology to the time the final report is issued. TAT is a useful general measure for identifying efficiency in the system. Delayed reports may compromise patient management. TAT may also provide information that may be used for peer review and performance evaluation for individual pathologists for hospital credentialing. The CAP LAP stipulates that TAT should be monitored at least for a period of time annually.

Monitors

The following TATs should be monitored:

- Intraoperative consultation (frozen section)

- Surgical specimens (biopsy, excision)
- Gynecologic pathology
- Nongynecologic cytology
- Preliminary and final autopsy report

Benchmarks

Intraoperative consultation (frozen section) TAT. A CAP Q-Probes study reported that 90% of frozen sections could be completed within 20 minutes.[39] The CAP LAP checklist item ANP.11820 states, "The laboratory at least annually evaluates turnaround time for intraoperative frozen sections." This applies only to cases with a single specimen requiring a single block and to frozen sections performed during regular business hours when a pathologist is on site. If there are delays, there should be sufficient documentation to identify the problem(s) when the 10% threshold is exceeded. The data can be collected if the time of specimen receipt and the time of reporting are recorded either electronically or in a written log in the gross room. Some preanalytic variables that may affect TAT include multiple simultaneous frozen section requests, the number of dedicated personnel performing the procedure, cryostat availability, resident participation in frozen sections, the need to review previous material, and the need to defer the final diagnosis.

Surgical pathology specimen TAT. The Association of Directors of Anatomic and Surgical Pathology recommends that acceptable TATs be determined on the basis of current literature, keeping in mind that acceptable TATs are also defined by the accrediting bodies. TATs are variable depending on case complexity and other factors, such as the presence of a residency-training program. The standards may change over time with the advent of new technologies and other factors. The LAP checklist item ANP.12150 states, "Reports on routine cases are completed within two working days." The checklist acknowledges that unusually complex or special specimens may require prolonged fixation and that special stains may require longer reporting times.[40]

Customer Satisfaction

Customer satisfaction in many industries is a large determinant of profitability and corporate survival. Pathologists' direct customers are clinicians; indirect customers include patients (the most important customers), Medicare, and insurance companies. Dissatisfaction with a private pathology laboratory may lead to a loss of business for the laboratory. However, because many institutions'

policies and procedures require clinicians to use a designated laboratory, many laboratories may feel protected and may shy away from surveys to monitor clinicians' satisfaction for fear of "opening a can of worms."

One recent publication[41] showed that while clinicians most often want improvement in aspects of communication (for example, timeliness of reporting, completeness of reporting, and notification of significant unexpected findings), they are not particularly worried about professional competence. Circulating clinician satisfaction surveys with a genuine effort to address the issues of concern usually creates a level of trust that leads clinicians to view the laboratory and pathologists as partners who are willing to improve their products. Furthermore, such surveys give pathologists the opportunity to understand and address the unmet needs of their clinician customers and to educate clinicians about unrealistic expectations.

Monitors

Monitors of customer satisfaction could include the following: satisfaction with intraoperative (frozen section) consultation services; satisfaction with the timeliness and completeness of surgical pathology reports; satisfaction with the notification of significant and/or unexpected findings; overall satisfaction with surgical pathology, cytopathology, and autopsy pathology services; satisfaction with pathologists' participation in conferences; and satisfaction with pathologists' availability to answer questions, review cases, and support research endeavors in academic institutions.

Benchmarks

A 2001 Q-Probes study[42] that evaluated physicians' satisfaction with the quality of professional interaction and diagnostic accuracy reported 96.3% and 96.1% median percentage values of excellent ratings and good ratings, respectively; reporting timeliness had a mean percentage value of 79.8%. In terms of percentages of below average/poor ratings, the lowest scores related to the communication of relevant information, notification of significant abnormal results, and timeliness of reporting.[42,43]

Responsibilities of the Laboratory Director

The laboratory director is responsible for all activities in the laboratory. CLIA '67 and CLIA '88 mandate certain direct responsibilities for the laboratory directors and allow laboratory directors to delegate other duties to qualified personnel. CLIA regulations stipulate, "The laboratory director is responsible for the overall operations and administration of the laboratory, including the employment of personnel who are competent to perform test procedures, and record and report test results promptly, accurately, and proficiently and for assuring compliance with the applicable regulations."[44] The laboratory director, if qualified, may perform the duties of the technical consultant, clinical consultant, or testing personnel or delegate these responsibilities to personnel who meet the qualifications. If some of the responsibilities are delegated, the laboratory director is still responsible for ensuring that all duties are properly performed. Laboratory directors must be familiar with various regulatory requirements (federal, state, accreditation, etc) and ensure compliance with these requirements. In view of the complexity of the processes involved in anatomic pathology, laboratory directors must also be actively involved in laboratory operations (including quality assurance measures) and have a system in place for effectively communicating with laboratory and administrative personnel to ensure that the laboratory is operating smoothly. Some of the responsibilities of the anatomic pathology director as specified by CLIA[44] are listed in Table 8-6.

Controversies in Anatomic Pathology: Immunohisto-chemistry Test Validation

The widespread use of immunohistochemistry (IHC) in the anatomic pathology laboratory has diagnostic and in some cases prognostic and predictive significance. Some antibodies used for IHC are classified as analyte-specific reagents and are regulated by the Food and Drug Administration as Class I in vitro diagnostic tests. For consistent and accurate results, IHC reagents must be optimized and validated. Antibody optimization is the process by which the laboratory serially tests and modifies component(s) (for example, pretreatment, enzyme digestion, pH of the buffer [pH 6 or pH 8 or 9], heating device use for antigen retrieval AR, primary antibody incubation time, detection system, and chromogens) of the procedure or protocol to achieve a consistent result. Antibody optimization must be completed before performing antibody validation. Antibody validation is the process of establishing the reproducibility of the IHC assays[45,46] to ensure that the assay performs as intended to detect the specified antigen. For test

Table 8-6. Responsibilities of the Laboratory Director

Oversees the production of quality services encompassing all phases of the test cycle
Provides adequate and appropriate environmental conditions for testing performed
Provides a safe environment for employees
Supervises high-complexity testing
Hires job candidates who have the appropriate education and experience
Reviews and documents new test procedures
Determines the individual responsibilities and duties of each consultant and technical staff
Ensures that approved procedure manuals are available to the relevant staff
Enrolls the laboratory in relevant Centers for Medicare and Medicaid Services (CMS)–approved proficiency testing programs
Performs and documents corrective actions when proficiency testing results are deficient
Ensures that test results are reported only when the system is functioning properly and that all necessary remedial actions are taken and documented whenever significant deviations from laboratory's established performance specifications are identified
Ensures that test result reports include pertinent information to allow interpretation
Ensures that consultation is available to the laboratory's clients on matters relating to the quality of the test results reported and their interpretation concerning specific patient conditions
Ensures that a sufficient number of laboratory personnel have experience or training to be able to provide appropriate consultation and properly supervise, accurately perform, and report test results

validations of IHC to be interpreted as "positive" or "negative," a minimum of 25 separate specimens must be tested or evaluated by an alternative validated method in the same laboratory or by a validated method in another laboratory. At least 10 samples should have high levels of the target antigen; 10 samples should have intermediate to low levels of the target antigen; and 5 samples should have no target antigen. The purpose of the validation is to evaluate the performance of the IHC on a range of clinical specimens to determine the sensitivity or specificity of the IHC reaction. The specimen used for the assay should be as close as possible to the clinical samples. All validated IHC assays need to be completely revalidated if significant changes are made to the assay or whenever new antibody lots are used. Three specimens—one with high levels of the target antigen, one with intermediate to low levels of the target antigen, and one with no antigen—should be sufficient for the revalidation of new antibody lots. It is preferable to have the negative and positive control tissues on the same slide; if these tissues are on separate slides, the laboratory must ensure that the control slides receive the same treatment as the test slides. Automation may be used to eliminate the variability that is inevitable with a manual process.

Inconsistency in the quality of the IHC assay due to lack of standardization may lead to inaccurate or unreliable results. The implications of inaccurate IHC results on patient care can be serious. For example, incorrect CD117 and actin stains may lead to the misdiagnosis of a spindle cell lesion as a smooth muscle tumor rather than a gastrointestinal stromal tumor, which in turn may lead to an incorrect treatment. The clinical significance of unreliable IHC has led to calls for standardizing and monitoring the IHC process.[45-51]

Processes in all phases of the test cycle may affect the quality of IHC studies. Preanalytic processes (eg, type of fixative, time to fixation, and duration of fixation) may affect antigen retrieval and the quality of the final product; analytic processes (eg, reagent optimization and validation, balancing the parameters of antigen retrieval with the length and type of fixation and the characteristics of the individual antibody, and personnel training and competence) and postanalytic processes (eg, result interpretation, accurate and clear reporting)[45-51] can also affect the accuracy of IHC staining.

Individual laboratories may choose to monitor any of the above processes. Possible monitors of the quality of IHC could include the rate of repeat tests, TAT of the IHC tests, and/or an audit for the appropriate use of IHC and/or interpretation of the staining.

Summary

Quality management plans in anatomic pathology are essential for quality products. Establishing and maintaining sound quality management plans often require time and effort. Efforts should be expended in monitoring all the phases of the test cycle, and should also include monitoring TAT and customer satisfaction. At the minimum, quality assurance efforts should satisfy regulatory compliance and address any observed laboratory issues, with the goal of improving the quality of laboratory products.

Case Example: Human Epidermal Growth Factor Receptor 2

Human epidermal growth factor receptor 2 (HER2) status is an important prognostic and predictive factor in the management of breast cancer patients.[48-52] Sound quality assurance measures are essential to providing accurate, reliable, and reproducible HER2 results. The CAP LAP requires that laboratories be in compliance with the American Society of Clinical Oncology (ASCO)/CAP guidelines.[53]

Because of its potential survival benefits, trastuzumab therapy is offered to breast cancer patients with HER2 amplification or overexpression in combination with other chemotherapeutic treatment. The accuracy of the HER2 result is essential as it determines possible benefits from trastuzumab therapy. However, the performance of HER2 testing may vary, with discordance rates of up to 20% in interlaboratory HER2 results.[54-56] The findings suggest that some patients who could benefit from trastuzumab may not be offered the drug because of false-negative test results, while some patients who may not benefit from the drug could be offered the treatment because of false-positive results, leading to unnecessary expenses and exposure to possible drug complications. These findings led to joint ASCO and CAP recommendations to address possible sources of variation and to standardize HER2 testing with the expectation of "minimizing inappropriate practice variation."[53]

The possible sources of variation were preanalytic (time to fixation, duration of fixation, and type of fixative and method of tissue processing) and analytic (assay optimization and validation, training and competency assessment of laboratory staff and pathologists, interpretation criteria, and proficiency testing).[45-53]

Familiarity with the ASCO/CAP recommendations on HER2 testing[53] is essential to determining the processes that should be monitored. Assuming that the test reagent is appropriately optimized and validated (with ongoing validation done biannually), some possible monitors to consider may include the duration of fixation in formalin (although the 6- to 48-hour recommendation is not scientifically validated), the time to fixation from specimen procurement, HER2 proficiency testing performance, and the rates of borderline results being repeated.

References

1. Levey S, Jennings ER. The use of control charts in the clinical laboratory. *Am J Clin Pathol.* 1950; 20(11):1059-1066.
2. Stout P. Frozen section diagnosis in surgery. *Surg Clin North Am.* 1956;36: 335-344.
3. Nakasawa H, Rosen P, Lane NM, Lattes R. Frozen section experience in 300 cases: accuracy, limitations and value in residency training. *Am J Clin Pathol.* 1967;49(1):41-51.
4. Wilson EB, Burke MH. Some statistical observations on a co-operative study of human pulmonary pathology. *Proc Natl Acad Sci USA.* 1957;43(12):1073-1078.
5. Wilson EB, Burke MH. Some statistical observations on a co-operative study of human pulmonary pathology, II. *Proc Natl Acad Sci USA.* 1959;45(3):389-393.
6. Wilson EB, Burke MH. Some statistical observations on a co-operative study of human pulmonary pathology, III. *Proc Natl Acad Sci USA.* 1960;46(4):561-566.
7. Gilchrist KW, Gould VE, Hirschl S, et al. Interobserver variation in the identification of breast carcinoma in intramammary lymphatics. *Hum Pathol.* 1982;13(2):170-172.
8. Zarbo RJ, Howanitz PJ, Bachner P. Interinstitutional comparison of performance in breast fine-needle aspiration cytology: a Q-Probe quality indicator study. *Arch Pathol Lab Med.* 1991;115:743-750.
9. Zarbo RJ, Hoffman GG, Howanitz PJ. Interinstitutional comparison of frozen-section consultation: a College of American Pathologists Q-Probe study of 79 647 consultations in 297 North American institutions. *Arch Pathol Lab Med.* 1991;115:1187-1194.
10. Gilchrist KW, Gould VE, Hirschl S, et al. Interobserver reproducibility of histopathological features in stage II breast cancer: an ECOG study. *Breast Cancer Res Treat.* 1985;5(1):3-10.
11. Valenstein PN, Raab SS, Walsh MK. Identification errors involving clinical laboratories: a College of American Pathologists Q-Probes study of patient and specimen identification errors at 120 institutions *Arch Pathol Lab Med.* 2006;130(8):1106-1113.
12. Zarbo RJ, Gephardt GN, Howanitz PJ. Intralaboratory timeliness of surgical pathology reports: results of two College of American Pathologists Q-Probes studies of biopsies and complex specimens. *Arch Pathol Lab Med.* 1996;120:234-244.
13. Kohn LT, Corrigan JM, Donaldson MS. *To Err Is Human. Building a Safer Health System.* Washington, DC: National Academy Press; 1999.
14. Raab SS, Grzybicki DM, Zarbo RJ, et al. Anatomic pathology databases and patient safety. *Arch Pathol Lab Med.* 2005;129(19)1246-1251.
15. Bartlett RC. Trends in quality management. *Arch Pathol Lab Med.* 1990;114(11):1126-1130.
16. Travers H. Quality assurance indicators in anatomic pathology. *Arch Pathol Lab Med.* 1990;114(11):1149-1156.
17. Nakhleh RE. Core components of a comprehensive quality assurance program in anatomic pathology. *Adv Anat Pathol.* 2009;16(6):418-423.
18. Raab SS, Tworek JA, Souers R, Zarbo RJ. The value of monitoring frozen section permanent section correlation data over time. *Arch Pathol Lab Med.* 2006; 130(3):337-342.
19. White VA, Trotter MJ. Intraoperative consultation/final diagnosis correlation: relationship to tissue type and pathologic process. *Arch Pathol Lab Med.* 2008;132(1):29-36.
20. Gephardt GN, Zarbo RJ. Interinstitutional comparison of frozen section consultations: a College of American Pathologists Q-Probes study of 90,538 cases in 461 institutions. *Arch Pathol Lab Med.* 1996; 120:804–809.
21 Ferreiro JA, Myers JL, Bostwick DG. Accuracy of frozen section diagnosis in surgical pathology: review of a 1-year experience with 24,880 cases at Mayo Clinic Rochester. *Mayo Clin Proc.* 1995;70: 1137–1141.
22. Khoo JJ. An audit of intraoperative frozen section in Johor. *Med J Malaysia.* 2004;59:50–55.
23. Jones BA, Novis DA. Cervical biopsy-cytology correlation: a College of American Pathologist's Q-Probes study of 22,439 correlations in 348 laboratories. *Arch Pathol Lab Med.* 1996;120(6):523-531.
24. Wright TC Jr. Massad LS, Dunton CJ, Spitzer M, Wilkinson EJ, Solomon D; 2006 ASCCP-Sponsored Consensus Conference. 2006 consensus guidelines for the management of women with abnormal cervical screening tests. *J Low Genit Tract Dis.* 2007;11(4): 201-222. Erratum in: *J Low Genit Tract Dis.* 2008;12(3): 255.
25. Katki HA, Wacholder S, Solomon D, et al. Risk estimation for the next generation of prevention programmes for cervical cancer. *Lancet Oncol.* 2009; 10(11):1022-1023.
26. Raab SS, Nakhleh RE, Ruby SG. Patient safety in anatomic pathology: measuring discrepancy frequencies and causes. *Arch Pathol Lab Med.* 2005; 129(4):459-466.

Challenge Questions

What is the main reason for having a quality management plan in the department?
Answer: See pages 137 to 138.

What are possible monitors of the analytic phase of the test cycle?
A. Intraoperative consultation–final diagnosis correlation
B. Gynecologic cytology-histology correlation
C. Intradepartmental peer review
D. Amended report review
E. All of the above.
Answer: E; see page 141 and Table 8-2.

What needs to be done to validate a new antibody for immunohistochemistry?
A. Antibody and other component optimization.
B. Antibody validation (reproducibility), 25 separate specimens compared to another method or laboratory.
Answer: B; see pages 147 to 148.

Describe a program for intradepartmental peer review for surgical pathology.
Answer: See page 143 to 145.

27. Renshaw AA, Cartagena N, Granter SR, Gould EW. Agreement and error rates using blinded review to evaluate surgical pathology of biopsy material. *Am J Clin Pathol.* 2003;119:797-800.

28. Renshaw AA, Gould EW. Comparison of disagreement and amendment rates by tissue type and diagnosis: identifying cases for directed blinded review. *Am J Clin Pathol.* 2006;126:736-739.

29. Nakhleh RE, Zarbo RJ. Amended reports in surgical pathology and implications for diagnostic error detection and avoidance: a College of American Pathologists Q-Probes study of 1,667,547 accessioned cases in 359 laboratories. *Arch Pathol Lab Med.* 1998;122(4):303-309.

30. Zarbo RJ. Interinstitutional assessment of colorectal surgical pathology adequacy: a College of American Pathologists Q-Probes study of practice patterns from 532 laboratories and 15,940 reports. *Arch Pathol Lab Med.* 1992;116(11):1113-1119.

31. Gephardt GN, Baker PB. Lung carcinoma surgical pathology report adequacy: a College of American Pathologists Q-Probes study of over 8300 cases from 464 laboratories. *Arch Pathol Lab Med.* 1996;120(10): 922-927.

32. Commission on Cancer. *Cancer Program Standards.* 2009 ed. Available at: http://www.facs.org/cancer/coc/cocprogramstandards.pdf. Accessed Apr 18, 2011.

33. CAP Cancer Protocols and Checklists. Available at: www.cap.org/cancerprotocols. Accessed Feb 15, 2011.

34. Srigley JR, McGowan T, Maclean A, et al. Standardized synoptic cancer pathology reporting: a population-based approach. *J Surg Oncol.* 2009; 99(8):517-524.

35. Onerheim R, Racette P, Jacques A, Gagnon R. Improving the quality of surgical pathology reports for breast cancer: a centralized audit with feedback. *Arch Pathol Lab Med.* 2008;132(9):1428-1431.

36. Imperato PJ, Waisman J, Wallen MD, et al. Improvements in breast cancer pathology practices among Medicare patients undergoing unilateral extended simple mastectomy. *Am J Med Qual.* 2003; 18(4):164-170.

37. Imperato PJ, Waisman J, Wallen M, et al. Results of a cooperative educational program to improve prostate pathology reports among patients undergoing radical prostatectomy. *J Community Health.* 2002; 27(1):1-13.

38. Paxton A. Thaw begins, changes to LAP checklists flow. *CAP Today.* 2009;23(6):5-8.

39. Novis DA, Zarbo RJ. Interinstitutional comparison of frozen section turnaround time: a College of American Pathologists Q-Probes study of 32,868 frozen sections in 700 hospitals. *Arch Pathol Lab Med.* 1997;121(6):551-567.

40. Association of Directors of Anatomic and Surgical Pathology. Recommendations for quality assurance and improvement in surgical and autopsy pathology. *Am J Surg Pathol.* 2006;30(11):1469-1471.

41. Zarbo RJ. Determining customer satisfaction in anatomic pathology. *Arch Pathol Lab Med.* 2006; 130(5):645-649.

42. Zarbo RJ, Nakhleh RE, Walsh W. Customer satisfaction in anatomic pathology: a College of American Pathologists Q-Probes study of 3065 physician surveys from 94 laboratories. *Arch Pathol Lab Med.* 2002; 127(1):23-29.

43. Nakhleh RE, Souers R, Ruby SG. Physician satisfaction with surgical pathology reports: a 2-year College of American Pathologists Q-Tracks study. *Arch Pathol Lab Med.* 2008;132(11):1719-1722.

44. CLIA regulations. Available at: http://www.cdc.gov/clia/regs/subpart_m.aspx#493.1407 Updated April 24, 1995. Accessed Dec 2, 2009.

45. Goldstein NS, Hewitt SM, Taylor CR, et al. Recommendation for improved standardization of immunohistochemistry. *Appl Immunohistochem Mol Morphol.* 2007;15(2):124-133.

46. Taylor CR. The total test approach to standardization of immunohistochemistry. *Arch Pathol Lab Med.* 2000;124:945-951.

47. O'Leary TJ. Standardization in immunohistochemistry. *Appl Immunohistochem Mol Morphol.* 2001;9:3-8.

48. Pritchard KI, Shepherd LE, O'Malley FP, et al. HER2 and responsiveness of breast cancer to adjuvant chemotherapy. *N Engl J Med.* 2006:354(20);2103-2111.

49. Villman K, Sjostrom J, Heikkila R, et al. TOP2A and HER2 gene amplification as predictors of response to anthracycline treatment in breast cancer. *Acta Oncol.* 2006:45(5);590-596.

50. Konecney GE, Thomssen C, Luck HJ, et al. Her-2/neu gene amplification and response to paclitaxel in patients with metastatic breast cancer. *J Natl Cancer Inst.* 2004:96(15);1141-1151.

51. Slamon DJ, Leyland-Jones B, Shak S, et al. Use of chemotherapy plus a monoclonal antibody against HER2 for metastatic breast cancer that overexpresses HER2. *N Engl J Med.* 2001:344(11):783-792.

52. Vogel CL, Cobleigh MA, Tripathy D, et al. Efficacy and safety of trastuzumab as a single agent in first-line treatment of HER2-overexpressing metastatic breast cancer. *J Clin Oncol.* 2002;20(3):719-726.

53. Wolff AC, Hammond EH, Schwartz JN, et al. American Society of Clinical Oncology/College of American Pathologists guideline recommendations for human epidermal growth factor receptor 2 testing in breast cancer. *Arch Pathol Lab Med.* 2007; 131(1):18-43.

54. Paik S, Bryant J, Tan-Chiu E, et al. Real-world performance of HER2 testing – National Surgical Adjuvant Breast and Bowel Project experience. *J Natl Cancer Inst.* 2002; 94(11):852-854.

55. Roche PC, Suman VJ, Jenkins RB, et al. Concordance between local and central laboratory HER2 testing in the breast intergroup trial N9831. *J Natl Cancer Inst.* 2002 ;94(11):855-857.

56. Perez EA, Suman VJ, Davidson NE, et al. HER2 testing by local, central, and reference laboratories in specimens from the North Central Cancer Treatment Group N9831 intergroup adjuvant trial. *J Clin Oncol.* 2006; 24(19):3032-3038.

Bibliography

CAP Accreditation Program. *Anatomic Pathology Checklist.* Northfield, IL: College of American Pathologists; June 17, 2010.

CAP Accreditation Program. *Laboratory General Checklist.* Northfield, IL: College of American Pathologists; June 17, 2010.

Nakhleh RE, Fitzgibbons, PL. *Quality Management in Anatomic Pathology. Promoting Patient Safety Through Systems Improvement and Error Reduction.* Northfield, IL: College of American Pathologists; 2005.

CHAPTER 9

Financial Management of the Laboratory

Elizabeth A. Wagar, MD
Isam-eldin A. Eltoum, MD, MBA
Richard E. Horowitz, MD

Contents

History

In 1965, the national health expenditure totaled $42 billion, and the health care industry represented 5.5% of the gross domestic product of the United States. By 2008, the national health care expenditures were $2.4 trillion and represented 16% of the gross domestic product. Laboratory expenditures are estimated to account for anywhere between 3% and 10% of this total. Medicare alone spent $7.1 billion for clinical laboratory services in 2008. The laboratory is big business and requires prudent and business-like management. According to Peter Drucker, an early general management theorist, a manager is responsible for producing a useful product or service, making work meaningful for employees, being cognizant of the organization's impact on the community, and making a profit. Pathologists need to know the parameters of income and expense as well as the methods for planning, evaluating, and controlling these parameters.

Laboratory income varies according to patient type (for example, inpatients versus outpatients), payer (private insurance versus Medicare versus a health maintenance organization [HMO]), and the type and the location of the laboratory (hospital versus outpatient clinic versus freestanding commercial laboratory). Hospitals and freestanding laboratories billed insurers or private parties on a fee-for-service basis until 1983, when the concept of prospective payment via diagnosis-related groups (DRGs) for Medicare hospital inpatients was implemented. This system classified hospital cases into one of approximately 500 groups, or episodes, that used similar hospital resources. Payment was based on the patients' diagnoses, not their length of stay, the resources used, and the procedures performed. At the same time, laboratory fees for Medicare inpatients were unbundled so that the technical component was part of, and paid through, the DRG, while the pathologist billed the professional component separately. In addition, the

Often administrators forget that hospitals are hierarchies of servants. The ultimate recipient of hospital services is the patient. The nurse and the primary care physician serve the patient directly. The specialist and the hospital-based physician and their staff serve the primary care physician directly and the patient indirectly. Hospital administration serves by providing the resources so that all the others can serve the patient. Many hospital administrators need to be reminded that they are servants, just like the rest of the people that work in a hospital, and they are there to serve the patient, not the bottom line.

professional component of most clinical pathology tests was defined not as a service billable to an individual patient, but as a professional service "to the provider" (ie, to the hospital), and payment for this service was again included in the DRG. Charges for Medicare outpatient clinical laboratory services were paid based on a fee-based schedule, which was the least of the amount billed, the local fee for a geographic area, or a national limit.

In the 1970s and 1980s, insurance companies, HMOs, and preferred provider organizations implemented a variety of cost-containment models, including capitation plans, discounted fee-for-service fee schedules, and negotiated hospital contracts, which usually included the laboratory fees. Often, these reimbursements were less than the Medicare payments and less than the actual cost to produce a laboratory result. In many instances, laboratories were forced to negotiate not only the cost of the test, but also the tests that could be performed. Some managed care companies are now targeting expensive molecular and genetic tests by requiring preauthorization. (See Chapter 10, "Financial Management of the Pathology Practice," for more information about reimbursement schedules.)

Other sources of hospital laboratory income include outreach programs with phlebotomy stations and even stat laboratories in medical buildings or clinics in the community. A laboratory courier service may be provided from hospitals and physicians' offices for reference laboratory services. Laboratories may also provide services such as substance abuse testing for employees of local businesses. Each of these income streams must be separately identified. Having additional income streams raises a variety of complicated financial issues regarding applicable deductibles, copayments, different contracted fee schedules, and the ever-looming hazard of unrelated business income compromising the tax-exempt status of a not-for-profit hospital. (See also Chapter 3, "Laboratory Operations.")

Responsibilities

The pathologist laboratory director is responsible for the financial management of the laboratory. Both the Clinical Laboratory Improvement Amendments (CLIA) and the Joint Commission charge the director to assume not only professional, scientific, and consultative oversight of the laboratory, but also responsibility for the organization of the facility. Thus, the laboratory director is ultimately responsible for the efficient and effective operation of the laboratory. The director establishes the laboratory's goals and objectives, supervises the budgeting process, monitors laboratory performance (including financial performance), and controls operations to meet the fiscal goals. In many laboratories, these services are provided by the laboratory director as a member of a pathology group that contracts with a hospital to manage the laboratory. The pathologist is usually an independent contractor when performing professional, scientific, and consultative duties; however, the managerial functions, including financial management of the laboratory, are appropriately in the purview of hospital administration, and the pathologist/director reports to, and may be evaluated by, hospital administration.

The laboratory director must have assistance in financial management. Depending on the size of the laboratory and the complexity of its operation, that assistance may come from the pathologist's executive assistant or the laboratory's chief technologist. In larger laboratories performing more than one million tests per year, an administrative officer or laboratory manager should be involved in the financial management of the facility. The very largest laboratories may employ financial officers. These financial assistants should report to the pathologist/director and are responsible for financial forecasting, planning, budgeting, contract management, managed care contracting, equipment leases, reference laboratory contracts, billing, collecting payment, bookkeeping, monitoring financial performance, and auditing. In executing the financial responsibilities of the laboratory, the pathologist/director and the laboratory manager work closely with the hospital administration—specifically, the administrator "in charge" of the laboratory, the chief financial officer, and the hospital accountants. Similarly, laboratory directors should seek counsel from the hospital's legal consultants when dealing with the many contracting issues facing the laboratory. In addition, since most financial operations are totally dependent on a functioning hospital information system, the clinical laboratory must establish a close and mutually respectful relationship with the hospital's information technology department. Finally, a compliance officer who ensures that the coding and billing operations are in compliance with various governmental regulations is essential to the fiscal operation of the laboratory.

A private stand-alone or commercial laboratory likely has a different financial structure than an in-hospital laboratory. The pathologist/laboratory director of a private laboratory may or may not have the ultimate decision-making responsibility in the budgeting process or financial management of the facility. Instead, a nonmedical financial officer often plays a major role in managing financial operations, and the business structure likely provides the appropriate auditing, accounting, and legal functions as well as billing and collection services.

Policies and Procedures

The management of the laboratory consists of planning, leading, organizing, and controlling, and the road map to successful management is the strategic planning process. The final step in that strategic plan is the development of the business plan and the budget. (See also Chapter 1, "Management Principles.") Thus, prudent financial management begins with a re-examination of the hospital's and the laboratory's vision and mission; a re-evaluation of the internal, external, and market assessments; an examination of the results of the most current strengths-weaknesses-opportunities-threats analysis; a confirmation of the laboratory's long- and short-range financial strategies; and, on the basis of these factors, the development of a business plan and the budget.

Business Plan

The business plan is a formal articulation of the strategic plan. The business plan states the goals of the project and says how those goals will be achieved. It also contains background information about the organization, describes the products and services provided, establishes a marketing plan and strategy, and recounts the past financial history of the organization. The critical sections of the business plan are the 12-month profit and loss projections, 5-year profit projections, cash flow projections, projected balance sheet, and break-even analysis. A business plan is essential for a stand-alone or commercial laboratory. The hospital laboratory generally does not develop a business plan separate from the hospital's business plan unless a joint venture or a new venture such as an outreach program is being considered.

Budgeting Process

The next step in the financial management of a laboratory is the budgeting process. Budgets are managerial financial tools that allow organizations to chart their commitments, plans, projects, and all

of its costs in one comprehensive document; it is the financial map of future activities.[1] Most organizations have a capital budget for major equipment or expenditures that are expected to extend over more than 1 year; a personnel budget, which details the personnel requirements of the entity; an operating or expense budget, which details the income and expenses of the organization; and an allocation budget, which details those items that are nominally called indirect expenses or overhead.

Some institutions segment budgets for different purposes. For example, an operating budget, which deals with activities already being performed, may be separated from an opportunities budget, which is devoted to innovation and new activities. Complex operations may have a critical factors budget, which identifies every product or service and the few major items that account for 75% to 80% of the total budget, and a milestone budget, which controls expenditures for a predefined result or a new product.

The methodology used to formulate the projection for a new budget varies with the institution. The simplest but least accurate method is to assess the previous year's expenditures and simply add a percentage that seems "about right" across the board for the upcoming fiscal year. A more accurate method, the standard budget, is based on the previous year's expenditures and realistically evaluates each line item for anticipated increases and decreases based on activities planned for the upcoming year. A favored methodology in government is the zero-based budget. Rather than starting with the previous year's expenditures, the manager starts fresh by identifying the results desired in a given area and asking what is needed to obtain those results. Zero-based budgeting requires significant planning; instead of incorporating this method in all areas of an institution, zero-based budgeting may be incorporated into specific sectors in which such planning may be of value. Sometimes zero-based budgeting rotates every 3 years through an institution to allow different departments to plan for obsolescence and/or changes in technology. Another budget methodology is the flexible budget, which may vary over the course of the fiscal year to adjust for changes in activity. Thus, with variations in utilization, adjustments can be made over the course of the year in the projections. The flexible budget basically separates fixed from variable costs and develops budget projections for various levels of activity. Finally, the case-mix budget accounts for different types of contracts that apply to the institution (eg, contracts with HMOs, preferred provider organizations, Medicare/Medicaid, and/or indemnity insurance providers).

Budget periods vary depending on the organization. For example, a calendar year with a January 1 start date may be typical for many businesses. Academic centers tend to follow the academic year, which begins on July 1. The federal government, on the other hand, begins its fiscal year on October 1.

The budgeting process is generally a 6-month–long activity and is based on a budget calendar (see Appendix 9-1). For a hospital laboratory operating in a fiscal year that starts on January 1, the process begins in the summer and ideally involves everyone in the laboratory, from the laboratory director and the pathologists to the technologists, phlebotomists, laboratory assistants, receptionists, and administrative assistants. The budgeting process begins with a review of the strategic plan and direction of the laboratory and a forecast for the upcoming year regarding changes in patient volumes, the patient case-mix, expected teaching activities, new procedures, obsolete activities, discontinued activities, the impact of new technology on productivity, anticipated inflation, and cost of living. The budgeting process also includes a prediction of changes in reimbursement from the government or the private sector. Everyone in the laboratory is asked for input regarding what they will need, or would like, so that they can provide better service in the coming year.

The various needs and wants of the laboratory constitute a "wish list," which is separated into equipment, personnel, and supplies categories. The laboratory director, along with the pathologists and the laboratory supervisors, prioritizes the requests in each category and submits these budget requests to the administration, generally in September for a calendar-year budget. A series of meetings follows wherein the laboratory director must justify the budget requests, often negotiate and accept trade-offs, and possibly even change some plans or projects. Laboratory directors must be able to defend all budget requests. The justifications that the administration are most likely to accept include enhancement of productivity, efficiency, and/or cost reduction; improvement in patient care and/or satisfaction; and necessity to meet safety or other governmental requirements. An important adjunct to the "needs" justification is an assessment of the clinical utility of the laboratory. It is always useful to get clinician support for the laboratory's budget requests, preferably in writing. Another important justification is the cost offset, in which expenditures in the laboratory result in savings in other departments, for example, acquiring a new, faster analyzer that could decrease turnaround time and thus length of stay. After the administration agrees to the laboratory budget, it takes several months to finalize the budget for the entire institution by the beginning of the next fiscal year.

The personnel budget projection requires estimates of the workload and of productivity (see "Outcomes and Metrics" for details regarding workload and productivity). Unfortunately, there are no reliable, universally accepted measures of work in the clinical laboratory. Most laboratories utilize a workload recording system that is built into the laboratory information system (LIS). This working system is valuable in the budgeting process as long as annual adjustments are made for changes in technology that impact the work necessary to do the test. However, such workload analyses should not be used to make interlaboratory comparisons. The personnel budget also has no standard measure of productivity. Many laboratories measure productivity by dividing workload (billable tests per year) by total full-time equivalents (FTEs) or paid hours. For example, if a laboratory that has 50 FTEs and performs 5,000,000 billable tests per year is anticipating a 10% increase in work, the laboratory would perform 5,500,000 tests and thus require 55 FTEs. But if the laboratory also anticipates a 5% improvement in productivity, then only 52.25 FTEs would be needed, and the personnel budget would request 2.25 new FTE positions. When justifying this budget to the administration, the laboratory would cite increased workload and productivity as well as improved service, leading to decreased turnaround times and possibly decreased length-of-stay.

The capital budget request is also based on the laboratory's "wish list." The capital budget, since it involves current investments for which future benefits are expected, usually over a period of years, includes purchases such as buildings, equipment that will be used for at least 3 years, and expensive computer software, as well as projects that have long-term impact on the organization. Such purchases typically require a process of technology assessment that includes issuing requests for information and requests for proposals (see Chapter 5, "Equipment, Supplies, and Space"). Also, capital budgets require a more detailed justification that includes a calculation of the return on investment, or the length of time necessary to recover the original cost of the investment.

Many laboratories now consider leasing certain equipment instead of purchasing it. Certain equipment, services, and reagents are available through reagent rental agreements. The advantage of reagent rental agreements is that the cost of major equipment acquisition is switched from the capital budget to the operating budget; the disadvantage is that such rental agreements are more expensive than purchasing the equipment. Many manufacturers will do cost-benefit analyses, but one should be sure that the components of the analysis are carefully defined, including the cost of the equipment, the interest on the loan, the buy-back cost at the end of the lease, the length of the lease, the level of technical service/maintenance, and the actual cost of the reagents.

The expense or operating budget includes the cost of reagents, supplies, purchased services (blood and blood products, reference laboratories), maintenance, physician fees, education, travel, quality assurance, depreciation, leases, transfers to other departments, marketing, transportation, communication, computers, safety, and rent and utilities for satellite laboratories. Again, the departmental "wish list" needs to be consulted to determine which new supplies or devices would be useful and/or what other operating changes are required. Expenses might also vary markedly with volume. For example, at volumes of <200,000 tests per year, the cost for a given test may be $2.92; but at volumes of >600,000 tests per year, the cost for the same test may be $2.51. Future test volumes should be assessed as part of the operating budget evaluation. To arrive at the proposed operating budget, the pathologist and laboratory manager should review the current operating budget; consider changes in work, test complexity, and programs; and multiply this amount by any anticipated percentage changes in workload and inflation.

The allocation budget details the overhead or indirect expenses that the hospital charges, or allocates, to the laboratory. The laboratory must pay for the space it occupies and the building, improvement, and the maintenance of that space as well as any utilities. These charges are based on the size (the space in square feet) of the laboratory. The laboratory, like all other revenue-producing departments, must also help support hospital administration, which does not generate any revenue itself. The amount of allocated administrative support is calculated on the basis of gross laboratory revenue. Similarly, the hospital's human resources department allocates costs to the laboratory based on a percentage of the personnel budget, and the purchasing department allocates costs based on a percentage of the total operating budget and the budgets of other hospital cost centers such as information technology services.

Once the major budget categories have been identified and quantified, the various expense, personnel, supplies, equipment, and overhead data are entered into a preliminary profit and loss estimate together with the income estimate. If the bottom line is adequate, then that figure may represent the next year's budget. However, if the bottom line is inadequate, and expenses exceed income, the budget must be adjusted by either decreasing expenses or increasing income.

Rate Setting

When income needs to be increased, or when a new test is added to the test menu, the laboratory is faced with the task of rate setting. There are several approaches to setting the rates or charges for a specific test. The most precise and correct approach is to determine what the test costs by performing a test cost analysis. If there is a single feature of financial management that a pathologist should understand, it is the calculation of cost per test.

Total costs are composed of two types of costs: fixed, or indirect, costs; and variable, or direct, costs. Thus, total costs = fixed costs + variable costs. The variable costs change with relation to the volume of testing. These costs typically account for 90% of the total costs. The calculation of the direct costs must include direct labor costs, ie, cost of the actual time required to perform the test, including preanalytic and postanalytic duties; direct materials costs, including the cost of reagents and disposables; and instrument costs, including lease/purchase, depreciation, maintenance, quality control, and calibration costs, all of which should be adjusted to annual test volumes.

Fixed or indirect costs do not change over a given period regardless of test volumes. Thus, fixed costs would include general laboratory supplies, indirect labor (such as the supervisor's salary and training), and other indirect expenses such as research. Fixed costs also must include general laboratory overhead categories such as specimen collection, specimen processing, result reporting, LIS management, laboratory management, continuing education (eg, medical technology classes), quality assurance, regulatory compliance, marketing, and communication. (for test cost

Analysis of Test Costs

Prime Cost
    Instrument cost including maintenance
    Direct material costs
    Direct labor costs

Indirect Costs
    General laboratory supplies
    Indirect labor (supervision, training)
    Other indirect labor (research)

Laboratory Overhead
    Specimen collection and processing
    Result reporting
    Laboratory information system
    Laboratory management and direction
    Continuing education (School of Medical Technology)
    Quality assurance
    Marketing
    Communication
    Depreciation

Hospital Overhead (Allocated Expenses)

Total Test Cost Is:
    Prime + Indirect + Laboratory and Hospital Overhead

How to Calculate the Prime Cost of a Test

Instrument Costs
    Purchase price ($)
    Life expectancy (years)
    Annual maintenance ($)
    Annual quality control ($)
    Annual calibration ($)
    Annual test volume (billable tests)

Direct Material Costs
    Reagents ($)
    Disposables ($)
    Annual test volume (billable tests)

Direct Labor Costs
    Preanalytical (minutes/test)
    Analytical (minutes/test)
    Postanalytical (minutes/test)
    Average hourly salary ($)
    Salary Cost x 1.3 (fringe benefits) =
        Total Direct Labor Cost

Figure 9-1. Test Costs.

analysis details, see "Outcomes and Metrics" section below.)

The most accurate method of rate setting is based on test cost analysis (Figure 9-1). Even though a number of computer programs can be used to perform test cost analyses, test cost analyses are tedious and not always part of the budgeting process, given the large number of tests performed in a laboratory and the continuing changes in technology. An expedient method of rate setting is to simply increase the cost of every test by the percentage needed to produce a positive bottom line. For example, if the projected laboratory income is $10 million, but the projected expenses are $11 million, the fee schedule could simply raise each charge by 10%. However, repeated percentage increases can lead to rates that are out of line with test costs. As an alternative, the laboratory could employ the Pareto principle (see Chapter 7, "Quality Management in Laboratory Medicine") and look at the common tests responsible for 80% of total tests (eg, complete blood counts, electrolytes, and urinalyses), and simply raise the charge of each common test by a minimal figure (eg, $1.00). Only a few changes would need to be made in the computer system; however, the test charge would no longer be associated with the test cost.

Operating Statement

Once the rates have been set, the fee schedule adjusted, and the budget approved, the various budget categories are apportioned monthly to form the basis of the operating statement, also referred to as profit and loss statement, earnings statement, in-

Every month the laboratory director received the Laboratory Operating Statement from the hospital and would spend a few minutes reviewing the numbers with the chief technologist. If there were any variances greater than 5%, the laboratory director would ask for an explanation. The laboratory director also knew that the associate administrator responsible for the laboratory would also receive this report, so it was essential that the director have answers before the administrator asked questions. Minor variances—usually dependent on variations in hospital occupancy or outpatient activity—were common. Variances in reagent costs were also common; for example, one month the expenditure for reagents was $100,000 over budget, but this was due to a bulk purchase; the budgeted amount had been allocated evenly over 12 months, while the actual purchase and payment were made in 1 month. Another time, a trend of decreasing inpatient Medicare revenue for 3 months was noted, even though the number of Medicare admissions had not varied significantly. An investigation revealed a glitch in the communication of coding data from the LIS to the hospital information system; although the patients' tests were performed and reported, the patients were not billed.

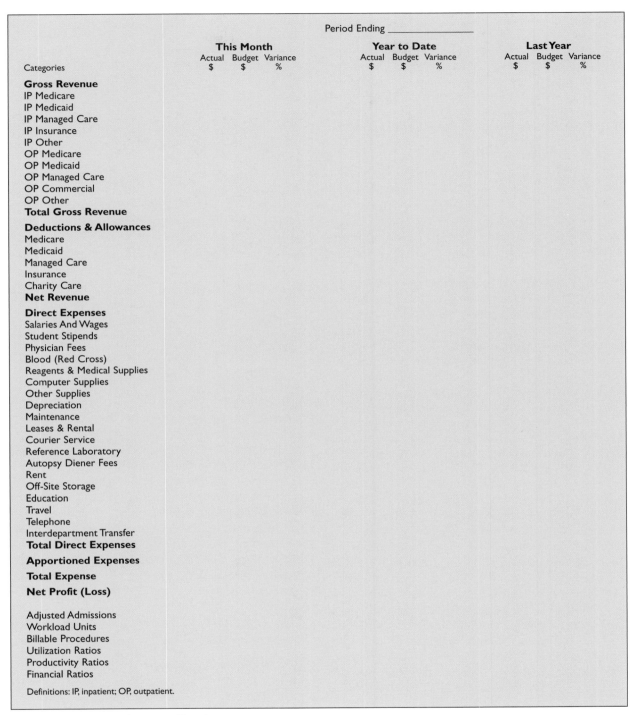

Period Ending _____

Categories	This Month			Year to Date			Last Year		
	Actual $	Budget $	Variance %	Actual $	Budget $	Variance %	Actual $	Budget $	Variance %
Gross Revenue									
IP Medicare									
IP Medicaid									
IP Managed Care									
IP Insurance									
IP Other									
OP Medicare									
OP Medicaid									
OP Managed Care									
OP Commercial									
OP Other									
Total Gross Revenue									
Deductions & Allowances									
Medicare									
Medicaid									
Managed Care									
Insurance									
Charity Care									
Net Revenue									
Direct Expenses									
Salaries And Wages									
Student Stipends									
Physician Fees									
Blood (Red Cross)									
Reagents & Medical Supplies									
Computer Supplies									
Other Supplies									
Depreciation									
Maintenance									
Leases & Rental									
Courier Service									
Reference Laboratory									
Autopsy Diener Fees									
Rent									
Off-Site Storage									
Education									
Travel									
Telephone									
Interdepartment Transfer									
Total Direct Expenses									
Apportioned Expenses									
Total Expense									
Net Profit (Loss)									
Adjusted Admissions									
Workload Units									
Billable Procedures									
Utilization Ratios									
Productivity Ratios									
Financial Ratios									

Definitions: IP, inpatient; OP, outpatient.

Figure 9-2. Operating Statement Template.

come statement, or management report (Figure 9-2). This is the most important report the pathologist/director uses to continually monitor the laboratory's financial condition. The operating statement indicates the various revenue sources, contractual deductions and allowances from revenue, and the net revenue. It also lists the laborato-

ry's direct and indirect expenses, apportioned or allocated expenses, and bottom line, or net. The operating statement may also include statistics on hospital workload (admissions or patient days), laboratory workload, and billable procedures as well as utilization, productivity, and financial ratios. A critical aspect of the operating statement is that it lists the budget projection for each category, the actual dollar amount received or expended, the amount for the same period during the previous year, the budgeted and actual year-to-date dollar amounts, and the previous year's year-to-date amount. The report also shows the variance in each category with each prior comparison. *Any variance of more than 5% requires investigation and explanation.*

Billing and Collection

Billing and collecting for the technical component of hospital laboratory services is generally the responsibility of the hospital and is usually performed automatically by the hospital information system (HIS). However, the LIS must communicate seamlessly with the HIS to receive patient demographic information and send data regarding the work performed. The laboratory's monthly operating statement should be used to verify the uniformity and consistency of the billing operation. Currently, most hospitals have numerous variations in fee schedules that depend on the details of contractual agreements, deductions, and allowances with a variety of payers, but again, these technical component billing activities are the responsibility of the hospital financial operation.

A critical aspect in this area is the management fee pathologists receive for providing professional clinical pathology services for Medicare to the health care institution. The management fee was bundled into the technical component reimbursement to the hospital (sometimes referred to as the "Part A" component) as part of the revisions to the Medicare program. (Management fees are discussed in greater detail in Chapter 10, "Financial Management of the Pathology Practice.")

The actual billing and collection for the technical component services described above are the responsibility of the hospital; however, the billing and collection for the pathologists' professional services for anatomic pathology and for consultations in clinical pathology are the responsibility of the pathology group. (Billing and collection are further detailed in Chapter 10, "Financial Management of the Pathology Practice.")

Outcomes and Metrics

Test Cost Analysis

Test cost analysis is a necessary component of financial analysis, rate setting, and budgeting in the clinical laboratory[2] and is important when developing the rationale for performing a given test in-house versus sending it to a reference laboratory. It also helps determine which analytes should be available on a given platform. Test cost analysis is an important factor in convincing hospital administration that client demand for a new test will produce a positive margin. Perhaps most importantly, it helps laboratory directors understand laboratory managers' priorities.

So how, exactly, would the cost of a new individual test be calculated? Assume that a new analyte that requires 1 minute of labor per test is being added to an automated analyzer platform already present in the laboratory.

- For 1 technologist ($36/hour)/60 minutes = $.60/minute
- Benefits (Social Security, workers' compensation, health, vacation, sick leave, etc) = 35% of hourly wage = $.21/minute
- Slack factor (breaks, etc) = 10% wages + benefits = $.08/minute
- Total labor = $.89/minute/test for labor costs

The cost of consumables (reagents, quality control, repeats/duplicates, calibrators, disposables) adds $0.30 per test. Thus, the total cost of labor plus consumables per test is $1.19. Note that the labor is much more expensive than the consumables; in this example, the labor cost is three times as much as the other variable (direct) costs. The cost may be considerably higher in some circumstances in which more time is required or in which the technologist must have a higher level of expertise. Micro-cost analysis up to this point only includes the variable (direct) costs. Typically, the fixed (indirect) costs are figured as an assigned cost for time required, so that the Total Cost/Test = Variable (Direct) Cost/Test + Fixed (Indirect) Cost/Test. Two templates for test cost analysis are shown in Figure 9-1.[3]

Break-Even Analysis

The evaluation process for establishing a new test in the laboratory should also include a break-even analysis. The break-even point is the point at which there is no profit or loss from performing the test, inclusive of all fixed (direct) and variable (indirect) costs. The break-even point is determined by the equation $V = (FC + I) / R - VC)$, where V is the volume of tests needed to break even, R is the expected revenue generated by the test, VC is

Workload by Laboratory Department

Month of _____

Department	Raw Count		Billable Workload		Total Workload*		Revenue Total	
	IP	OP	IP	OP	IP	OP	IP	OP
Blood Bank								
Microbiology								
Hematology								
Immunology								
Chemistry								
Surgical Pathology								
Cytology								

* Total Workload = Billable Workload x 1.3
The 1.3 factor includes Repeats, Standards, QC Testing.

Definitions: IP, inpatient; OP, outpatient.

Monthly Workload Comparisons

Month of _____

Category	Budget	Current Month	Previous Month	Previous Year	Year to Date (YTD)	Previous YTD
Raw Count						
Total Workload						
Revenue						
Inpatient						
Outpatient						
Patient Days						
Admissions						

Figure 9-3. Two Examples of Workload Analysis.

the total variable cost per test, FC is the fixed cost per test, and I is the net income.

Workload Recording

There are no universally accepted workload recording methods that can be used as an external benchmark to assess the efficiency of laboratory work. However, every laboratory needs some measure of the amount of work being done for internal benchmarking and for budgeting purposes. Workload analysis is a measure of the tasks required to perform an individual test procedure. This workload analysis can include specimen preparation and set-up, instrument time, the running of standards and controls, and reporting results. Since humans do not work with machine-like consistency, a personal, fatigue, and delay allowance can be incorporated to account for the "human element."[3]

An example of the difficulties in determining workload is the former workload metric provided by the College of American Pathologists (CAP). The CAP program measured paid, worked, and workloaded labor hours, which represented three different labor performance levels of the laboratory. None of these factors were easily verifiable by standard information systems. Also, the "unit value" for each test did not include time values for certain preanalytical and postanalytical functions that may represent major costs, such as accessioning specimens, preparing quality controls and standards, and other functions. The CAP workload recording method also did not correlate well with costs in some surveys. In 1993, the CAP decided to discontinue the program as a distinct entity, given the variability in procedures in health care institutions in the US.

However, there is still value in analyzing the differences between billable hours and worked hours. Also, a comparison of available labor hours for test-related labor production versus hours needed for teaching, administration, and/or development (ie, non–test-related hours) can be defined. Estimates can be generated for idle time, by laboratory subsection, and in the development of proposals for laboratory staffing. Two common methods for analyzing workload are shown in Figure 9-3.

Assets	Liabilities
Current Assets	**Current Liabilities**
Cash	Notes Payable
Petty Cash	Accounts Payable
Temporary Investments	Wages Payable
Accounts Receivable	Interest Payable
Inventory	Warranty Liability
Supplies	Unearned Revenues
Prepaid Insurance	**Total Current Liabilities**
Total Current Assets	
Investments	**Long-Term Liabilities**
Property, Land, Equipment	Notes Payable
Land	Bonds Payable
Land Improvements	**Total Long-Term Liabilities**
Buildings	
Equipment	
Less Depreciation	**Stockholder Equity**
Total Property, Land, Equipment	Common Stock
Intangible Assets	Retained Earnings
Goodwill	**Total Stockholder Equity**
Trade Names	
Total Intangible Assets	**Other Liabilities**
Other Assets	
Total Assets	**Total Liabilities and Stockholder Equity**

Figure 9-4. Balance Sheet Template.

Productivity Analysis

A corollary to workload recording is productivity analysis. Productivity is essentially a measure of output compared to the resources invested and is an important factor in projecting personnel needs and budgets. A number of productivity ratios are available, as follows:

- Billable tests /FTEs, or /salary $, or /total expenses
- Total revenue /FTEs, or /salary $
- Total expense /FTEs, or /salary $, or /patient days

The laboratory director should work closely with hospital administration in choosing and calculating productivity metrics.

Financial Performance

As long as each component of the ratio is calculated consistently, the ratios can be meaningful measures of productivity. Some laboratories also monitor measures or ratios of financial performance or utilization. Examples of these calculations include:

- Total revenue per billable tests
- Total revenue per admission or patient days
- Billable tests per admission or patient days
- Total cost per billable tests
- Supply cost per billable tests

The operating statement is used to continually monitor the laboratory's financial condition. It indicates the various revenue sources, the contractual deductions and allowances from revenue, and the net revenue. It also lists the direct and indirect expenses, the apportioned or allocated expenses, and the bottom line, or net. It may also include statistics on hospital workload (admissions or patient days), laboratory workload, and billable procedures as well as utilization, productivity, and financial ratios. The operating statement also lists the budgeted dollar amounts for each category and the actual amounts received or expended, and compares these amounts to the previous months' and years' amounts. The interested reader is again directed to the example of an operating statement template in Figure 9-2.

The balance sheet or statement of assets and liabilities is one of the major financial statements used by accountants and businesses; it presents an organization's financial position at the end of the fiscal year and contains valuable information for management, administrators, government agencies, and others. Hospital laboratories generally do not have a separate balance sheet, but free-standing independent laboratories and private laboratories run by pathology groups need one. A typical balance sheet template is shown in Figure 9-4.

Another important metric is the cash flow statement. Various iterations have existed for some time to describe the flow of funds in a business.[4] It is a generally accepted accounting practice to provide an assessment of the movement of cash resources through a financial system. The cash flow statement is partitioned into three segments: cash flow resulting from operating activities, cash flow resulting from investing activities, and cash flow resulting from financing activities. Money entering the business is called cash inflow, and money going out of the business is called cash outflow. Typically, a cash flow statement is viewed monthly or annually to assess changes in the cash balance, or the amount of cash on hand. A simple example of a cash flow statement is shown in Figure 9-5.

Examples of cash flow operating activities (both positive and negative) include cash received for test performance services, salaries for laboratory technologists, depreciation, and payments for supplies and reagents. Examples of cash flow investment activities include the purchase of a building for a laboratory and loans to customers. Examples of cash flow financing activities include proceeds from issuing shares, payment of dividends, and, for not-for-profit institutions, receipt of donor-restricted funds for long-term purposes.

The operating statement, the balance sheet, and cash flow statements are compiled through a process called the accounting cycle, which consists of two subprocesses: (1) data entry and (2) book closure. In the data entry phase, one identifies the transaction, amount of money, transaction date, and type of activity (gain or loss) as well as the account to which the transaction belongs. A journal entry is then made. The accounting journal and the general ledger chronicle all financial transactions and classify them as either debits or credits. The general ledger, which forms the central hub of all financial records, is composed with subledgers, such as assets, cash, accounts receivable, sales, and expenses, that form the same entries in the income, balance sheet, and cash statements. Each entry impacts two accounts simultaneously to keep the equation, assets = liability + owner equity, balanced at all times. For example, a debit to account receivables also impacts the cash account. At the end of the account cycle, the book closure step ascertains the fidelity of the actions through the conduction of a trial balance. If discrepancies are identified, the entries are adjusted appropriately so that a final, honest, reconciled balance is achieved. Compiling these accounts into financial statements closes the books and ends the account cycle.

For small laboratories and stand-alone large laboratories, the financial accounting steps are usually visible to the stakeholders as well as the pathologist, even if he or she is not the owner of the laboratory. However, for a large enterprise, the laboratory is one unit of production, and the accounting books are often embedded in the institution as financial statements. However, pathologists almost always play a direct role in managerial accounting activities that include cost accounting, capital budgeting (particularly for equipment), and creating the operating budget.

Discussion and Controversies

Dual Financial Management

One controversy peculiar to pathology and laboratory medicine is the dual role the pathology practice group has in the financial management of the laboratory. Controversies can frequently arise in settings in which collaboration is required between administration and a laboratory director.

The ultimate responsibility for a clinical laboratory under CLIA '88 resides with two entities: (1) the owner of the laboratory and (2) the laboratory director. When these two entities are separately organized, controversies occur, especially in the area of financial management. Budget issues are probably the most frequent sources of friction. Space and facilities allocation and human resource issues, such as staffing levels and staff competence requirements, have budgetary impact, which often causes controversies.

The laboratory director can best manage dual management by having primary involvement in the budget process. Membership in key budget committees and regular meetings with laboratory managers regarding budget development ensure that laboratory directors receive the appropriate input. To actively engage in the budget process, a laboratory director also needs to know the basic terms and definitions of the process. It is also es-

ABC Clinical Laboratory Cash Flow Statement, 1-1-09 to 12-31-09	
Cash Flow from Operations	$137,000
Cash Flow from Investments	$12,000
Cash Flow from Financing Activities	($37,000)
Net Increase (Decrease) in Cash	**$112,000**

Figure 9-5. Cash Flow Template.

Case Examples

How Much Does it Cost to Perform a Potassium Test?

You are the laboratory director of a clinical laboratory in a 250-bed hospital. To justify asking physicians to order only medically necessary tests instead of metabolic panels and emphasize the low cost of testing on your automated analyzer at the next medical staff meeting, you calculate the direct cost for a single potassium test that takes 30 seconds using the following information:

- For 1 technologist (salary = $30/hour) = ?$/30 seconds
- Benefits (Social Security, workers' compensation, health, vacation, sick leave, etc) = 35% of hourly wage = ?$/30 seconds
- Slack factor (breaks, etc.) = 10% wages + benefits = ?$/30 seconds
- Total labor = ?$/test for labor costs
- Consumables per potassium test = $.15/test
What is the total direct (variable) cost of a single potassium test? *(Answer = $.52)*

In activity-based costing, one should look at the whole testing cycle (process thinking), including preanalytic, analytic, and postanalytic steps, and then determine the costs of those steps, including costs related to labor, reagents, supplies, equipment depreciation, etc, as well as indirect costs.

How Do I Assess the Replacement Value of an Instrument?

You are the laboratory director of an anatomic pathology laboratory in a 250-bed hospital. You went to a meeting and found a new $10,000 microtome with throw-away blades that you want to buy to replace an old, outdated one that uses a knife that takes a lot of the histotechnologist's time to sharpen. How would you create a capital equipment justification budget? In addition to the narrative rationale, include the financial metrics such as net present value, payback period, and return on investment. (You may want to seek the help of your accounting department.)

sential that laboratory directors have a grasp of monthly variances as they occurred over the past year, which requires frequent communication with laboratory managers and supervisors.

Many laboratories are currently undergoing a "space crisis," which is related to the expansion of tests performed in-house as well as the increasing footprint sizes of many new automated systems. Laboratory directors must have an understanding of the allocation budget to justify space and facilities for the clinical laboratory (see Chapter 5, "Equipment, Supplies, and Space"). The space allocation requires the analysis of the percent of revenue, personnel budget, and the operating budget. In nonhospital settings, activity- or department-specific revenues should be analyzed and compared to space requirements for specific equipment and facility needs (ie, automation, biosafety requirements, etc).

Personnel controversies in dual management may occur when the budgeting process is considering FTE cuts in the laboratory. The laboratory director needs to be intimately involved in such a process, since ultimately the stipulated requirements for personnel qualifications are the laboratory director's responsibility. Personnel cannot be shifted easily if the changes require replacing staff with less-qualified individuals in sections in which moderate- or high-complexity testing is performed. The laboratory director must be intimately familiar with these requirements as described in CLIA '88 and CLIA '03 (see Chapter 12, "Laboratory Laws and Regulations"). Another factor affecting laboratories is staff availability. With the average age of laboratory technologists increasing, each retirement reduces the ability to swiftly replace competent individuals. Administration may request "cross-training" to solve a personnel shortage. However, while cross-training may be easily applied in core laboratories and highly automated laboratory sections, it is less applicable in highly specialized testing areas such as transfusion medicine and microbiology. Regardless of the financial controversy, the best solutions for the clinical laboratory involve thoroughly analyzing the financial data, frequently reviewing budget variances in a timely manner, and clearly understanding the regulatory requirements for clinical laboratory personnel.

Conflicting Agendas within the Laboratory

Pathologists, technologists, and other technical staff have differing needs, responsibilities, and interests in the laboratory. The technologists are hospital employees, and they want more pay, greater benefits, and better working conditions; while the pathologists, who may be members of an independent practice group, want to keep expenses low so the administration looks favorably on their ability to manage the laboratory's fiscal resources. Balance and wisdom are required to address these wants and needs as part of the budget cycle. To better engage in controversies regarding personnel, pathologists should be aware of the laboratory technologists' salaries and benefits. Also, the pathologist/director should be familiar with any generalized personnel issues such as union contracts and institutional work rules (see Chapter 4, "Personnel Management").

Controversies with the Medical Staff

A sophisticated medical staff that reads all the latest medical literature and demands immediate availability of every new test that is purported to be useful can place a heavy financial burden on the laboratory. Here, test cost analysis combined with estimates of clinical utility are useful for cogent decision making. The laboratory director should seek ways to interact with hospital and medical staff leadership so that when operational demands or financial controversies occur with medical staff, wise counsel is available. An essential way of interacting is by membership on hospital and medical staff committees where finances are routinely discussed. (See also Chapter 2, "Competencies and Interactions of the Involved Pathologist," pages 18 to 21.)

Challenge Questions

Examples of direct or variable costs include:
A. Salary
B. Computers
C. Reagents
D. A, B, and C
E. A and C
Answer: E; see page 155 and Figure 9-1.

Over the next 5 years, the hospital is constructing a new building to expand the clinical laboratory. The most relevant analyses the laboratory director should review include:
A. The operational budget
B. The allocation budget
C. Cash flow analysis
D. The capital budget
E. B and D
Answer: E; see pages 153 to 157 and 161.

In reviewing the latest Operating Statement, it is seen that revenue is down, while personnel costs, test volume, and number of admissions are unchanged. What are possible causes?
Answer: See pages 156 to 157.

References

1. Travers EM. *Clinical Laboratory Management.* Baltimore, MD: Williams & Wilkins; 1997.
2. Harmening DM. *Laboratory Management. Principles and Processes.* 2nd ed. St. Petersburg, FL: FA Davis Co; 2007.
3. DiLima SN, ed. *Medical Laboratory Management.* Gaithersburg, MD: Aspen Publishers; 1996.
4. Travers EM, Delahunty DC, Hunter LL, McClatchey KD, Rudar JM. *Basic Cost Accounting for Clinical Services. Approved Guideline.* Wayne, PA: NCCLS: 1998. Document GP11-A.

Appendix 9-1.
Typical Budget Calendar

Calendar for the Budgeting Process			
Month	**Action**	**Responsible Party**	
July	Review laboratory and hospital strategic plans; create wish list.	All staff	
August	Prioritize wish list.	Director and Pathologists	
September	Submit individual budgets to hospital administration; negotiate with administration; preliminary profit and loss, test cost analysis, rate setting.	Director	
November	Submit final budget to administration.	Director	
December	Receive final approved budget from administration.	Director	

CHAPTER 10

Financial Management of the Pathology Practice

C. Bruce Alexander, MD
Richard E. Horowitz, MD
Ronald L. Weiss, MD, MBA

Contents

Introduction

This chapter will introduce the terms and concepts that are essential to the financial success of a pathology practice. This chapter is not meant to make the readers financial experts, but rather to acquaint pathologists with the principles and nomenclature used by financial professionals. To understand and work with financial professionals (accountants, auditors, risk managers, etc), pathologists must know what they are saying, what questions to ask, and, most important, what can be expected from them regarding financial services. Financial operations are not static; contracts are frequently amended, tax laws and regulations often change, and governmental payment policies are modified at the whims of Congress and/or state legislatures. The bureaucracy of insurance companies can also vary considerably. Keep these thoughts in mind while reviewing this chapter.

Nothing in this chapter should be construed as a formal recommendation or advice; such advice should come only from your independent legal and financial advisors.

History

Prior to 1983, most hospitals billed for laboratory services on a fee-for-service basis and were paid by insurers or private parties. Pathologists practicing in community hospitals were employees or had a contract to provide pathology services. Some were "percentage" contracts, with payment based on a percentage of gross billings or percentage of net receipts. Some were based on patient days. There were many other varieties of contractual services. The Social Security Act of 1964 created Medicare and Medicaid. In 1983, the new concept of prospective payment utilizing diagnosis related groups (DRGs) for Medicare hospital inpatients was implemented. As noted in Chapter 9, "Financial Management of the Laboratory," this system classified hospital cases into one of approximately 500 groups with similar resource use. Payment was based on diagnoses, not on the length of stay or the procedures performed. At this same time, for Medicare inpatients, laboratory fees were unbundled so that the technical component was part of, and paid through, the DRG, while the professional component was billed separately by the pathologist. In addition, the professional component of most clinical pathology tests was defined not as a service billable to an individual patient, but as a professional service "to the provider," that is, to the hospital. Payment for this service was included in the DRG paid to the hospital. Anatomic pathology services were also unbundled, with the hospital billing for the technical component and the pathologist billing for the professional component. In most instances, the pathologists formed an independent billing entity after DRG implementation. However, in other cases, the hospital served as the billing agent for the pathologists or pathology group.

Parallel to changes in governmental payment mechanisms, insurance companies, health maintenance organizations (HMOs), and preferred provider organizations (PPOs) implemented a variety of cost-containment models in the 1970s and 1980s, including capitation plans, discounted fee-for-service fee schedules, and negotiated hospital contracts. These contracts usually included the laboratory fees, which often paid less than Medicare reimbursement rates and less than actual costs, depending on regional economics in the United States. In many instances, laboratories were forced to negotiate not only test cost, but also which tests might be reimbursed. More recently, some managed care companies began targeting expensive molecular and genetic tests by requiring preauthorization for such tests. These changes' cumulative effect on clinical laboratories in the governmental and private sectors was to transition the clinical laboratory from a revenue center to a cost center, especially for inpatient services.[1]

Integrated health care organizations, such as the Mayo Clinic and Kaiser Permanente, were among the first to introduce the concept of the multi-specialty physician group and managed care models. Kaiser Permanente (referred to as the Permanente Medical Groups), which was founded in 1945 as a consortium of a health insurance plan, multiple hospitals, and independent physician-owned groups, evolved in the era shortly after World War II in response to labor benefits negotiations in the northwest United States and is still prevalent on the West Coast. Other integrated health care organizations, such as The University of Texas MD Anderson Cancer Center, developed formal academic ties, becoming degree-offering institutions in their own right. Pathologists working in such an environment may be partners or employees of the larger multi-specialty medical group, with the group contracting with the plan, and the hospitals providing professional services.

Free-standing clinical laboratories once had a variety of billing practices. Some billed patients or insurance companies for laboratory tests. In some instances, the laboratory billed the ordering clinician, and the clinician in turn billed the patient, usually with a healthy mark-up. A variety of questionable practices were also common, with clinicians receiving "discounts" for volume or early payment to a clinical laboratory. Price fixing laboratory tests in a community was not unheard of in this environment.

Because of competition from commercial laboratories, the College of American Pathologists (CAP) modulated its position favoring direct billing of hospital patients or insurance carriers for pathology services. In line with the American Medical Association (AMA) code of professional conduct, it opposed fee-splitting with referring physicians and opposed the solicitation of physicians for laboratory referrals. It also opposed ownership of laboratories by nonphysicians and condemned advertising. Late in 1965, the United States Justice Department opened an investigation of possible antitrust violations, and in July 1966, a formal antitrust action was filed in the federal district court in Chicago alleging violations of the Sherman Antitrust Act. A consent decree was finalized on July 15, 1969, in which the CAP and its members were "enjoined and restrained" from any and all of the following actions: restricting in any manner any person from owning or operating a laboratory, referring specimens to any laboratory, performing services for any person, or associating with any laboratory; preventing any person from accepting advertising or exhibiting at any meeting; boycotting any laboratory; limiting any compensation arrangement; and fixing fees in any manner. This decree remains in effect and has allowed the enormous expansion of the independent commercial laboratory industry.

After 1983, Medicare outpatient clinical laboratory services were paid based on the clinical laboratory fee schedule (CLFS). Non-Medicare outpatient laboratory tests are now paid for in a variety of ways. Large referral laboratories usually receive payments for testing based on contracts with hospitals and other health care institutions. A hospital may contract for its "send-out" testing with one or more such reference laboratories, sometimes including discounts for larger volume utilization. The hospital in turn will then bill patients or their insurance providers. Other arrangements also exist with outside clinical laboratories. For example, some physician groups can contract with a specific laboratory that will then directly bill the patient for services rendered. These are typically physician groups linked by specialty (eg, neurology) with needs for esoteric testing from a unique laboratory provider. Direct-access testing is also available in some states but limited by other states. Under such arrangements, a laboratory test does not require a physician order but instead can be directly requested by a patient. Usually such arrangements require cash payment by the patient, since most insurance providers and Medicare/Medicaid require a physician order to indicate medical necessity. This type of laboratory business has progressed extensively in areas such as genetic testing, which has mechanisms that allow patients to mail their specimens to the laboratory. However, recent inquiries and actions by the US Food and Drug Administration may limit direct-access testing in the future.

In academic settings, pathologists' payment arrangements vary depending on the institution. The pathologists may officially be paid through a university payroll system, but the income generated by the individual professional practice group for a department is the source of funds for these pathologists' salaries. Other faculty members (usually those with basic science research programs) may be partially paid by the university directly and partially paid for clinical services provided from practice group resources. Tenure versus non-tenure faculty tracks may be defined by the revenue sources by which an individual physician is paid. With the advent of prospective payment and the distinction between Medicare Part A and Medicare Part B, some academic pathology departments have joined their faculty practice group, including all departments in a given school of medicine for billing and contracting purposes.[1,2]

Private practice pathologists may be invited to serve as adjunct faculty for a local school of medicine and/or its pathologists. Under these arrangements, rotations of residents or medical students to a private institution occur. Many of these "voluntary" appointments are unpaid unless direct administrative responsibilities for students are part of the position description. These voluntary positions may be important to the private practice group in that they lend prestige to the group and provide access to potential future associates and the latest academic developments in the field.

Practice Categories

The CAP *Practice Characteristics Survey,* published in 2008, lists the percentage of pathologists in each of several practice categories[3]:

Practicing in a Pathology Group	74%
Independent Laboratory	28%
University Medical School	21%
Multi-Specialty Group	16%
Hospital Employee	12%
Solo Practice	4%

The total percentage exceeds 100 because many pathologists have more than one position; for example, as noted previously, a private-practice pathologist may have a voluntary or adjunct appointment at the local medical school and is thus represented in two categories. It is of interest that pathologists' participation in university medical schools and multi-specialty groups nearly doubled since the previous survey in 2004.

The pathologists practicing in pathology groups may be partners, employees, or per diem workers. The partnership may be one of individuals or of professional corporations, and the terms of employment and the nature of the contractual relationships vary, from formal contracts to letters of agreement to handshakes. Pathologists in an independent commercial laboratory are generally employees. However, many hospital pathology groups have their own independent laboratory whose financial operation is entirely separate from that of the hospital laboratory.

A pathologist might also be a partner in the hospital practice, an employee of the independent laboratory, and/or a shareholder or owner of the independent laboratory. In university medical schools, pathologists may be employees of the academic department or members of a pathology or multi-specialty group within the school and might receive additional income for performing additional work at a county or Veterans Affairs hospital. Pathologists in multi-specialty groups may start as employees and later attain partnership status.

The number of pathologists working solely as hospital employees has not changed significantly since 2004, and the number of pathologists in solo practice has declined from 5% in 2004 to 4% in 2008. Other practice categories for which the CAP does not have detailed data include government service, medical examiners' offices, and non-laboratory industries. In most of these categories, pathologists are employees, but many pathologists have multiple jobs, which may include working at a Veterans Affairs hospital, teaching at a university, or consulting for industry. Clearly, pathologists have many opportunities for multiple activities, depending on their location, skills, and preferences.

Sources of Income

Just as there are various pathology practice categories, there are various ways to classify pathologists' sources of professional income. The major groups are:

- Government
- Private insurance
- Managed care
- Hospital or academic salary
- Private patient pay
- Management fee

Within each of these groups are subgroups, each of which may have different payment schemes. Government payers include Medicare, Medicaid, State Children's Health Insurance, and the Civilian Health and Medical Program of the Uniformed Services. Each of these subgroups include further distinctions between inpatient and outpatient services and between professional (Part B) and technical (Part A) services that follow different rules, fee schedules, and payment policies. Private insurance companies also vary markedly in their rules, regulations, and payment method-

ologies. Private insurers may have special agreements with hospitals that impact pathology income, and certain rules that determine whether a service is "allowable," how much will be paid, what copayments are due, and whether any payment will be received at all depend on the specific insurance plan for individual patients. Other conditions include the patient's completion and payment of a "deductible" amount or exceeding of an annual "maximum."

Managed Care Organizations

Managed care organizations (MCOs), which are reluctant to pay for laboratory services, pose a major challenge for pathology practices. Often, MCOs require that laboratory testing be performed at a specific laboratory. Also, when an MCO has a contract with a hospital, the MCO and/or hospital administration may put pressure on the pathologist to accept a heavily discounted fee for professional services. Some MCOs operate on a capitation basis (an amount per patient per month paid up front by the carrier for laboratory and pathology services). When working with an MCO operating on a capitation basis, it is most important to know the demographics of the patient population—for example, a younger, healthier group of patients that require fewer services versus an older group of patients that requires more services and thus justifies a higher capitation fee. Many MCOs not only negotiate individual fee schedules with hospital pathology groups but also pay for selected preapproved tests only.

Salary Arrangements

Hospital salary arrangements are generally fairly simple. However, recent surveys indicate that relatively few pathologists are directly employed by hospitals. One should assume that hospital salary arrangements, if existent, are firmly based on an appropriate contract.

Academic practice plans may be complex, with certain consultative income excluded and other funding sources subject to certain payments to support academic activities. The internal income generated by the laboratory and pathology professional services may be the basis for each year's calculated salary, with additional salary provided for administrative or teaching functions. In some academic settings, secondary consultations are entirely attributed to the individual pathologist who reviews the case. In other academic settings, consultative monies are distributed as a percentage return to the pathologist to account for institutional support expenditures (clerical, support staff, overhead, etc). In other academic environments, consultative and outside incomes are distributed through an outreach program based on a measure of effort (eg, relative value units [RVUs]). Still other academic institutions view consultations as part of the institution's overall mission, and all funds revert to the umbrella division or department.

Cash from uninsured private patients is the only pure payment, but these types of payments are exceedingly rare. Most revenue is generated through Medicare, insurance carriers, MCOs, and PPOs. A certain proportion of billing must also be written off as charitable care to maintain a laboratory's nonprofit status. Income sources are exceedingly complex and are in continual flux as contractual relations, patients' insurance statuses, and rules and regulations change, usually without warning or input. Thus, pathology practices must engage knowledgeable, sophisticated billing services that keep up with all contracts, changes, allowables, and deductibles.

The advent of prospective payment and DRGs for Medicare inpatients and the distinction between professional and technical components of pathology services inaugurated a new payment scheme for most pathologists. Today, only the professional component of the pathology testing services provided to an individual Medicare inpatient can be billed on a fee-for-service basis (using a fee schedule), and this charge can no longer be bundled with the hospital's bill for the technical component of the services. The professional component is paid by the Medicare Part B Trust Fund, and this payment is known as the Part B payment. Part B revenue is often reviewed for determination of an individual pathologist's salary since it is directly attributable to the cases reviewed.

Part A

Part A represents the technical component of a test and represents the cost involved in performing a test—in personnel, equipment, reagents, and facilities. An example is the technical component assigned for preparation of slides for microscopic review (histology). The technical component of the test, which is typically provided by the hospital, was included in the DRG payment and could not be billed separately.

The Centers for Medicare and Medicaid Services (CMS) regulations stated that for most clinical pathology tests, the pathologist does not provide a specific professional service to individual patients; therefore, pathologists could not separately bill Medicare patients for the professional component of clinical laboratory tests. The government acknowledged that pathologists performed professional services in the clinical laboratory but noted that these services were for the laboratory or the hospital as a whole. Thus, CMS established the Medicare management fee (also known as the payment for professional services to the provider in the Part A payment), a source of income unique to pathologists. These services are designated as professional services to the provider (the hospital) and are based on cost reports supplied by the hospital. Along with the DRGs, Part A payments are paid to the hospital out of the Medicare Part A Trust Fund. Recovering these payments from hospitals is a continuing challenge for pathology practices.

Further justification for the management fee is provided by the Clinical Laboratory Improvement Amendments (CLIA), which requires that laboratory directors ensure the following:

- The laboratory's testing systems provide quality services in all aspects of test performance (ie, the preanalytic, analytic, and postanalytic phases of testing) and are appropriate for the patient population.
- The laboratory's physical and environmental conditions are adequate and appropriate for the testing performed.
- The environment for employees is safe from physical, chemical, and biological hazards, and safety and biohazard requirements are followed.
- A general supervisor (eg, a high-complexity testing technologist) provides day-to-day supervision of all testing personnel and test results reporting and on-site supervision of specific minimally-qualified testing personnel when they are performing high-complexity testing.
- The laboratory employs a sufficient number of appropriately educated, experienced, and/or trained personnel who provide appropriate consultation, properly supervise, accurately perform tests, and report test results in accordance with the written duties and responsibilities specified by the laboratory director.
- New test procedures are reviewed, included in the procedure manual, and followed by personnel.
- Each employee's responsibilities and duties are specified in writing.

Table 10-1. What Does a Pathologist Do?

If a laboratory director, must be a physician licensed to practice medicine and surgery	Monitors QA corrective actions
Establishes appropriate relationships and communications with medical staff, administration, and other departments	Establishes QA and quality control methods relating to materials and tolerance limits
Assumes responsibility for the qualifications and performance of staff, including MDs, PhDs, MTs, etc	Establishes QA systems of correction
Ensures the prompt performance of adequate examinations in sufficient depth to meet the needs of patients	Establishes QA procedures for proficiency testing methods and systems of response
Approves procedures necessary for obtaining specimens satisfactory for examination	Determines the appropriate turnaround times for specific patient conditions
Is responsible for all laboratory reports, including their delivery to the appropriate persons, with steps taken to avoid misinterpretation	Determines the criteria for stat testing for specific procedures
Assumes professional responsibility and liability for results reported and their cost	Establishes alert levels
Performs at least an annual review of all clinical laboratory procedures	Determines formats for reporting
Ensures that procedures and tests outside the capabilities of the department are not performed	Establishes referral criteria for pathologist review
Establishes and manages an appropriate quality assurance (QA) program for specific disciplines and activities of the clinical laboratory	Establishes data collection and retention criteria
Provides 24-hour medical consultation services	Evaluates the clinical relevance of normal and abnormal results
Determines patients' needs for specific clinical laboratory procedures	Educates the medical staff on the application of procedures to clinical situations
Determines the appropriate analyte(s) for specific diseases or conditions	Responds to queries from the medical staff (informal consults)
Determines the specific analytical method for analyte(s), including research, development, instrument, and reagent(s)	Prevents the overuse and improper application of procedures
Establishes a clinically verifiable correlation for the analytical method used	Interprets test results
Establishes appropriate reference ranges for age and sex	
Establishes levels of precision and accuracy	
Establishes levels of sensitivity and specificity	
Selects the appropriate reference laboratory for the correlation of results	
Determines the effects of medications on test results	
Determines the effects of other analytes on test results	
Determines the effects of other disease states on test results	
Establishes QA procedures	

Source: Hanson DJ. Lack of payment for clinical pathology services: the Part A battle. *The American Pathology Review*. A Publication of the American Pathology Foundation. Spring 1996.

The Management Fee

When asked "What is a pathologist?" James D. Barger, MD, president of the CAP from 1981 to 1983, replied "A pathologist is what a pathologist does." Daniel J. Hanson further expanded the definition of a pathologist (Table 10-1). To convince hospital administration to pay Part A payments to the pathology practice, pathologists must emphasize their work duties as they relate to the professional component of providing clinical pathology testing or professional services to the provider. These duties include:

- Complying with the Joint Commission expectations that the director of a laboratory will "assume the professional, scientific, consultative, and organizational responsibility for the facility."

- Interacting with medical staff to design systems and protocols for ideal utilization of the laboratory for patient care.

- Evaluating, selecting, and validating the best tests, methodologies, supplies, and equipment.

- Establishing standards for, and monitoring the performance of, laboratory personnel.
- Ensuring that tests, examinations, and procedures are properly performed, recorded, interpreted, and reported.
- Ensuring the quality of testing procedures.
- Ensuring the hospital laboratory's compliance with state licensure laws, Medicare conditions, Joint Commission standards, the CAP Laboratory Accreditation Program, and federal CLIA '88 certification standards.

Several advisories from the Office of Inspector General (OIG) of the Department of Health and Human Services caution against hospitals providing only token or even no reimbursement to pathologists for Part A services in return for the opportunity to have an exclusive contract for performing and billing Part B services. In fact, hospitals' refusal to adequately compensate pathologists for Part A services may violate federal Stark antikickback laws.[4]

Calculating the amount of the payment for these services that the hospital should pay to the pathology practice involves a time study and the reasonable compensation equivalent (RCE), which is the amount of allowable annual compensation for services furnished by physicians to providers that are not covered by the prospective payment system that are paid by Medicare on a reasonable cost basis. In 2004, the RCE for pathologists ranged from $208,000 in nonmetropolitan areas to $215,700 in large (over one million people) metropolitan areas per annum.[5] For example:

1. Assume there is a 6-person pathology group in a hospital, with each pathologist performing anatomic pathology services and supervising a section of the clinical laboratory.

2. Determine the percentage of clinical laboratory tests performed for Medicare patients.

3. Perform a time study to determine the number of hours each pathologist spends performing the activities detailed above.

4. Total these hours. For example, for 6 pathologists each working 50 hours per week, it would be reasonable for each to spend 10 hours per week in the clinical laboratory performing the services described above for a total of 60 hours per week for the group doing Part A work.

5. If 50% of the clinical laboratory testing is for Medicare patients, then 30 hours per week is devoted to performing Part A services for Medicare patients.

6. If the current RCE is $215,700 per year for a full-time (40 hours/week) pathologist, then the

appropriate fee to the group would be $215,700 x 3/4 = $161,775.

A similar calculation can be performed for non-Medicare patients if the payer refuses to pay a professional component fee for clinical laboratory tests or services. Other services a pathology group may provide to the hospital that may be additionally compensated include serving as the medical director, providing education for hospital staff, and serving on hospital (not medical staff) committees. Recently, some have argued that overseeing anatomic pathology services (histology and cytology laboratories, flow cytometry, cytogenetics, etc) requires as much time and effort as overseeing, for example, clinical chemistry or microbiology, and that these services should be similarly compensated by the hospital.

Table 10-2. Chart of Accounts for a Pathology Practice

Income
Professional Fee
Director's Fees
Management Fees
Interest Income
  Total Income

Expenses
Partners' Professional Fees
Associates' Professional Fees
Pension Contribution
Billing Service
Consultants' Fees
Bank Charges
Taxes & Licenses
Office Personnel Salaries
Payroll Taxes
Telephone
Gifts
Insurance
Travel
Meetings
Advertising
Auto
Interest
Office Supplies
Professional Management
Legal
Accounting
Dues
Rent
Promotions
Entertainment
Pension Administration
Pathology Assistants
Postage & Delivery
  Total Expenses

Profit (Loss)

Responsibilities

Hospital Pathology Group

Every member of the community hospital pathology group has a vital interest in, and a major responsibility for, the financial management of the group. Obviously, the ultimate basis of the group's fiscal viability is correct billing—the first and critical responsibility of each pathologist in the group. Beyond that, each member of a group, partners in particular, have a fiduciary responsibility for the group finances. In most large groups, one of the senior partners is designated the chief financial officer (CFO) for the group. That person accepts fiduciary responsibility and is legally the custodian of the group's funds. The CFO may establish a finance committee to spread the responsibility and the workload and/or may delegate some of the work to a business manager or accountant. The

CFO is responsible for establishing financial policies and a chart of accounts (Table 10-2), planning and budgeting, and billing and collection. The CFO also determines a compensation policy that includes bonus, profit-sharing, and expense-sharing formulas; banking, investment, and pension fund management; and insurance, tax planning, and contracting details. Because the pathology group is often very dependent on the hospital information system for patient demographics and insurance information, it is crucial that the group's CFO develop a good relationship with the hospital CFO and the hospital information technology personnel to provide the representing attorney with reliable information. Without patient demographics, the pathology group cannot appropriately and legally bill Medicare, other carriers, and patients. Similarly, the group is dependent on the staff of physicians' offices for patient information when performing outpatient laboratory testing.

The Accountant

Every pathology group needs an accountant. The accountant is usually an independent outside contractor. The accountant should be familiar with the billing practices and varying income sources that are unique to the practice of pathology. The accountant's responsibilities include daily bookkeeping, generally in conjunction with the practice's billing service; monthly bill paying, accounting, and financial reporting; annual auditing; and developing the annual financial statements and balance sheet. The accountant is also responsible for ensuring compliance with government fiscal, pension, and tax laws and regulations and preparing tax returns.

The Attorney and Others

The pathology group's attorney is essential for drafting and/or evaluating all contracts, both internal (within the group) and external (with the hospital or MCOs). Other specialists that a group might wish to engage include insurance agents who can provide group malpractice insurance, general liability insurance, directors and officers' liability insurance, and errors and omissions liability insurance.

Academic Pathology Group

In academic pathology practice groups, financial management responsibilities may reside with a departmental chief administrative officer (CAO). Such individuals typically have an MBA or a business background. CAOs are responsible for coordinating budgets, financial statements, billing/accounts receivable data, research accounts management, practice group accounts management, and departmental chair accounts management. In addition, depending on the salary structure (academic and hospital), the CAO may have human resources responsibilities in the department. Some academic departments have both a CAO and a CFO, with the CFO's financial responsibilities distinct from the CAO's personnel and administrative responsibilities. In most instances, the CAO and/or CFO reports to the chair and/or hospital management, depending on the reporting and salary structure.

Commercial Laboratory

In independent commercial laboratories, fiscal responsibility depends on the executive administrative structure and is often similar to that of other industries. A major difference between other industries and commercial laboratories is the presence of a chief medical officer or laboratory medical director, who typically has the responsibilities as defined by CLIA '88 for the laboratory director with the appropriate designations. Because each laboratory site requires a laboratory director, large reference laboratory sites typically have their own chief medical officers. Smaller regional reference laboratory sites may cover multiple sites and are subject to the maximum of five laboratories per laboratory director as defined by CLIA '88.

Most independent commercial laboratories employ pathologists in a given specialty; for example, a pathologist may be hired for clinical microbiology, hematopathology, and cytology. If the reference laboratory provides anatomic pathology services, specific anatomic pathology specialists may be hired. Larger-volume surgical pathology specialties, such as gastrointestinal surgical pathology and dermatopathology, are frequently represented in commercial laboratories that provide anatomic pathology services. A growing trend is for commercial laboratories to hire pathologists; according to the most recent CAP pathology practice survey, 28% of pathologists reported having a working relationship with independent laboratories.[3]

Independent commercial laboratories may be privately or publicly owned. CLIA '88 requirements are the same regardless of the ownership model. There are numerous moderately sized private laboratories, which often serve a regional set of physician offices and clinics. Larger laboratories—for example, Quest and LabCorp—may be publicly or privately held. The business models for these larger enterprises are typically a multi-laboratory model, with smaller laboratories performing common large-volume tests, and flagship laboratories performing the more esoteric testing, which includes molecular pathology, cytogenetics, microarrays, bioinformatics, molecular microbiology, and esoteric drug and metabolic testing. Another large laboratory model is the model associated with large academic environments. In these settings, full anatomic pathology services are often included in addition to routine and esoteric testing. Examples include ARUP Laboratories and Mayo Reference Laboratories.

A natural tension exists between smaller hospital-based laboratories and larger reference laboratories. The hospital laboratory is typically a customer of the large reference laboratory. For "send-out" tests, it is important to have an appropriate contract with a larger reference laboratory. Certain regulations apply; for example, the reference laboratory must be fully identified on patient results, including the name of the laboratory director, an address, and contact information. As with all laboratory tests, the reference laboratory must provide reference ranges or result guidelines. The laboratory director must review for the institution all quality markers for the reference laboratory, including CLIA accreditation for all US laboratories and preferably other quality markers (eg, CAP or International Organization for Standardization accreditation). The hospital typically pays the reference laboratory under a contract, and there is always the desire on the part of the hospital to minimize this direct expense. The question of utilization is often referred to the pathologist laboratory director for mechanisms to limit costs and decisions related to bringing reference laboratory testing in-house. Also, pathologist laboratory directors should be wary of compliance violations if they choose to perform outside consultations or other services for a reference laboratory contracted to their hospitals. Such actions may be viewed as a form of "kickback" by the federal government.

Planning and Budgeting

Planning and budgeting for the community hospital pathology practice is not always done, and when done, is often not done well. The basic process begins with the creation of the mission, vision, and value statements of the practice. Completing internal, external, and market assessments are critical to performing a strengths, weak-nesses, opportunities, and threats (SWOT) analysis, which leads to the development of strategies; other key activities include developing a business plan and ultimately a budget. Often, these activities are not major priorities for most hospital practices. However, each pathology practice should endeavor to complete these processes annually for budgets and every 5 years for SWOT analysis and strategic planning. The pathology group's CFO can lead the process, but all partners and members should participate. Guidelines for activities that warrant further planning, including management principles and discussions of business mergers or partnerships, are available[6-9] (see Collaborative Strategies, pages 188 to 189).

The planning goals of the hospital are not always or necessarily congruent with the goals of the pathology practice. Thus, the pathology group must develop its own plan and budget separate from those of the hospital. Obviously, the hospital's strategic plan is an important driver of the pathology group's activities and needs to be carefully considered when making plans for the group. If, for example, the hospital is planning a liver transplantation program, the hospital must plan for the space, equipment, and technologists to perform the specific laboratory tests that will be required, but the pathology group will have to either recruit a pathologist with special expertise in transplantation pathology or ask one or more of its members to attain additional training. Thus, the pathologist/director must be involved in the strategic planning processes of both the hospital and hospital laboratory; both the hospital administration and the Joint Commission expect the pathologist to be involved in planning, designing, directing, integrating, and improving the laboratory service.[1] However, since the pathology practice is a separate entity, it must also separately develop and implement a plan for the pathology group. (See also Chapter 1, "Management Principles," and Chapter 9, "Financial Management of the Laboratory.")

In the typical community hospital pathology practice, the culmination of the planning process is the creation of the budget and the revenue and expense report. The budget predicts the major income categories, which include fees from direct patient billing, capitation, and other managed care contracts; management fees from the hospital and other professional fees; and interest and other income. The budget also contains expense categories, which include pathologists', associates', and consultants' fees; pension plan contributions;

pathology assistants' or secretaries' salaries (if employed by the pathology group rather than the hospital); administrative fees to the director and/or the CFO; bank charges; taxes; licenses; legal and accounting fees; office supplies; travel; dues; subscriptions; entertainment; promotion or marketing costs; rent; depreciation; charitable contributions; and billing service costs.

The budget is not only a guide to operations, but also a measure of performance, and must be reviewed on an ongoing basis. One tool that can be used to quickly review the budget is the monthly variance report, which compares each income and expense item with the expected or budgeted amount and compares the current month's numbers with the numbers for the previous month and the same period the preceding year. Any variance greater that 5% should be investigated, and a description of the cause of the variance should be added to the budget line item. Also, specific explanations may be required by the CFO and at different percentages, depending on the type of line item. Additional information regarding the types of budgets and their management is given in Chapter 9, "Financial Management of the Laboratory."

Although planning and budgeting in the academic pathology practice is somewhat different from planning and budgeting in a community hospital pathology practice, similar principles apply. Often, the academic department budget is created in coordination with the school of medicine budget and/or the hospital budget. The departmental CAO or CFO drafts a budget that includes the estimated expenses and/or salaries of specific laboratory section personnel (eg, laboratory managers or supervisors), research managers, practice group faculty, and departmental chair. The CAO or CFO creates a department budget that includes specific sections that may include school of medicine, hospital, department, and faculty practice group revenue or expenses. The hospital revenue generated by the clinical laboratory (Part A payments) may represent a "blind spot" in budget planning for an academic pathology department. If the revenue numbers are not provided, the budget will principally be "cost-center" based and reflect only the costs for the various clinical laboratory expenses, such as personnel, capital equipment, and supplies.

In independent or commercial laboratories, the planning and budgeting process is generally more sharply defined and is used to guide the laboratory's operations. Public businesses have reporting requirements. Private independent laboratories' methods for managing planning and budgeting are similar to those of other moderately sized private businesses. While the revenue for independent commercial laboratories is complex, it may not be as complex as that of the hospital laboratory, which interfaces with multiple insurance contractors, Medicare (with DRGs), Medicaid, MCOs, and PPOs. The revenue in independent commercial laboratories is more likely to be contract based, with multiple hospitals and institutions. Thus, contracting and managing contract expectations are of core importance to independent commercial laboratories. Most contracts are written with an expectation of certain volumes of test utilization. If utilization does not meet expectations (ie, lower volume), the laboratory's planning and budgeting process may require that the hospital agree to a higher per-test payment at the next contract renewal. Similarly, if a given test volume increases significantly, the independent commercial laboratory may be able to provide a discount at the next contract renewal.

The overall management of an independent reference laboratory is highly dependent on strategic planning.[9] The strategic plan is the means by which to define its competitive strategy and involves establishing the mission (what we want to do), vision (what we want to be), and value (who we are and what we cherish) statements assessing its differential competitive advantage (what we do better than anyone else). The strategic plan typically encompasses more than one fiscal period and is often prepared as a 5-year plan. Although it does not replace the budget, the strategic plan should be used to drive the budget and specific business plans. The strategic plan includes both an internal analysis of the laboratory's effectiveness and ability to meet the plan goals as well as an external situational and environmental analysis of the laboratory's competitors and the relevant forces that would facilitate or impede the success of the plan. Importantly, the situational and environmental analysis includes an assessment of current and potential customers and their known needs and preferences. This market can then be segregated into preferential targets. Once the market is reasonably well defined, one can then judge success by the portion, or share, of the market one is able to successfully serve and retain.[10-13]

As discussed elsewhere in greater depth, the SWOT analysis is a critical element of any business and strategic planning process. SWOT, which stands for strengths, weaknesses, opportunities, and threats, encompasses a systematic thinking process for thoroughly understanding what the practice or organization does well, what is done poorly or not at all, what opportunities can be exploited in the marketplace, and what constraints—particularly those from competitors—exist in the marketplace. An organization is handicapped in any important planning process if it does not clearly understand these four elements.

The strengths and weaknesses should not only encompass those of the individual members of the practice, but also those of the existing processes in which services are delivered. SWOT analysis includes infrastructure elements such as client services, marketing, logistics, information technology, billing/finance, technical operations (eg, histology, immunohistochemistry, and other technical anatomic and clinical pathology services), compliance, quality systems, legal services, and administrative services. Strengths and weaknesses all lie on a continuum and are clearly interrelated.

The culmination of this analytic process is the business plan and the budget. The purpose of the business plan is to state the specific goals and means to attain those goals for a business venture or project. The business plan may be used to convince internal and/or external stakeholders (ie, investors) of the value of the project or venture. The business plan serves as a means for decision making and should contain as much in the way of known relevant information and assumptions as is needed to make decisions. It typically includes information and assumptions about financing, staffing, equipping, supplying, managing, and marketing the venture. It may also include "best-case" and "worst-case" projections, with applicable risk assessments for each. The business plan often involves a detailed market potential analysis, a competitor analysis, and environmental (eg, regulatory, legal) assessments.

In an independent laboratory, the budget is a plan for generating and spending revenue and includes an inventory of revenue and the planned expenses necessary to generate and maintain that revenue. It is a best-estimate forecast that typically encompasses a 12-month period or fiscal year. Although seldom precise, the budget is the measuring stick of a practice's or organization's effectiveness at providing their goods and services. As such, it serves as the means to compare actual performance against the planned performance. Any difference in individual revenue and expense line items is considered a variance, which can either be positive or negative as compared with budgeted line items. Significant variances (as defined by management) are a source for investigation, particularly when expenses are over budget.

Manager performance in independent reference laboratories can also be measured by the managers' ability to meet or beat their budgeted areas of responsibility. Budgets are often described as "top-down," "bottom-up," or a combination of both. A top-down budget is formulated entirely by senior management. In contrast, a bottom-up budget is developed by the line managers and staff and then presented to senior management for modification and/or approval. In one variation of the bottom-up budget, senior management sets the revenue (sales) part of the budget based on their best forecasting and then allows line management to set their expenses in a way that best ensures that the revenue projections are met or exceeded. Budgets can also be broken down into operating budgets, which are used to plan the expenses necessary to providing the operating goods and services of the practice or organization, and capital budgets, which are reserved for physical plant and equipment purchases, that is, those that can be capitalized (or amortized) and depreciated over time rather than expensed. (See also Chapter 5, "Equipment, Supplies, and Space.")

Billing and Collections

The discussion so far has covered the "preanalytic" (strategic planning) and "analytic" (business planning and budgeting) aspects of laboratory finances. The "postanalytic" phase of financial management requires that the "practice" is thoroughly familiar with, and knows how to properly use, several coding systems and a variety of fee schedules. Also, the pathology group or laboratory leadership (ie, the CFO) should know how to choose a billing service and what to expect from billing and collection agencies.[14,15] (See also Appendix 10-1.)

Alphanumeric coding systems provide a universal nomenclature for communicating, storing, and retrieving information on health conditions, diseases, procedures, and services. These systems are widely used by health care providers, health care institutions, insurance providers, governmental agencies, and others in creating medical records, storing data, compiling statistics, and filing claims for reimbursement for procedures and services. Currently the most widely used system for describing diseases and injuries is the International Classification of Diseases, 9th Edition, Clinical Modification (ICD-9-CM), and the most widely used system for coding procedures and services is the Healthcare Common Procedure Coding System (HCPCS).[16,17]

ICD-9-CM is a clinical modification of the World Health Organization's ICD-9. It is maintained by representatives from the American Hospital Association, CMS, the National Center for Health Statistics, and the American Health Information Management Association. The codes include three-digit (XXX), four-digit (XXX.X), five-digit (XXX.XX), and alphanumeric (V-numeric and E-numeric) versions that describe varying levels of specificity. For example: "482" represents "Other bacterial pneumonia"; 482.0 represents "Pneumonia due to *Klebsiella pneumoniae*"; and 482.83 represents "Other gram-negative bacteria." The most current version of ICD was published by the World Health Organization in 1993 as ICD-10-CM and has been implemented in some European counties. ICD-10-CM or ICD-10-PCS (Procedure Coding System) is due to be implemented in the United States, effective October 1, 2013. There are currently 14,025 codes used in ICD-9-CM, while there is expected to be more than 155,000 diagnostic codes in ICD-10-CM.

HCPCS codes are of two types: Level I codes and Level II codes. Level I codes are specified within the Current Procedural Terminology (CPT). CPT was developed and is maintained by the AMA. Level II codes are developed and maintained by CMS for those products, services, and procedures not included in CPT. CPT codes are further divided into three categories: Category I, Category II, and Category III. Category I codes are for established services and procedures that have distinct, commonly practiced, well-documented clinical efficacy. Category II codes are used to track the use of services or procedures and analyze the quality of care of these services from an evidence-based, outcomes-directed perspective. Category III codes are used for the assessment of an investigational product, service, or procedure, including those under future consideration for assignment of a Category I code.

CPT utilizes a five-digit format with a specific textual descriptor. The pathology and laboratory code series is 80047-89398 and includes the surgical pathology code series 88300-88399.[18,19] An example is "88305, Level IV – Surgical pathology, gross and microscopic examination." Additional alpha or numeric code modifiers (XXXXX-XX) are often used to ascribe additional specificity to these codes. For example, "-TC" is used with an appropriate five-digit code when only the technical component (eg, histology services) of a procedure is billed for (eg, 88305-TC). Or, the "-26" modifier is used when only the professional component of a physician-performed services is billed for (eg, 88305-26). There are general rules for selecting the appropriate code(s) to use when describing a procedure or service. In the pathology and laboratory series, the code that most accurately describes the rendered service or the specific analyte tested for should be selected. In the absence of such a specific code, the next level of specificity is to use the code for the specific methodology used, if such a code exists. In the absence of the analyte code or the methodology code, one should use the "unlisted procedure" code.

For the surgical pathology code series 88300-88309, the unit of service is the specimen. More specifically, it is the specimen that is "submitted for individual and separate attention, requiring individual examination and pathologic diagnosis." If two or more specimens from the same patient are submitted on the same day of service and separately identified (ie, distinctively labeled or otherwise identified by the health care provider who obtained the specimens), each specimen is considered a separate unit of service. Many specimen types are defined in CPT by specific codes (eg, gallbladder is only designated as 88304). Any certain tissue specimens are bundled together into specific codes (eg, tonsils and/or adenoids, uterus with or without tubes and ovaries) and should not be unbundled into separate, multiple codes. Ancillary services like histochemical stains (eg, 88312, special stains; 88342, immunohistochemical stains) are coded for each separately identifiable stain performed per specimen.

Physicians are required by law to submit diagnosis codes (ICD-9-CM) together with HCPCS codes to CMS when billing for reimbursement for procedures and services. Most if not all other third-party insurance companies, as well as health care organizations, also require the use of ICD-9-CM and CPT. Correct coding is required not only to ensure that the procedure or service provided is paid for, but also that the process complies with the specific requirements necessary to avoid fraudulent billing practices, especially with Medicare and Medicaid patients.

Compliance is one of the latest watchwords in coding and billing; it means documenting medical necessity. Using Medicare as the generally accepted standard, coverage (ie, benefits) policies require that services meet a "reasonable and necessary" or "medical necessity" standard. CMS has established coverage policies and an integrity program aimed at ensuring correct coding and payment of services. CMS polices these policies through a variety of means, most notably the OIG and the Department of Justice. Further, CMS administers the claims review and reimbursement process through contracts with private insurance companies. Most private insurance companies and health plans follow many of the same coverage policies and procedures established for Medicare. The health care provider is the individual with primary responsibility for ensuring compliance with all medical necessity requirements.

The pathologist performing the coded service is the individual whose name is submitted on the reimbursement claim. The pathologist is likewise responsible for avoiding billing fraud at the coding level. The types of billing fraud that are targeted by the OIG include billing for items or services not rendered, providing medically unnecessary services, upcoding, unbundling, coding inpatient services as outpatient services, and submitting duplicate billings. The pathologist who performs the coded service is responsible for correct procedural coding. Because of this, it is important to clearly explain and document all services provided in the final interpretive report and then bill for only those services so documented. When done properly, the final report provides the justification for all billing should any issues subsequently arise, including claims, challenges, or denials by insurers.

Model compliance plans have been developed and published for hospitals, laboratories, pathologists, and billing companies. It behooves every health care provider to be familiar with the key elements of compliance to prevent inadvertent coding and billing mistakes. The civil and criminal penalties for fraud and abuse, particularly for services provided through the public insurance plans—Medicare and Medicaid—can be substantial. The Department of Health and Human Services developed the OIG Compliance Program for Individual and Small Group Physician Practices in an effort to develop "a higher level of ethical and lawful conduct throughout the entire health care community" by establishing internal controls the OIG believed would "significantly advance the prevention of fraud, abuse and waste." These plans include seven common elements the OIG believes to provide a solid basis from which pathology practices can develop an effective internal compliance program:

- Develop written policies and procedures for coding and billing.

- Designate a compliance officer.
- Conduct effective training and education programs.
- Develop effective lines of communication.
- Enforce standards through well-publicized disciplinary guidelines.
- Conduct internal monitoring and auditing.
- Respond promptly to offenses and develop corrective action.

The activities of a compliance program, whether managed within the laboratory or with the hospital or institution, include the following procedures:

- Designate a compliance officer and/or a compliance committee.
- Develop specific written policies, standards, and procedures for the coding, billing, marketing, and claims processing of laboratory services.
- Conduct effective periodic training and education programs.
- Enforce standards through well-publicized disciplinary guidelines.
- Implement systems to monitor compliance with the standards and procedures.
- Create a "hot-line" to receive reports of alleged wrongful conduct.
- Conduct internal monitoring and auditing.
- Promptly investigate and remediate identified instances of noncompliance.

As a part of the process for reviewing coding claims, CMS utilizes a system known as the Correct Coding Initiative (CCI; see www.ntis.gov/products/cci.aspx), whose authorized distributor is the National Technical Information Service. CMS established the CCI "to promote national correct coding methodologies and to control improper coding that lead to inappropriate payment of Medicare Part B claims." These methods, or "edits," are intended to identify mutually exclusive, gender-specific procedures and service codes that may or may not be legitimately billed by a single provider for a single beneficiary on the same day of service. The edits are based on coding conventions in the AMA's CPT manual, national and local coverage policies and edits, coding guidelines developed by national societies, analysis of standard medical and surgical practice, and a review of current coding practice.

There are two general categories of CCI edits: mutually exclusive edits and column 1/column 2 edits (formerly known as comprehensive/component edits because the second code in the pair is considered integral to the first code). CMS allows the use of modifiers to override certain edits in both categories. The two CPT modifiers of particular application to these edits are "-91" for repeat clinical diagnostic laboratory tests and "-59" for distinct procedural services.

CMS has also established frequency limits, known as the medically unlikely edits (MUEs), for many CPT services. These limits were developed as a means for CMS to curtail the excessive use of certain services. Claims submitted in excess of an MUE should be denied by the insurance carrier. Some limits are published, while others are given very limited distribution to prevent individuals from exploiting the coding system. For example, the published MUE for 88331, frozen section, is "11."

Compensation for medically necessary procedures and services is typically based on fee schedules. Given that Medicare is the single largest third-party payer in the United States, the fee schedules for both physician services and clinical laboratory services serve as models for most other fee-for-service schedules from private insurance companies. Medicare uses the physician fee schedule (PFS) for physician professional services and the clinical laboratory fee schedule (CLFS) for outpatient clinical laboratory services.

Medicare pays for nonphysician services, including the technical component of laboratory tests provided to hospital inpatients, through Medicare Part A insurance, and hospitals are reimbursed for their costs through payments for the DRGs, as described previously. Medicare contracts with private insurance companies around the country to receive, review, and administer claims for Part A services from eligible providers. These insurers are referred to as fiscal intermediaries.

All physician services (other than those provided through Medicare Advantage, the Part C managed care plan) are paid on a fee-for-service basis through Medicare Part B for inpatients, outpatients, and "non-patients" (ie, those seen in independent physician offices). Part B services also include clinical laboratory testing for outpatients and non-patients. Medicare beneficiaries must elect to participate in Part B services. Participation in Part B services is voluntary; to participate in Part B services, individuals with annual incomes of less than $85,000 per year and couples with annual incomes of less than $170,000 must pay an additional monthly premium. A means test is applied to incomes above those levels, with commensurately higher premiums. Premiums

fund approximately 25% of the Part B payments; general tax dollars support the remainder. The annual deductible is a defined amount of costs required of the patient annually, and a 20% copayment (payment by the individual patient as a percentage of charges) applies to most services. Medicare contracts with private insurance companies to administer Part B services claims. These entities are referred to as carriers. In most geographic jurisdictions, the same insurance company is both the fiscal intermediary and the carrier.

Medicare reimburses for physician services on the basis of the PFS. From the inception of Medicare in 1965 until 1992, Medicare physician services were paid on a "customary, prevailing and reasonable charge" basis. On January 1, 1992, Medicare began a 4-year phase-in of the resource-based relative value scale (RBRVS) system, a comparative work methodology based on RVUs and developed in part by researchers at Harvard University. For each physician service based on CPT codes, the fee schedule is determined using the following equation:

$$(\text{RVU-W})(\text{GPCI}) + (\text{RVU-PE})(\text{GPCI}) + (\text{RVU-PLI})(\text{GPCI}) \times \text{CF} = \text{Fee}$$

where RVU-W is physician work, RVU-PE is practice expense, RVU-PLI is professional liability insurance, GPCI is the geographic practice cost index, and CF is the conversion factor. For example, 88305 "Tissue examination by pathologist" has the following professional components:

RVU-W = 0.75
RVU-PE = 0.26
RVU-PLI = 0.01
Total RVU = 1.02
GPCI = varies by geographic location (assume 1.0)
CF = $36.066 (CY2010)
Fee schedule amount = $36.787

Certain CPT codes have both a professional component and a technical component. In the case of pathologist services, the technical component is for histology services, including slide preparation and staining. In the example above, the technical component of the 88305 service has a total RVU of 1.80 and a fee schedule amount of $64.919. The combined, or "global," RVU for both the technical component and professional component is 2.82, with a fee of $101.76. Pathologists who have their own histology laboratory can globally bill if they perform both the technical component and the professional component. However, many pathologists buy histology services from another entity, typically a hospital. In that case, the hospital bills Medicare for the technical component, and the pathologists bill Medicare for their professional component or allow the hospital to bill the professional component on their behalf (through "assignment").

Medicare payment for Part B outpatient clinical laboratory services is based on the CLFS. The CLFS was authorized by Congress and became effective July 1, 1984. Prior to that date, as noted above, clinical laboratory services were paid on a "customary, reasonable and prevailing charge" basis. The new CLFS was set at 60% of those rates. Medicare instructed each carrier to establish its local fee schedule. In 1985, Congress established the National Limitation Amount (NLA), the ceiling set on the services covered by the CLFS. Initially, the NLA was set at 115% of the median of all carrier fee schedules. By law, the CLFS is annually updated based on the previous year's Consumer Price Index. Since 1985, however, Congress has either cut, frozen, or raised the CLFS and has reduced the NLA to the current level of 74% of the median. The net effect has been to reduce the CLFS by 40% during this period despite increases in the complexity and cost of clinical laboratory services. For the 2010 calendar year, the CLFS was adjusted upward 1.9%. In the future, the CLFS will be adjusted according to the provisions of the Affordable Care Act of 2010.

In addition to using the Medicare PFS and the CLFS, both of which are formulated by the government (ie, CMS), pathology practices must develop their own intrinsic fee schedules, which are used to bill non-Medicare patients. Such fee schedules can be used creatively to develop panels of tests for specific diseases and/or clinicians as long as such panels are not applied to Medicare patients. The intrinsic fee schedules may be used as a starting point in negotiating fees with insurance companies and MCOs. These fees should be reasonable and customary for the community; however, there should not be any collusion or price-fixing with other pathology groups because such actions would constitute a violation of antitrust laws and the Consent Decree of 1969.

A billing system requires the seamless interfacing between the hospital information system (HIS), the laboratory information system (LIS), and a billing service (see also Chapter 6, "Management of Pathology Information Systems"). The HIS provides patient demographic and insurance information and transmits it to the pathology group's billing service or LIS. The LIS must accurately record the tests performed and attach the appropriate codes and electronically transmit that information to the billing service. In some instances, the hospital serves as the billing service or agent for the pathology group; however, it is prudent to use a separate, outside billing agency, if for no other reason than to avoid any potential conflicts and retain confidentiality. The billing service receives the demographic, insurance, and test coding information from the HIS and LIS, and must be aware of the various insurance fee schedules and rules and regulations for deductibles, allowables, etc. The billing service also should be aware of any contractual relations, such as discounts and capitation rates, the group has with individual MCOs. The billing service then sends bills electronically to the proper payer.

The billing service should be helpful in establishing intrinsic fee schedules and analyzing contracts with MCOs and insurance companies. The billing service is responsible for correct automated patient billing, electronic insurance claims processing, and claims denials appealing and adjudicating. The billing service is also responsible for collecting payments, depositing payments in the group's bank (lock box), following up on delinquent accounts, and referring bad debts to a collection agency. The billing service should also provide an "800" number and address patients' billing questions or disputes. At a minimum, the billing service should provide the following four monthly reports:

- Charges and Receipts by Financial Class and Patient Type (Cash Flow)
- Accounts Receivable by Financial Class
- Accounts Receivable Aging
- Account Analysis by Ordering Physician, CPT, ICD-9, and Payer

Billing services generally charge a percentage of collections; this fee is usually negotiable, and different percentages may be established for the various categories of charges, eg, anatomic pathology versus clinical pathology, or CMS versus insurance. See Appendix 10-1, "What to Expect from a Billing Service."

Insurance and Risk Management

Community hospital pathologists and pathology groups carry a number of insurance policies including malpractice, health, life, disability, general liability, umbrella, and errors and omissions insurance. If there is no formal group or if the group is composed of individual professional corporations, each pathologist or professional member carries

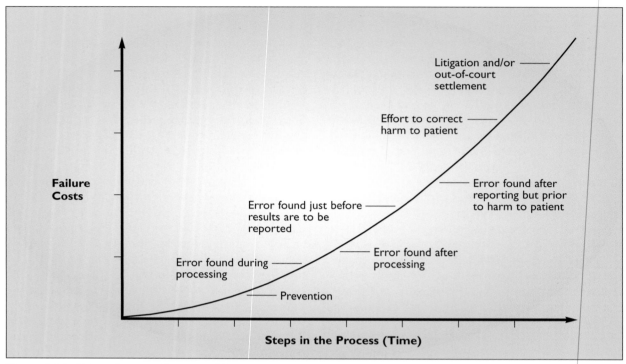

Figure 10-1. Failure Cost as a Function of Detection Point in a Process.

its own insurance policies. If the group has a formal organization, eg, a partnership that employs other pathologists, the group may be responsible for all or some of the insurance coverage. In formal groups with appointed officers and directors, additional officers and directors insurance is needed.

A brief primer on the essence of medical malpractice and risk management is essential (see Chapter 13, "Legal Affairs for Pathologists").[20-22] With the recent health care reform, greater attention will be paid to preventing errors and to the cost of errors (Figure 10-1).[1]

Risk is a chance of harm or loss. Risk should be viewed as threats to patient and employee safety, facility integrity, business continuity, and financial stability. Risk should be identified and categorized within each of these overlapping spheres, and risk-prone activities should be well understood. Examples of risk include analytical, diagnostic, clerical, and billing errors; privacy and security breaches; loss, compromise, or mislabelling of specimens; critical value notification; equipment malfunctions; employee injuries; and damage to facilities or equipment.

Risk management is a medical-practice and/or organization-wide activity, directed at identifying, monitoring, and mitigating or eliminating risk, that involves incident management, communication, claims management, and liability insurance.

Large organizations have risk management departments and designated risk managers. Smaller organizations and individual practices may lack these dedicated resources but should not fail to incorporate risk management activities into their policies and procedures. Risk management is everyone's responsibility, as is quality management. The two go hand-in-hand and rely upon many of the same key elements, including identification, monitoring, reporting, corrective action, individual responsibility, communication, process improvement, and education and remediation.

Medical malpractice represents a tort against an individual and requires that negligence be established and proven. Tort law includes the four elements of negligence: duty, breach of duty, injury, and proximate cause (see also Chapter 13, "Legal Affairs for Pathologists"). Each element must be substantiated to establish negligence and malpractice. In medicine, duty means a "duty of care" that health care providers have accepted on behalf of their patients. Implicit and explicit standards of care exist in medicine, whether at the local or national level. A breach of that duty could mean a failure to act (omission) or an inappropriate act (commission). There must also be a measurable injury to the patient. Finally, the breach of duty must be the proximate cause of that injury. Pathology malpractice generally involves diagnostic errors in surgical pathology; the majority of these errors are due to either a false-negative or false-positive diagnosis of cancer. The most problem-prone specimens are breast specimens, cervical specimens, and skin biopsies. It is also estimated that clinically significant errors are relatively rare. In a blinded review of 5000 sequential biopsies (1998 to 2003) by The Doctors Company (www.the doctors.com), clinically significant errors occurred in only 0.08% of cases.

A medical malpractice action is initiated when the injured party (the plaintiff) files a claim against the person(s) and/or organization(s) believed to have caused the injury (the defendant). Any state-specific statute of limitation on such a filing must be met. It is then the responsibility of the court to determine the facts of the case and either substantiate the claims or dismiss them. The court accomplishes this through a proscribed process that involves discovery and witness testimony. Discovery refers to the process of identifying all of the relevant facts in the case through subpoenas for documents, interviews (depositions and interrogatories) with those involved in the case, and review of any material (eg, histologic slides) on which the claim of malpractice is made. This process is designed to uncover, for both parties, facts on which the case will be judged and affords the opportunity (time) for the parties to reach an out-of-court settlement. Once at trial, the plaintiff has the burden of proof to substantiate all of the four elements of malpractice beyond a preponderance (51%) of evidence.

The discovery process is facilitated by each side requesting copies of all relevant materials. These materials may include specific documents as well as pathology materials; for example, in the case of claims against anatomic pathologists, the plaintiff may request and/or subpoena all of the remaining tissues, slides, and blocks for review by their own expert pathologist(s). Although court orders should not be ignored, it is generally recognized that such materials often represent the only existing material in a case and are subject to the dangers of loss or irreparable damage. Every attempt should be made to provide access to these materials so as to preserve their existence and integrity. For example, providing recuts from the blocks may suffice as long as they contain the original diagnostic material, or granting full and easy access to the materials on the laboratory's premises may meet the plaintiff's review requirements. A ruling from the court can be requested if there is any reluctance to provide controlled access.

Witness testimony is used in malpractice cases to either establish material facts or to provide expert opinions. Material witnesses can be compelled to testify through subpoena. Expert witnesses participate voluntarily and are compensated for their time and expertise. Both parties can offer expert testimony to substantiate or repudiate claims and opposing expert opinions. Because of the highly technical nature of medical malpractice claims, these explanations facilitate informed decision making if the case is tried in court. Expert testimony is also helpful in establishing the standard of care in a particular case.

Attorney–client privilege means that all verbal and written communications between a party and their legal counsel, as well as attorney work-product compiled as part of the case, are considered exempt from the discovery process. Attorney–client privilege facilitates the free exchange of information necessary to build or defend a case.

Hospitals, laboratories, and pathology practices generate an abundance of records. Accrediting, licensing, and law enforcement agencies require that many of these be retained and accessible for various lengths of time. The specific requirements for record protection should be contained in a record retention policy. For example, the CAP requires that most anatomic pathology reports be retained for 10 years and clinical laboratory reports be retained for 2 years. The policy should also specify the disposal methods for such records when their retention period expires. Patient records should be destroyed at that time to protect personal health record privacy and confidentiality. Organizational policy may require the indefinite retention of some records. All records involved in a claim (eg, a medical malpractice claim) against an organization or individual(s) should be retained and protected from destruction as required by the applicable laws. Effective document control is essential to a well-run practice or organization (see also Chapter 7, "Quality Management in Laboratory Medicine"). Commercial tools are available to facilitate document control and management. An important but often overlooked repository of documents is the email present on computer hard drives and servers. "E-discovery" laws now exist to protect these records from loss or wanton destruction and allow such records to be subpoenaed.

Privacy and security are essential to the practice of medicine. Particularly in health care organizations, patients enjoy protections against the indiscriminate disclosure of their protected health information. Hospitals, laboratories, and pathology practices must comply with all applicable laws, including the Health Insurance Portability and Accountability Act (HIPAA) and the Health Information Technology for Economic and Clinical Health Act, which specify the ways in which records are to be protected and the steps required to obtain patient authorizations for disclosures. Any unauthorized disclosures of protected health information are considered serious breaches of privacy and are subject to potentially severe penalties. Electronic information security is also an important part of these laws.

Health care providers incur liability for their own acts of omission or commission as compared to the accepted standards of practice in their specialties. Individuals and organizations can also be held liable for the acts of others that occur as a result of their recognized duties and responsibilities; this is referred to as "vicarious liability." For example, the medical laboratory director of a clinical laboratory can be held liable for the acts of a medical technologist for whom the director is responsible if the technologist has acted in an inappropriate manner in the discharge of his assigned duties.

Professional liability or medical malpractice insurance is recommended for all medical practitioners, including pathologists. It provides financial protection against malpractice claims of acts of omission or commission. Insurance coverage can be formulated on either a "claims-made" or "occurrence-based" basis. The more commonly used claims-made insurance covers any claims that are brought during the policy period, including claims that may have occurred but were not filed before the policy was in force. The policy period only remains in force as long as the insurance premium is paid. Allowing the policy to lapse eliminates any coverage; however, one can usually purchase "tail-coverage" to maintain the policy indefinitely. Physicians often do this prior to retiring from practice.

An occurrence-based policy only covers incidents that occur during the policy period, regardless of when the actual claim is filed. It is prudent for all members of a pathology practice group to have the same malpractice carrier and identical policies. Hospital-based practices are required by the hospital contract to carry a minimum amount of malpractice insurance for both the group and the individual pathologists in the group. When a pathologist is a hospital employee, the hospital or health care facility should provide malpractice insurance.

Similarly, a pathologist in an independent laboratory or academic pathology practice is almost always covered by malpractice insurance. In large academic medical centers, the institution may provide self-coverage; in other words, the insurance risk is carried by the institution. However, the institution may hire an insurance carrier for the administrative functions or for an umbrella of protection above some predetermined ceiling, for example, a claim greater than $3 million to an individual or greater than $10 million to the practice. Similarly, large reference laboratories may also be self-insured. Small to moderately sized laboratories typically ask their pathologists or pathology group to provide their own medical malpractice insurance as part of the contract agreement to work for the private laboratory.

Health, life, and disability insurance is often provided by a group practice or may be purchased individually by each pathologist. There are many types of each insurance, and policy selection is very much dependent on the specifics of the individual and his or her family, such as the individual's age, the ages and number of children, and spouse's income and insurance plan. When evaluating disability insurance, it is important to know how long the waiting period is, how *disability* is defined, and whether there is a return of premium if no disability occurs by the end of the policy term (usually age 65).[23]

Pathologists who serve as officers or directors of a pathology group, whether in community practice or in academia, should secure directors and officer liability insurance in the event they are sued in conjunction with the performance of their duties as they relate to the group. This usually includes employment practices liability and sometimes fiduciary liability, the former of which involves harassment and discrimination suits. Errors and omissions insurance covers performance failures and negligence in the group's provision of services, rather than the performance of the officer per se.

Pension Fund Management

One of the major reasons pathologists form individual professional corporations is to design and manage their own pension fund. Knowledge of pension fund management is critical even when the fund is managed by the professional group or by an employer, particularly when a pathologist participates in the management of the group plan(s). Knowledge of the types of available plans, the advantages of each, and the fiduciary responsibilities they entail is essential for each pathologist. The following are common pension vehicles.

401(k) Plan

The term 401(k) is a reference to a section of the Internal Revenue Code that describes a retirement savings plan in which a worker can save funds and defer the income taxes on the saved funds and their earnings until the funds are withdrawn at retirement. These plans are primarily employer sponsored and allow employees to elect to have wages directly deposited into their retirement account. It also provides an optional opportunity for the employer to provide some level of matching funds and/or profit-sharing as a benefit to their employees. This retirement fund is then managed either by the employer or by a third party for the benefit of the employees. Employees are usually allowed to select from a number of different risk-based investment vehicles. Employer participation in these funds can be either "defined benefit" or "defined contribution." A defined benefit is a promise made by the employer to provide a designated retirement benefit, or pension. This is most common for publicly traded companies in which the main investment tool in the fund is company stock. A defined contribution plan designates a specific dollar amount that is deposited into the fund each period, rather than the promise of a specific benefit amount at retirement. (See also "Roth Individual Retirement Account.")

403(b) and 457 Plans

401(k) plans apply to for-profit companies. Nonprofit organizations have a similar retirement funding tool, known as a 403(b). For governmental entities, the plan is referred to as a 457 plan.

Individual Retirement Account

The Internal Revenue Code includes provisions for making tax-deductible contributions into individual retirement accounts (IRAs). Currently, the limit on tax-deductible contributions is 100% of earned income or $5000, whichever is less. Upon retirement, withdrawals are taxed as income net of the original contribution. There are multiple forms of IRAs, including those that have pre-tax deductions and those that have post-tax (Roth IRA) deductions.

Roth Individual Retirement Account

Also know as a Roth 401(k), this form of IRA does not defer the taxes on the initial amount. After-tax dollars are used, and any gain in value over time is then tax-free at withdrawal.

Profit-Sharing and Bonuses

As an incentive benefit of employment, many organizations offer the opportunity to share in their profits. Profit-sharing plans, which rely on any of a number of different formulas to define their calculation and administration, can be used as sources of bonus compensation. They can also be used to reward high performance and share any gains made by the organization. For publicly traded companies, profit sharing may be in the form of stock or deferred stock options. In pathology practices, some groups pay base salaries and then divide any excess practice revenue at the end of the year among the members of the group, either equally or based upon a distribution plan to which everyone has agreed. In some settings in which cost savings are important, the ability to successfully control costs can lead to a sharing of the net gains at the end of the year.

Pension Administration

When a pathology group manages the pension plans for the members and employees of the group, they incur a fiduciary responsibility for the plan and a heavy burden of moral and ethical responsibility, particularly if the plan loses money. Therefore, most pathology groups use a pension fund administrator and an investment advisor or investment manager to make the investment decisions and manage the necessary paperwork. The selection of an administrator and advisor is not easy and requires extraordinary due diligence on the part of the group's officers, CFO, and investment committee, if any. If the markets rise and the pension plans thrive, the advisor takes credit, but if the markets slump and the pension plan falters, whoever selected the advisor is at fault.

In academic settings and independent laboratories, the pension plan depends on the institution supporting the laboratory. Academic medical centers that are part of state or other government oversight often have "old-fashioned" defined benefit pensions. These plans pay into a centrally managed financial agency that then invests the funds to support a defined pension amount. Defined benefit pensions may be calculated as a percentage of salary (for example, the average of the three highest salary years), based on age at retirement, and/or based on the years of employment at a given institution. Such institutions may also offer 403(b) or 457 plans, resulting in a combination of funds available at retirement. Most independent laboratories provide 401(k) defined contribution retirement plans. These types of plans are by far the more common vehicles for retirement planning in the private sector. As noted above, some large laboratories may also contribute to these plans or provide other inducements to save, such as stock options. Recently, the 401(k) contribution statute has been revised to allow "opt-out" mechanisms, which encourages more retirement savings in the general population.

Accounting and Auditing

Pathology and laboratory medicine is big business. The average hospital generates $1 million per bed per year in revenue. For a 500-bed community hospital, that means a gross revenue of $500 million. If the laboratory accounts for 10% of this total, then the laboratory would generate $50 million per year. If the pathology group is responsible for 10% to 20% of the laboratory revenue, their revenue would be between $5 million and $10 million. The management of such a large amount of money requires acceptable accounting practices. The typical group practice engages an outside accountant to provide some or all of the following services.

Accounting or management accounting is defined as the recording, classifying, and summarizing of financial transactions in a way that facilitates interpretation. Management (or managerial) accounting is the process used in planning, coordinating, and controlling the operations of a practice or organization. Management accounting represents all of the financial information necessary for managers to make informed day-to-day business decisions and is used to track the performance of the organization's operations. Management accounting includes cost accounting, pricing, sales management, profit analysis, forecasting, and variance analysis (ie, comparing actual performance to that planned in the budget). The day-to-day component of management accounting is bookkeeping, which the accountant performs in close coordination with the billing service. In most instances, the accountant's services include bill payment.

In contrast to management accounting, financial accounting involves the preparation and communication of financial statements, including the income statement, balance sheet, and cash flow statement. Financial accounting is the formal reporting system required by owners, stockholders, banks, and other outside agencies, and is used to summarize an organization's financial performance into regular monthly, quarterly, and annual reports. Financial accounting is governed by the rules of Generally Accepted Accounting Principles.

Debit and Credit

Debit and credit are the two sides of all individual transactions recorded in an accounting system. The left-handed side of an account (often referred to as the "T" account) is the debit side, and the right-handed side is the credit side. For each recorded transaction, debits must equal credits. Asset accounts are increased on the debit side and decreased on the credit side. For liability and owner's equity accounts, increases are recorded as credits, and decreases are recorded as debits. This serves to preserve the equation used in accounting, assets = liabilities + owner's equity. (For further information regarding how these categories operate, please refer to Chapter 9, "Financial Management of the Laboratory.")

General Ledger

The general ledger, or chart of accounts, is the collection of all individual accounts used for both management and financial accounting purposes. The chart of accounts is grouped into general categories: assets (eg, cash, accounts receivable, investment income), liabilities (eg, accounts payable, debt), owner's equity, revenue (eg, sales, interest income), expenses (eg, salaries, wages, benefits, supplies, reagents, bad debt, utilities, depreciation), gains (profits), and losses.

Balance Sheet

The balance sheet is a financial accounting statement used to summarize the assets, liabilities, and owner's equity of an organization as of a specific date (month end, quarter end, and/or year end). As such, the balance sheet is often referred to as a "snapshot" of the financial condition of the organization. Typically, each of these three categories are presented in their own sections, following the flow of the equation, assets = liabilities + owner's equity.

Operating Statement

Variously referred to as the "profit and loss," "income," or "earnings" statement, the operating statement summarizes the income and expenses of an organization's operations over a specified period of time (month, quarter, and/or year). It presents, in columnar form, the list of sources of revenue followed by the list of expenses. Net income (margin or profit) is then represented by the equation, net income = revenue – expenses. The income statement depicts the organization's operating margin or loss for management and all outside stakeholders.

Funds Flow Statement

The cash flow or funds flow statement tracks the flow of cash and cash equivalents in and out of the organization. It ties back to the balance sheet as the amount of cash in the asset section of that statement. Cash is usually separated into operating, investment, and financing (borrowing) sections. The cash flow statement is an important tool in monitoring the short-term financial viability of an organization (ie, its liquidity and solvency). It also provides additional information about changes in an organization's assets, liability, and equity.

Audit

An audit is an evaluation of an organization's accounting processes and financial information. It is used to confirm the validity and reliability of accounting and finance practices. Financial audits can be either internal or external. Internal audits are performed to provide better assurance to management that their processes and necessary checks and balances are working effectively. External audits are performed for the same reasons, usually by a third-party accounting firm, and are often required by interested stakeholders (eg, owners, lending institutions, stockholders) and generally performed at the end of the fiscal year as a part of "closing the books" on that period.

The final function of the accounting operation is tax planning, including the preparation of local, state, federal, employment, payroll, and business taxes, and fulfilling the reporting requirements of the various entities, partnerships, professional corporations, and pension plans. In academic or independent laboratory practices, accounting operations may be several layers removed from the pathologist. However, most pathologists who engage in a practice group, whether in a private reference laboratory or an academic setting, should be somewhat familiar with accounting operations.

Contracting

The legally binding articulation of the business of a pathology practice resides in the various contracts which are executed. These include partnership agreements, buy-in and buy-outs, professional service agreements, employment agreements, hospital contracts, contracts with managed care organizations, and contracts for services such as accounting and billing. The CAP *Professional Relations Manual,* 12th edition (2003), is a thorough compendium and guide to professional practice and contractual relations; it is an essential reference for all pathologists. The professional services agreement, ie, the contract or agreement between an individual pathologist and a pathology partnership, pathology group, or other employer, is discussed in Chapter 11, "The Pathology Position."

Contracting with Hospitals

The contract with the hospital is the pathology practice's most crucial financial instrument. It defines the fiscal basis of the group. Hospitals are becoming increasingly aggressive in their attempts to control hospital-based physician groups. They demand greater jurisdiction over contracting with insurance companies and HMOs, and they exert greater control over staffing and budgeting for the laboratory. Hospitals are also encouraging competitive bidding for pathology services, and they are increasingly reluctant to pay any management fees to the pathology group. The execution of a successful hospital contract requires planning and negotiation. It is important to know the hospital's strategic plan—where it is going—and what the pathology practice can do to enhance the hospital's mission and vision. It is important to know how the pathology group is perceived by the medical staff. Is the staff supportive or critical? What needs to be done to assure that the medical staff leadership supports the pathology group's contract? It would also be of value to know how other hospital-based groups have fared in their negotiations. And, as in other negotiations, it is valuable to have a negotiating plan, knowing what items are essential, what items are "nice to have," what the "fall-back" positions are, and what the "deal-breakers" are.

The pathology group negotiator must be well prepared. Table 10-3 is a checklist that may be useful in preparing for the negotiation of a hospital contract. The contract should clearly identify the pathologist(s) as independent contractors rather than hospital employee(s) and should stipulate that the hospital may not interfere with the pathologists' professional judgment or activities and that pathologist(s) can practice elsewhere as long as their services to the hospital are not compromised.

Table 10-3. Hospital Contract Questions

In the "Definitions" section, the pathology department needs to be clearly defined as far as its location—for example, is it only the laboratory in the hospital, or does it also include hospital-owned, off-site satellite laboratories or surgical centers? The department should also be defined in terms of its function, ie, the services it provides and controls. (For example, are blood gases done by the laboratory or by pulmonologists?)
The professional independence of the pathologist must be confirmed, and the technical and administrative responsibilities must be described and delineated by the granting of appropriate authority.
The relationship of the pathologist/director to the laboratory personnel must be defined. If the laboratory personnel are hospital employees, the pathologist must be given the right to establish performance standards and the right to hire and fire.
If the space, equipment, and supplies are the responsibility of the hospital, the pathologist should retain the right to make purchasing decisions.
A convenient way to characterize the responsibilities of the pathologist/director is to include a list of services or a fee schedule as an exhibit to the contract and indicate that the pathologist has the exclusive right to control and supervise those procedures for the hospital's patients.
The contract might specify the individual to be the director of the laboratory and to whom the director reports. (Is it only to administration, or is there a reporting responsibility to the medical staff?)
The contract might also specify a successor director or a succession plan if the designated director is unable to fulfill the position.
The contract may also require that the pathologist maintain the highest professional standards and perform other services for the hospital, such as participating in medical staff and hospital educational and peer-review activities, participating in medical staff research projects, serving on the medical staff executive committee and/or other committees, and performing autopsies.
The pathologist must be awarded exclusivity (ie, no other pathologist, unless an associate, may provide pathology services in the hospital).

The contract should also specify the type and amount of malpractice and liability insurance the pathologist must carry. It must be clear in authorizing the pathologist to bill separately for services and must ensure that the hospital agrees to provide the pathologist with the patient demographic and insurance information necessary for billing.

A convenient way to characterize the responsibilities of the pathologist/director is to include a list of services or a fee schedule as an exhibit to the contract and indicate that the pathologist is authorized the exclusive right to control and supervise those procedures for the hospital's patients. The contract might specify the individual to be the director of the laboratory and to whom the director reports—it may be only to the administration, or there may be a reporting responsibility to the medical staff as well. The contract might also specify a successor director to be appointed or a succession plan to be followed in the event that the designated director is unable to fulfill the position. The contract may also require that the pathologist maintain the highest professional standards and perform other services for the hospital, such as participating in medical staff and hospital educational and peer review activities, participating in

medical staff research projects, serving on the medical staff executive committee and other committees, and performing autopsies. Some of these services may be compensable, either through the management fee (professional service to the provider) or as separate service. The pathology group may hire or contract with an outside entity to provide autopsy diener or pathology assistant services, and these should be reimbursed by the hospital.

The contract should not force the pathologist to use the hospital as a billing agent or as a negotiator with third parties such as MCOs. The hospital usually retains the right to approve the pathologist's fee schedule. The pathologist should be paid an additional fee for providing professional services to the hospital—the management fee or professional component fee and the contract should specify how this fee is to be calculated. Most hospital contracts will have a no-cause cancellation clause, which effectively limits the term of the contract. However, a no-cause cancellation may be modified to allow remediation or be subject to negotiation or arbitration by the medical staff organization. Although the contracting process might seem contentious at times, a mutually satisfactory agreement can be reached when persons of good will negotiate in good faith with patient welfare always in mind.

Managed Care Contracting

Contracting with MCOs is one of the most troublesome and vexing duties of a pathology practice. The rapid rise and dominance of MCOs has come about because they are touted as being able to stem the rapid rise in health care costs, and in some regions of the country, they have achieved market domination. If a pathology practice chooses to negotiate its services directly with MCOs, the pathologist/director must learn how MCOs are governed and how they operate. In some communities, pathologists might have the opportunity to become leaders in the managed care environment by becoming leaders in PPOs or independent practice associations (IPAs). In such situations, the pathologist is involved in rate setting and able to direct the flow of laboratory services. Even if they are not in MCO leadership positions, pathologists can become indispensable to MCOs by virtue of their involvement in utilization reviews and in application of practice parameters, clinical pathways, and outcome and performance evaluations.

The types of managed care agreements or contracts that pathology practices need to understand include PPOs, participating physician agreements with IPAs, direct service agreements with HMOs, and capitation agreements with IPAs or HMOs. Insurance companies are responding to government health care reform activities by forming limited networks, which are merely another variation of managed care with restricted access and lower reimbursements. Before negotiating with any MCO, the items outlined in Table 10-4 should be determined. It should be clear that these are not simple negotiations. The MCOs and insurance companies have full-time physician negotiators

Table 10-4. What You Need to Know Before You Negotiate a Managed Care Contract

Who owns and/or controls the managed care organization (MCO)?
How many patients are covered? (Covered lives.)
What are the demographics of the patients: ages, occupations, etc?
What are the practice patterns of the participating clinicians? How do they use the laboratory?
What is the benefits package, ie, what constitutes patient eligibility, deductibles, and what are the copayments?
How does the MCO define: • Covered service: What tests will be paid or excluded? Are there carve-outs? • Medical necessity: How do test orders have to be justified? • Authorization: What tests have to be preauthorized by the MCO?
What are the quality and utilization review policies?
What are the insurance requirements? Is there mutual indemnification?
What is the term of the agreement, and what are the details surrounding termination? Is there an "evergreen" clause? Is there a covenant not to compete?
What are the payment terms? Are Medicare rates used? Is it a fee-for-service, is it a discounted fee-for-service, and are there withholds or risk pools? If reimbursed by capitation, how has the fee been determined? Is there an incentive or bonus plan?
Does my laboratory have exclusivity, or are other pathology services used?
Are there restrictions concerning membership in other MCOs?
What are the appeals, grievance, and dispute resolution policies?

whose main mission is to decrease costs by limiting testing and paying less for services.

Hospitals, academic medical centers, and independent laboratories also have experienced professionals that exclusively navigate these kinds of agreements. In some situations, all the physicians serving an academic medical center create an umbrella practice plan group for the purposes of such negotiations. Given their small size and influence, community hospital pathology practices are at a disadvantage in their dealings with MCOs, and it may seem expedient to allow hospitals to negotiate for these groups. However, hospitals have very different priorities than pathology practices. An alternative is to form a negotiating team with other hospital-based groups, radiologists, emergency medicine physicians, anesthesiologists, and hospitalists. Often, these groups' situations and priorities align with those of the pathology group. Such

Negotiating with managed care organizations regarding fees, allowable tests, and which tests require preauthorization can be terribly frustrating. There is always the specter of costs and benefits, and the MCO never thinks the costs justify the benefits. Several years ago, I was negotiating the surgical pathology fee schedule and insisted that a malignant breast biopsy required additional immunohistochemical and molecular analyses as part of the routine work up. Even after I told the MCO representative that the surgeons and oncologists demanded the studies and that it was the standard of practice in the community, he replied, "Well, Doc, you do those tests if you want to, but we're not going to pay for them!"

Table 10-5. The Advantages of Collaboration

Economies of scale, resulting in decreased costs.
Elimination of duplicative top and middle management (the most expensive employees), thus decreasing costs. For example, three separate laboratories may have three chief technologists and three chemistry supervisors, whereas a single merged laboratory has only one of each.
Centralization can increase productivity and efficiency and quality.
Alliances can provide core competencies and technologies that are not available to any single entity.
By being more efficient and having advanced technology, alliances can capture an increasing market share.
Improvement in the contracting position with hospitals and managed care organizations.
Alliances can share expertise in management, billing, and contracting.
Alliances can share templates for performance measurement and outcome analysis.
Alliances have access to capital for computers and new technologies that are essential for efficient and cost-effective operations.

Table 10-6. Assessing the Existing Entities in a Potential Collaboration

Organization and management
Facilities and equipment
Personnel policies, compensation packages, union agreements
Existing hospital and other contracts
Scope of current services
Staffing and productivity
Financial assessment, balance sheets, and profit and loss statements
Fee schedules, revenue analysis
Legal analysis

a negotiating group would have the resources to hire an experienced attorney or negotiator who can get the best deal possible for the hospital-based physicians.

The 2010 health care reform plan (Patient Protection and Affordable Care Act) authorizes accountable care organizations beginning in 2012. These organizations will be another type of integrated network designed to manage patients across a continuum of care that includes doctors' offices visits, outpatient care, inpatient hospital care, postacute care, and pathology and laboratory services. Presumably this will be a "bundling" of all services; pathologists will have to be prepared to function in this environment. It is likely that the accountable care organizations will be required to provide quality outcomes analysis for patient care analysis. Pathology and laboratory medicine, being the resident database of these outcomes, will have an important role to play in these activities.

Collaborative Strategies

Medicine's economic challenges are being met by a variety of collaborative strategies by hospitals, pathology practice groups, independent laboratories, and even universities. Such collaborations can take the form of mergers, acquisitions, outsourcing, or other less formal cooperative ventures. Collaboration or centralization may involve an entire laboratory or a single test. For example, in one European country, all cervical cytology is performed in just one or two laboratories. The advantages of collaboration by pathology practice groups are outlined in Table 10-5.

A successful collaboration requires a thorough and detailed planning process, which begins with a statement of intent that outlines the rationale for the collaboration and a roadmap for implementing and evaluating the collaboration. A steering committee with representatives from each collaborating entity should perform an initial market assessment and prepare a preliminary strategic plan that articulates the mission and major goals of the merger. The steering committee should also establish a preliminary schedule, assign duties, prepare letters of intent and confidentiality, and engage legal and tax consultants to aid the process.

The next step in collaboration is to assess the existing entities to determine congruence or identify differences that need to be addressed. The most important assessment is the assessment of the culture of the entities. Is one organization in a rapid growth phase with aggressive and confident marketing and innovative operations, while the other is old and staid, with a declining market share and aging, risk-averse management? The most common cause of merger failure is not legal or financial, but rather divergent cultures or organizational personalities. It is essential to carefully evaluate all aspects of potential collaborators, as listed in Table 10-6.

If the assessments indicate that a merger is possible, the steering committee should develop a feasibility analysis that includes an organizational model. This model proposes the governance and financial structure of the merger. An additional operations model that identifies the services that will be provided and the locations where such services will be performed should be developed. In addition, a cost-benefit analysis and ultimately a proforma and business plan that implement the organizational, operational, and financial models of the merger should be developed. Essential also is a time table or implementation schedule and an assignment of responsibilities. When all of the above have been reviewed, modified, and approved by the leadership of each entity, the collaboration can move forward.

Mergers and acquisitions in the independent laboratory environment include the process of buying, selling, and combining companies. These activities are generally solicited and welcomed, particularly as strategic decisions. However, they may also be unsolicited, or "hostile." Independent laboratories and pathology practices engage in mergers and acquisitions for similar reasons. Mergers and acquisitions can be multifactorial in nature. As a component of the analysis, there likely is a recognition that the merger will lead to greater market competitiveness, lower costs, and/or more effective service operations.

Mergers or acquisitions may involve one competitor buying out another. Or they can involve complementary business strategies that produce synergy when aligned. One entity may fill another's gap in the market, service menu, etc. The distinction between a merger and an acquisition can be somewhat arbitrary. A merger generally results when two or more companies agree to combine their assets and operations into one entity (a "merger of equals"). In contrast, an acquisition implies that one or more entities are subsumed into another as the result of a buyout of assets and operations (a "takeover"). The new entity, whether the result of a true merger or acquisition, may choose to do business under one of the existing names or under a new name or attempt to maintain the name and brand identity of one or more of the involved entities.

These activities can involve publicly traded companies, private companies, investment groups (venture or equity partners), or some combination thereof. The exchange of value generally involves cash, stock (if available), and/or debt financing. Besides ensuring a "good fit," the most important step in this process is to perform an accurate business valuation so a fair market price can be set for the transaction. For publicly traded companies, business valuation may involve a multiple of the firm's total market capitalization based on total stock value, or it may involve some multiple of current sales revenue (eg, 1.5 times annual sales) or a multiple of (eg, 15 times) the firm's annualized earnings below interest payments, taxes, and depreciation and amortization. Valuations are often performed by independent outside experts (eg, merger and acquisition advisors or companies).

Although not a collaborative strategy per se, a pathology practice, independent laboratory, or academic organization may decide for economic (eg, lower cost) or strategic operational reasons (eg, a lack in necessary expertise, quality, capacity) to contract with another party or organization to take over a business function. Most business functions or infrastructure support services—for example, human resources, personnel management, finance, billing, sales, legal services, information technology, marketing, transportation—can be outsourced. Certain companies advertise that they specialize in doing so and often refer to themselves as "management services organizations." In the extreme, entire operating units can be outsourced. For example, a hospital could outsource its clinical laboratory services to an outside entity such as a commercial laboratory company. Most practices and laboratories outsource special or unique laboratory tests. The outsourcing of other services requires similar evaluations and due diligence. (See Chapter 3, "Laboratory Operations.")

Marketing and Public Relations

Marketing and public relations, which are essential pursuits that require special education and experience, are generally outsourced by a pathology practice group or laboratory (see Appendix 10-2).

Personal Financial and Estate Planning

There are several important financial functions that pathologists must address on an individual basis. These include personal planning of finances, management of educational loan repayments, personal budgets, and estate planning. Every pathologist needs to plan appropriately for his or her family's future, as discussed below.

Financial Advisors

Financial advisors come in many shapes and sizes. They include lawyers, bankers, stockbrokers, insurance agents, accountants, and financial plan-

Table 10-7. Creating a Personal Budget

Income. Wages, bonuses, interest income, investment income
Taxes. Federal, state, and local income taxes; Social Security; Medicare
Home Expenses. Rent or mortgage, insurance, property taxes, repairs, maintenance, home owners' association dues, improvements, utilities
Food. Groceries, lunches, restaurants
Family Obligations. Child support, alimony, day care, babysitting
Health. Medical and dental insurance, unreimbursed expenses, drugs, copayments, fitness
Transportation. Car payments, gasoline, repairs and maintenance, license fees, auto insurance, tolls, bus, taxis
Debt Payments. Credit cards, student loans
Entertainment/Recreation. Cable television, movies, computer, hobbies, subscriptions, dues, vacation
Miscellaneous. Toiletries, household products, clothing, personal products
Gifts and Donations.
Investments and Savings. 401(k) or individual retirement accounts, stocks/bonds/mutual funds, college fund, savings

ners. Some financial advisors are registered or licensed; others are not. Generally, individuals or firms that get paid to give advice about investing in securities must register with the Securities and Exchange Commission and/or state securities agencies. Pathologists can request a specific financial adviser's registration form, known as the "Form ADV," to garner more information about the advisor, including whether he or she is properly registered with the appropriate agencies. Some financial advisors charge by the hour; others provide their services free of charge but are promoting specific financial or insurance products. There is no magic formula for finding the ideal financial adviser, but it is essential to find one. A simple way to find an advisor is to ask a successful friend or relative about who they use. Or, when joining a pathology group, one can ask about the financial advisors used by the senior members.

Loan Repayment

Newly-minted pathologists who are still facing enormous student loan debt may question why any financial planning is needed. Loan repayment is an essential component of any personal financial planning. Expeditious loan repayment re-

quires that all loan information is available, including the type of loan, its terms, any grace periods, and the time and payment cycles. This information should be obtained by undergoing exit counseling in the academic institution before entering practice. The terms of a loan may be negotiated or modified; for example, a standard loan may be modified to an extended loan or a graduated loan. Repayment may be altered to be income based, income contingent, or income sensitive. Some loans may be forgiven for public service, and the repayment of some loans may be postponed or deferred for a variety of reasons including military service, post-active duty, or economic hardship. As part of the financial plan, loan forbearance and loan consolidation should be actively and periodically reviewed.

Budget

The budget, an essential component of the personal financial plan, is necessary for managing personal financial affairs and provides a profile of income and expenses. Budget allocations should be reviewed regularly. A personal budget also provides important information for negotiating a salary or a professional fee. Creating a budget generally requires three steps: (1) identifying how money is being spent, (2) evaluating the current spending habits and setting goals that take into account long-term financial objectives, and (3) tracking spending to ensure that it stays within those guidelines. The broad categories that need to be identified in the budget are listed in Table 10-7.

Insurance

Property insurance on a home or renter's insurance on the contents of a rented home or apartment is essential. Automobile insurance is generally required. Health insurance and disability insurance may be provided by an employer or may have to be purchased individually or through a professional corporation.

Term life insurance provides coverage for a specified term of years in exchange for a specified premium. Term life insurance policies do not accumulate cash value. Term insurance is generally considered "pure" insurance in which the premium ensures protection in the event of death only. Permanent life insurance is life insurance that remains in force (in-line) until the policy matures (pays out). Permanent insurance builds a cash value that reduces the amount at risk to the insurance company and thus the insurance expense over time. The owner of the policy can access the cash value of the policy by withdrawing money, borrowing the cash, or surrendering the policy and receiving the surrender value. The four basic types of permanent insurance are whole life, universal life, limited pay, and endowment insurance. Other insurance products include accidental death, survivors' life, long-term care, and annuities insurance. Various types of life insurance are available and must be thoroughly investigated and integrated into one's tax and retirement planning. Personal liability or umbrella coverage is also a prudent purchase.

Consumer Credit and Debt

A number of organizations and individuals offer credit counseling and debt management advice to consumers. Before engaging such an advisor, one should make certain they are a member of the Association of Independent Consumer Credit Counseling Agencies and are accredited by the Better Business Bureau. A credit counseling or debt management program should evaluate one's financial situation, assist one in creating a budget to help manage finances, and work with creditors to obtain possible reductions. Categorical reductions to consider include finance charges, late fees, and/or over-limit charges; monthly payments; and debt pay-off time. A credit counseling service can also suggest methods of debt consolidation. A debt consolidation plan combines all unsecured debt, such as debt from credit cards, department store cards, credit lines, and unsecured personal loans (including student loans), into a single payment. Ideally, such a plan should retire the most expensive obligations early, resulting in lower interest and other finance charges and lower monthly payments.

Savings and Investments

The US Securities and Exchange Commission has an excellent website called Beginners' Guide to Investing (http://www.sec.gov/investor/pubs/begininvest.htm), which links to a number of online publications that can help consumers define their investment goals, make a financial plan, determine risk tolerance, choose investment products, and select a financial adviser. Defining investment goals simply means listing and prioritizing those things that one wishes to save for—for example, a new car, a home, college for children, or retirement. Each goal should take into account how long one has to meet each goal. A financial plan includes a net worth statement of assets and liabilities, a budget, and a debt manage-

ment program. Risk tolerance is a personal decision. It depends on how much money will be needed and when, as well as one's personal approach to financial risk-taking. If one saving for retirement has 35 years before he or she retires, one may want to consider riskier investment products. If one chooses to invest in less risky products only, one's money will grow more slowly. On the other hand, if one is saving for a short-term (5 years or less) goal, it is wiser to choose less risky products because a loss is less likely with less risky products for short-term scenarios.

There are innumerable types of investment products including stocks, bonds, mutual funds, exchange traded funds, and real estate. The selection of the best investment vehicle(s) requires the knowledge of the individual's financial plan and the advice of an expert and specialist. Once an advisor and products have been selected, one has an ongoing obligation to assess the progress of one's investments by reviewing monthly statements, evaluating performance in relation to projections, and reviewing the value of the investments in current dollars. Also, every investor should be aware of any fees paid for financial services and the criteria necessary to sell an investment.

Retirement and Estate Planning

The American Institute of Certified Public Accountants has an excellent website, 360 Degrees of Financial Literacy (http://www.360financialliteracy.org/), which has tools and tutorials to assist in personal financial management. Retirement planning is the culmination of the personal financial plan and the estate plan, and provides for the conservation and transfer of one's wealth. These are highly specialized and technical endeavors that require the special expertise of several financial planning professionals including accountants, attorneys, and insurance agents.

The obvious first step in this planning process is to articulate the objectives, ie, to provide for the best use of the assets during one's lifetime and anticipate and provide for lifetime needs such as a child's education, retirement, income replacement in the event of disability, and asset management in the event of incapacity. The plan should also address the succession or transfer of assets upon death to ensure that the estate that passes to the decedent's heirs is maximized and distributed according to the wishes of the decedent and the needs of the family.

A critical step in estate planning is selecting people who will implement the plan, namely, the executor, trustee, and possibly guardian and conservator. The next step in the planning process is to determine assets, liabilities, insurance, retirement plans, and other instruments to make certain that the chosen objectives for your estate planning can be met. The plan is actualized in the form of a number of documents including trusts, wills, powers of attorney, and advanced directives. There are several different types of trusts, including family trusts, by-pass (or generation-skipping) trusts, "Q-tip trusts," and trusts for charitable giving, all of which have significant tax implications and need to be drafted for an individual's specific situation. Finally, an estate plan, once drawn, cannot be placed in a vault; it must be re-evaluated periodically, as financial situations and tax laws inevitably change.

Challenge Questions

The RVU includes a calculation for:
A. Practice expense
B. Professional liability insurance
C. Physician work
D. A and C
E. A, B, and C
Answer: E; see page 178.

A defined contribution plan for retirement:
A. Is calculated from salary, age, and length of work
B. Can be a 401(k) plan
C. Is paid from an annuity
D. Requires an employer to match employee contributions
E. None of the above
Answer: B; see page 183.

What are the essential elements of a hospital pathology contract?
Answer: See pages 185 to 187 and Table 10-3.

References

1. Alexander CB, McDonald JM. Cost-based (Part A) pathology physician services: origin, current spectrum, and future. *Clin Lab Med.* 1999;19(4):783-796.

2. Alexander CB. Pathology graduate medical education (overview 1926 - 2005). *Hum Pathol.* 2006;37:923-928.

3. *Trends in Pathologist Workforce. Results from the 2007 Practice Characteristics Survey.* Northfield, IL: College of American Pathologists; 2008. Available at: http://www.cap.org/apps/docs/advocacy/workforce_survey_07.pdf. Accessed Nov 12, 2010.

4.. Kusserow RP. OIG Management Advisory Report OEI 09-89-0331: Financial Arrangements between Hospitals and Hospital-Based Physicians. Washington, DC: US Department of Health and Human Services, Office of Inspector General. Jan 31, 1992. Available at: http://oig.hhs.gov/oei/reports/oei-09-89-00330.pdf. Accessed Nov 17, 2010.

5. Rules and Regulations. Updates to the Reasonable Compensation Equivalent (RCE) Limits, Section 415.70. *Fed Reg.* Aug 1, 2003;68(148):45458-45459. Available at: http://209.83.188.231/HSM/uploaded Files/HealthLaw_Library/HealthLawLibraryContent/Reasonable%20Compensation%20Limits.pdf. Accessed Nov 17, 2010.

6. Cooper RS, Mulligan JT. *A Guide to Successful Mergers and Joint Ventures for Pathology Groups and Laboratories.* [Monograph.] Cleveland, OH: McDonald, Hopkins, Burke & Haber Co LPA; 1996.

7. Drucker PF. *The Five Most Important Questions You Will Ever Ask About Your Organization.* San Francisco, CA: Jossey-Bass; 2008.

8. Drucker PF. *The Essential Drucker.* New York, NY: Harper Collins; 2001.

9. Practice Management Committee. *Professional Relations Manual.* 12th ed. Northfield, IL: College of American Pathologists; 2003.

10. Valenstein P. Strategic planning. In: Garcia LS, ed. *Clinical Laboratory Management.* Washington, DC: ASM Press; 2004:499-512.

11. Lepoff RB. Financial management: setting the stage. In: Garcia LS, ed. *Clinical Laboratory Management*. Washington, DC: ASM Press; 2004:493-498.

12. Winn WC Jr. Financial decision making: the endgame of the planning and analytical process. In: Garcia LS, ed. *Clinical Laboratory Management*. Washington, DC: ASM Press; 2004:551-554.

13. Tolzmann GC, Vincent RJ. Costs, budgeting, and financial decision making. In: Garcia LS, ed. *Clinical Laboratory Management*. Washington, DC: ASM Press; 2004:525-550.

14. Baselski VS, Weissfeld AS, Sorrell F. Approaches to billing laboratory services. In: Garcia LS, ed. *Clinical Laboratory Management*. Washington, DC: ASM Press; 2004:567-573.

15. Baselski VS, Weissfeld AS, Sorrell F. Charges and fees for laboratory services. In: Garcia LS, ed. *Clinical Laboratory Management*. Washington, DC: ASM Press; 2004:574-580.

16. Buck CJ, ed. *2010 ICD-9-CM for Physicians*. Standard ed. Vol 1, 2, 3. Maryland Heights, MO: Saunders/Elsevier; 2010.

17. *Principles of CPT Coding*. 4th ed. Chicago, IL: American Medical Association; 2005.

18. Abraham M, Beebe M, Dalton JA, et al. Pathology and laboratory guidelines. In: *CPT 2010 (Current Procedural Terminology)*. Professional ed. Chicago, IL: American Medical Association; 2010:385-428.

19. Weiss RL. Coding, coverage and compensation of pathology and laboratory medicine services. *Clin Lab Med*. 2007; 27(4):875-892.

20. Forensic Pathology Committee. *The Pathologist in Court*. Northfield, IL: College of American Pathologists; 2003.

21. Davis GG. *Pathology and Law*. New York, NY: Springer-Verlag; 2004.

22. Ahlin PA, Weiss RL. Risk management and compliance in pathology and laboratory medicine. *Clin Lab Med*. 2007:27(4)859-874.

23. Anderson V. Hospital laboratory outreach: benefits and planning. *Clin Lab Med*. 2007;27(4):791-806.

Appendix 10-1.
What to Expect from a Billing Service

Choosing and monitoring a billing service for the professional practice is the responsibility of the group's financial officer, but the success or failure of the billing service impacts all members of the group. The following are some issues to keep in mind:

- Experience in pathology billing
- Experience interfacing to your specific hospital information system and laboratory information system
- Experience in electronic insurance claims processing
- Experience in managed care contract management, eg, discounts, capitation
- Experience in fee schedule and contract analysis
- Customer relations issues: address on bills, "800" phone line, patient sensitive telephone response, email address for billing inquiries
- Patient payment options: check, credit card, time payment
- Delinquent accounts follow-up; collection service
- Banking services including lock box
- Reporting services
  - Charges and receipts by financial class (cash flow)
  - Accounts receivable by financial class
  - Accounts receivable aging
  - Account analysis by ordering physician, by CPT, by ICD, by payor (all critical for utilization review)
- Marketing services
- Other services, eg, CMS incentive payments via Physician Quality Reporting Initiative (PQRI)
- Cost of billing service
  - Percentage of billings or collections?
  - Same percentage for anatomic pathology and clinical pathology?
  - Extra charges for postage, delinquency letters, collection attempts, etc
- Name of single contact person or liaison to interface with pathology group

Appendix 10-2.
Marketing and Public Relations

Marketing and public relations may be accomplished independently by the pathology practice group or in concert with the hospital. Although everyone participates in marketing and public relations to a certain extent every day, a formal public relations program requires professional consultation. The following suggestions can assist in communicating with marketing and public relations professionals.

Marketing

- Definition: The execution of the total business activity that directs the flow of goods and/or services from producer to consumer. It is not only sales, but something all successful businesses and individuals do every day.
- Essence of Marketing
  - Who are our customers? Defining the market.
  - What do they deem important? Defining consumer needs and wants.
  - What is our business? Defining and positioning the product or service.
  - The marketing plan.
  - Advertising and sales.
  - Pricing.
  - Service.
- Market Research and Analysis
  - Answer questions: Who are our customers and what do they deem important?
  - Formal surveys of customers and potential customers, including satisfactions surveys and questionnaires for all customers such as physicians, nurses, patients, and managed care organizations (MCOs).
  - Informal surveys from rounds, physicians' dining room: Ask "customers" what they like or don't like about your services or the services of your competitors.
  - Analyze the competition: What do they have that we don't?
  - Evaluate market share, eg, how many of the obstetrician-gynecologists in your hospital send their patients' Pap smears to your laboratory?
  - Evaluate consumer motivation and buying behavior, eg, price, loyalty to institution.

- Product Planning
  - Answer question: "What is our product?" on the basis of the market analysis.
  - Drives research and development to modify and/or develop new products or services, eg, new tests, new forms, fax reporting, standing orders for critical pathways (practice parameters).
- Strategic Planning
  - Implement the products/services from planning phase.
  - Integrate all parties into the overall laboratory strategic plan.
  - Explain marketing thrust to employees.
- Advertising and Sales
  - Role of pathologist: Sell your competence.
  - Sales representatives: Use medical technologists.
  - Brochures and price lists: Professionally produced.
  - What are you selling? Expertise? Service? Price?
  - Evaluate success of advertising.
- Pricing Policy
  - Who is responsible? Pathology group or hospital?
  - Who is billing?
  - Varying fee schedules, custom panels.
  - Discounts: For volume, early payment, survival; must know baseline and incremental costs before thinking about discounts.
  - Special deals: Per diem, capitation, Medicare.
  - Cost-based pricing vs price-based costing.
- Service
  - Service representative same as sales representative.
  - Courier and receptionist training and motivation.
  - Supplies, lock box.
  - Reporting system.
  - Complaint management: Need a well-defined system that ensures prompt replies and solutions; no delegation; remember the customer is always right, and always say "Thank you."
  - New services especially for managed care: Utilization review and management and performance measurement systems.
- Evaluation of Marketing Strategy
  - Sales: Revenue.
  - Satisfaction.

Public Relations

- Everyone should be doing public relations (PR) all the time.
- Definition: PR is "Doing good and getting credit for it."
  - Advertising is under your control but expensive.
  - Publicity is free but controlled by the media.
  - The public views publicity as more credible and honest than advertising.
- Elements of a PR Program
  - Identify the "publics" you wish to influence.
  - Who will make the buying decisions? Doctor, office staff, or MCO? Who are your "targets"?
  - Articulate your organizational goals.
  - Decide on the public image that you wish to project.
- Who are the "Publics" of a PR Program?
  - Internal: The employees. Goal is to establish and maintain esprit de corps.
  - External: Customers, shareholders, administrators, vendors, payers, regulatory and government agencies. Goal is to project a great image, eg, the superior education and competence of your staff.
- PR Strategies
  - Written materials.
    - Brochures, pamphlets, flyers: All should be professionally produced unless you have a really skilled desktop publisher in your laboratory.
    - Newsletter: Requires editor and trained staff.
    - Use the College of American Pathologists (CAP)-produced newsletter (NewsPath).
    - Monthly column in professional staff bulletin(s).
    - Annual report (see Chapter 2, Appendix 2-6).
    - Written materials must be readable, interesting, and professional, and have aesthetic appeal.
    - Audio-visual materials for in-house television networks or local TV stations (available from the CAP).
  - Corporate identity materials.
    - Should be designed so that when anyone thinks of "laboratory," they think of *you*.
    - Should be attractive, memorable, distinctive, and consistent.
    - Examples: Logo, stationery, brochures, signs, forms, cards, uniforms for couriers.
  - News releases.
    - Should be newsworthy. New diagnostic test or new therapeutic triumph.
    - Newspapers and TV stations receive 200 to 400 per day; 90% are discarded without being read.
    - Selection based on interest of editor, significance of information to readers/listeners, and personal relationship with editor.
    - Total length 100 to 300 words.
    - First sentence must tell entire story with drama.
    - Background data on separate "fact sheet."
  - Public service announcements.
    - Must provide public service.
    - Limited to 15 seconds.
    - Usually event-related: One-time use only.
  - Events.
    - Lab Week open house.
    - Health fairs.
    - Public displays in shopping centers.
    - Piggyback onto hospital events.
  - Public speaking/speakers bureau.
    - Obtain training (CAP or AMA).
    - Within hospital or local medical society.
    - To community: Rotary, Elks.
  - Telephone information service ("hotline").

CHAPTER 11

The Pathology Position

Richard E. Horowitz, MD
Michael O. Idowu, MD, MPH
Gene P. Siegal, MD, PhD

Contents

Where Do Pathologists Work?

Pathologists work in a variety of settings: 75% of pathologists work primarily in community practice (54% in pathology group practices, 10% as hospital employees, 5% as solo practitioners, and 6% as employees of multi-specialty groups such as Kaiser-Permanente), 11% work in academic or university practice, 9% work in independent or commercial laboratories, and 5% work in other venues as medical examiners or in industry or government.[1] More than half of community pathology practice groups have at least 10 pathologists.

In community hospital pathology practices, pathologists are usually generalists who dedicate the majority of their time (65%) to anatomic pathology, 15% of their time to supervising and managing the clinical laboratory, 6% of their time in clinical pathology consultation, and the remainder of their time in teaching, research, and other activities.[2] In larger pathology practices—particularly those covering several hospitals—or in larger multi-specialty groups, pathologists often must subspecialize; for example, a pathologist who supervises the blood bank, attends transfusion committee meetings, and performs difficult cross-matches and transfusion reactions in all the group's hospitals might need to have additional certification in transfusion medicine. Similarly, if the testing volume is sufficient, a pathologist may perform cytopathology or hematopathology only or in addition to performing routine surgical specimen tests, frozen sections, and autopsies. In some practices, each pathologist is assigned a domain in the clinical laboratory and an area of special interest in surgical pathology. Experienced pathologists (eg, those who have spent several years in academia) entering such a practice may be offered the opportunity to buy into the practice and become a partner.

In a university-based teaching hospital or academic medical center, pathologists are usually employees or members of an academic practice group. In this setting, pathologists are not only expected to provide services related to patient care work but also participate in translational or clinical research and teach residents, medical students, and occasionally allied medical sciences students. Therefore, academic medical centers expect that prospective academic pathologists are interested in scholarly activities, teaching, and service work, since these are the basic requirements for retention and promotion. Recently, some academic institutions, finding their faculty unable to compete with full-time experimentalists, have created non–tenure-track clinical-care and/or education-based positions that place more emphasis on teaching and service work and less emphasis on extramurally funded research work or publications.

The impetus for choosing an academic pathology career varies, but it often includes a strong desire to create new knowledge, educate, and develop an international reputation in a particular area or field. The influence of a mentor, among others, should not be underestimated. If pathologists are interested in working in an academic medical practice, they should not only obtain sound residency and fellowship training (subspecialty training is virtually a given in many academic institutions), but also show that they are driven by scholarly pursuits (eg, by giving poster or platform presentations at national meetings, publishing their research in peer-reviewed journals, and undertaking teaching activities during their training).

Possible disadvantages of an academic pathology career may include lower income, academic politics, lack of autonomy, and less family and leisure time. Some of the disadvantages of academic practice may be perceived rather than real, as they may be encountered in other practice settings. Many rewards are associated with academic medical practice, including recognized expertise in a specific subspecialty; the "luxury of specialization"; intellectual stimulation; challenges from trainees, colleagues, and patients; the opportunity for regional, national, or international recognition; meeting presentations; the satisfaction of publishing; the satisfaction of helping junior colleagues reach their goals; and the opportunity to pass along knowledge to future generations of pathologists. These advantages may more than compensate for the perceived disadvantages of working in academic practice.

Independent commercial or reference laboratories like LabCorp, Ameripath, or Quest are large laboratories that employ pathologists. Subspecialty training may or may not be needed, depending on the needs or composition of the laboratory. Similarly, pharmaceutical, diagnostic, and biomedical research industries may require pathologists to serve as practitioners or consult-

> **Some fortunate young pathologists** face a dilemma with multiple job offers, some from a medical school and others from a community hospital. The community hospital practice will generally pay better, but the academic center carries more prestige. What to do? Sadao Otani, MD, gave the following advice: "Take the academic position first. You can always go from the university to private practice, but going from private practice to the university is almost impossible."

ants. A research background or related training is an asset in these settings.

In government pathology laboratories or establishments (local or federal government laboratories, Veterans Affairs hospitals, etc), pathologists are usually primarily responsible for clinical activities. There are also opportunities to work at the medical examiner's office as a forensic pathologist, which would require subspecialty training in forensic pathology. Pathologists may also work in health and regulatory agencies such as the Food and Drug Administration or a state department of health. In such settings, pathologists may have administrative, research, or regulatory responsibilities, rather than diagnostic responsibilities.

Some pathologists may work in a nonpathology specialty practice in which they are employed by another medical or surgical specialty; for example, a urology or gastroenterology specialty group may employ a pathologist to look at all their prostate or endoscopic biopsies. As discussed in Chapter 8, "Quality Assurance in Anatomic Pathology," this arrangement, which often corresponds to the arrangement in "pod" laboratories, is highly controversial and subject to a rapidly changing legal scene. Some believe such arrangements are unethical because those who are not pathologists (in this case, urologists or gastroenterologists) may benefit or profit from their referrals to the pathology services in which they have a business interest, which is in violation of the Stark law. This kind of arrangement potentially raises the issues of kickback, self-referral, and billing irregularities. Therefore, it is prudent to exercise caution when entering into these types of arrangements and probably best to stay clear of them altogether.

Not unexpectedly, different practice situations have different challenges. One should consider the following questions before making an employment decision: Do you see yourself as a generalist or a subspecialist? Do you enjoy teaching and interacting with trainees? Do you want to participate in research activities? Do you want to publish (articles, book chapters, books, etc)? How hard do you want to work; or, more specifically, how much time do you want to commit to work versus your other interests? Regardless of the position you select or the environment in which you choose to work, you should expect to work hard. However, you should realize that you may need to work a lot harder in some settings than in others.

You should also ask, "Which is more important to me, financial security or job security?" Currently, it appears that private pathology practices offer more monetary compensation than academic or other non-private practices. Although the issue of job security is somewhat nebulous in the current economic climate, government establishments and large, financially stable institutions may offer more job security than a small private pathology group. Answering the above questions may help pathologists decide whether they want an academic versus nonacademic position, diagnostic versus research responsibilities, or private versus nonprivate pathology position, and so on. These questions should be seriously considered; the more flexible you are, the more opportunities you will have.

What Will Be Expected?

The practice of pathology is being re-shaped by rapidly advancing molecular, genetic, and digital technologies.[3-5] The anatomic pathologist no longer simply recognizes an image and gives it a name, but uses advanced technologies to make diagnostic, therapeutic, and prognostic determinations. The clinical pathologist no longer merely generates data, but uses advanced technologies to analyze data and transform them into clinically relevant information for patient care.

This rapidly changing health care environment mandates that pathology residents' education and training encompass a broad spectrum of skills and knowledge. For new pathology graduates, the expected minimum competencies in anatomic pathology include accurate autopsy, surgical, and cytopathology diagnoses; rapid and accurate intraoperative consultation; accurate and thorough gross dissection, with judicial and reasonable use of special stains and studies; and the ability to interact effectively with surgeons, oncologists, and other physicians. It is essential that pathologists be able to work independently, yet know when to seek help.

Pathologists who are new to a practice generally have smaller workloads and slower turnaround times than experienced pathologists; within 1 year, however, new pathologists should be working at a level comparable to that of the more senior members of the group. Clinical pathologists are expected to have sufficient knowledge of clinical medicine, experience, and perspective, which enables them to integrate laboratory data with clinical information, handle clinical laboratory consultations, provide test interpretation, and advise clinicians about test strategies. It is also expected that pathologists have some expertise in laboratory and quality management, including familiarity with inspection, accreditation, and regulatory compliance strategies, and are able to supervise a section of the laboratory.

A critical expectation, particularly in the community hospital setting, is that pathologists have knowledge of molecular and genetic applications in pathology. Newly minted pathologists must understand and be able to convey the principles and methodologies of all new techniques, including immunohistochemistry, flow cytometry, nucleic acid amplification testing (ie, polymerase chain reaction), microarray testing, laser capture microdissection, cytogenetics, pharmacogenetics, microRNA analysis, various nucleic acid sequencing technologies, and fluorescence, chromogenic, or other in situ hybridization strategies. Because most community practices send these tests to a reference or university laboratory, new pathologists do not necessarily need to be able to perform these tests, but they must know which tests are available, what their indications are, and how their results should be interpreted.

New pathologists should also have good written and verbal communication skills, good interpersonal skills, and good leadership and teaching skills. Knowledge of committee meeting methods is also important (see Appendix 2-3). One recent survey found that new pathologists tend to be deficient in communication and interpersonal skills, which appear to be the principal attributes that determine success in the practice of pathology.[6]

Where to Find a Job

In difficult economic times, with a shrinking job market and fewer available positions, finding one's "dream job" may seem daunting. Pathologists must incorporate strategy and planning to successfully navigate the job market. It is worth re-emphasizing that the best time for pathologists to start planning their strategy is early in their residency programs, not when they are about to finish their fellowships. Part of this strategy should include getting involved in organized medicine, at the very least as a junior or resident member of one or more medical specialty societies, such as the College of American Pathologists (CAP), the American Society for Clinical Pathology (ASCP), the United States and Canadian Academy of Pathology (USCAP), the American Society for Investigative Pathology, the American Medical Association, or local or state medical associations. Besides specifically helping your specialty and the practice of medicine in general, becoming involved in organized medicine early in your career is an excellent way to network with potential employers.

There are several ways to discover employment opportunities. Even in this electronic age, "word of mouth," or networking, still plays a major role in the job search. Many employers indicated that they use this method. When a community pathology group needs a new associate, the most common initial step is to call the residency program director or the pathology department chair of the local medical school and ask if any upcoming graduates meet the group's current needs or requirements. Thus, just getting by with average evaluations during your training may not serve your best interests. To determine whether you would be an attractive candidate for a pathology group position, you should ask yourself, "Would my department or residency program recruit me if they had an opening?"

Pathology positions are advertised in virtually all the major pathology journals. This is often a legal requirement for many academic institutions and hospitals; for a subset of these employers, posting such positions helps them meet their institutional affirmative action plan or the requirements of the Equal Employment Opportunity Commission. A number of professional organizations also advertise pathologist positions on their websites. These include but are not limited to the CAP (www.healthecareers.com/cap), the ASCP (www.ascp.org/careercenter), Pathology Outlines (www.pathologyoutlines.com/jobs.html), and USCAP (www.nature.com/naturejobs/science/partners/modpathol). In addition, by registering with the CAP or the ASCP on their websites, you can choose to receive email notifications when new positions become available. The role of social networking sites is yet to be determined.

Additional job-search tools include recruiters and search firms; professional coaching services that help individuals develop their resumes or curricula vitae (CV) and individualize their job search are also available. (Institutions usually pay recruiters, so one should be wary of recruiters who ask for a fee.) Applicants can also meet potential employers at annual pathology meetings, where employers often post openings and occasionally interview candidates.

How to Evaluate the Position

After years of medical training, new pathologists may be tempted to accept any job offer. However, job satisfaction, job performance, and, ultimately, happiness are all related to how comfortable a person is with his or her surroundings. Richard J. Hausner, MD, a leader in both the CAP and the American Pathology Foundation and a noted community pathologist from Houston, has clearly and emphatically articulated that to achieve overall professional and personal fulfillment, a pathologist must thoroughly evaluate the town in which the position is located, the medical community, and the pathology group before accepting an offer of employment.[7]

Evaluating the Town

Since the town or city in which the position is located will likely also be your new home, you should consider the following:

- **The geography and climate.** You should determine whether the location's climate meets your lifestyle needs. For example, pathologists who prefer warm weather and mild winters may not want to seriously consider a job in the Midwest. Another factor to consider is whether the location is near to important family members.

- **The economy, cost of living, taxes, and unemployment rate.** The location's cost of living may help put monetary compensation in perspective. Usually, higher salaries are offered in regions with higher costs of living. For example, it costs approximately three times as much money to live in La Jolla, California, as it does to live in Birmingham, Alabama. But you should consider: Is the starting salary and fringe package of the position offered in La Jolla three times that of the position offered in Birmingham, or are there other factors that compensate for the difference? Taxes also vary from one city to another; in some cities, one may pay city taxes in addition to federal and state income taxes, and property taxes may be higher in some localities than in others. In addition, a city's unemployment rate may affect the mood of the city and could be a surrogate marker for the city's crime rate and growth potential.

- **The school system.** Parents of school-age children should evaluate the cost and quality of the city's public and private schools. This process may include visiting prospective school systems. You might discuss educational opportunities with pathologists who have children enrolled in the schools.

- **The recreational and cultural environments.** Your recreational or cultural interests should be considered when evaluating the location. Do you enjoy outdoor activities such as mountain climbing, hunting, and surfing? Large metropolitan areas have lots of cultural diversity but may not satisfy your recreational interests. Do you enjoy going to theaters, symphonies, and live shows? Then a small town with a lot of outdoor activities may not satisfy your interests.

- **The residential areas: costs, convenience, commuting.** How much living space is necessary? How much will a house or an apartment cost? If a person desires a large house with ample space, working in a big city like New York may not be ideal unless he or she is willing to commute from the suburbs. Commuting time should be considered, particularly if the position requires that a person be on-call for frozen sections at night and on weekends. Of course, you should also factor in future plans, such as having a family and raising children.

- **The needs of your spouse or partner.** A pathologist who has a spouse or partner must choose an environment that meets their needs also. What do they like to do? Will the town or city satisfy their interests? Are they planning to work, and, if so, how easy will it be to find employment? Is it a two-physician or two-pathologist search? It goes without saying, then, that the views of your spouse or partner are critical and must be considered.

Evaluating the Hospital and Medical Community

Because job satisfaction is determined in part by the job's physical and medical environment, it is essential to evaluate the following:

- **The institution's mission.** What is the vision of the institution? What is the history of the institution? Is the institution modern and well maintained?

- **The size and financial health of the hospital.** Is the hospital competently managed? The size of the hospital may be an indirect measure of a pathologist's workload. The financial health of

the institution may determine how long you will remain employed. Pathologists should also consider the size and number of other hospitals in the region and/or the size and number of hospitals affiliated with their primary practice group.

- **The number and types of specialists and procedures.** This profile may indicate the variety and complexity of the cases the pathologist encounters.

- **Ownership, medical staff governance, and pathologists' roles.** How are pathologists regarded? Do they take part in the administration of the institution? The answers may indicate how seriously pathologists' opinions are regarded. An institution in which pathologists actively participate in institutional committees and administration is likely to seriously consider pathologists' opinions.

- **The size and number of other hospitals and competitors.** What is the composition of the medical community? Are there competing medical or surgical specialty groups? Are there any other pathology groups in the area? Have there been any recent mergers? All these factors may determine the market share of the patient population. Major competition between pathology groups or hospitals, especially in an area with a limited number of patients, may increase pressure to generate revenues.

- **Relationship of the hospital and the medical staff to the medical school.** This is especially important in academic medical centers, where pathologists may have dual appointments, with clinical activities in the hospital and research and/or educational activities in the medical school.

Evaluating the Pathology Group

Pathologists should evaluate the viability of the pathology group and consider whether they will fit into the culture of the group. In some practices, pathologists spend more of their waking hours with their colleagues than with their families. Before you seriously consider joining a group practice, you should research the following:

- **The group's relationship with the hospital.** How long has the group been with the hospital? How many hospitals are affiliated with the group? Does the group have a contract with the hospital? What type of business arrangement or contract does the group have with the hospital? What are the terms of the contract? If the group covers more than one hospital, how much traveling is involved?

- **The group's organization.** How is the group organized? Will you be replacing an associate, or will you be an additional associate of the group? The group's hiring of an additional associate may be an indication of the group's growth or expansion. If you are replacing an associate, you need to consult the associate that you are replacing before or shortly after the interview. Inquiring about the group's employment history is prudent; rapid turnover may be a sign of problems.

- **The group's track record with associates.** What is an associate's potential for growth, advancement, and self-actualization? You may need to talk to current and past associates for an honest appraisal.

- **The group's reputation.** You should speak with nonpathology physicians and staff to acquire valuable information regarding the group's reputation.

- **The accreditation of the hospital and/or laboratory.** Are there any current accreditation issues, or have there been accreditation issues in the past? Because they may affect the viability of the laboratory, problems with accreditation may determine how long you will be with the group. You may politely request to review the last laboratory accreditation inspection review.

Some of the senior faculty in your training program, either through networking or from previous trainees now in practice, may be able to provide insight into some pathology group practices in the region or even different parts of the country. Evaluating a pathology group requires a great deal of effort. In the final analysis, your long-term satisfaction and avoidance of a potentially painful experience depend on thorough evaluations. However, even with careful planning and evaluation, you may find your planned long-term relationship with a pathology group to be short-lived. You should take this into consideration and plan accordingly.

Curriculum Vitae with Cover Letter

The first salvo in the "job campaign" is to prepare a curriculum vitae (CV) and an accompanying cover letter (appendices 11-1 and 11-2). A CV should provide potential employers with a summary of your academic accomplishments. Employers often use this document to determine whether an applicant should be considered for a position and subsequently invited for an interview. The CV should be updated at least twice a year and more frequently if necessary. Trainees' CVs should reflect their abstract or poster presentations at national, local, and regional meetings; presentations at tumor boards and grand rounds; committee memberships; and publications. Resume- or CV-writing software can be used to compose an effective CV. It is strongly recommended that you have an experienced faculty member or mentor review the CV and provide suggestions for improvement. The presentation of your CV is as important as its content, so the CV should be informative, attractive, and detailed. Because many employers do not have or take the time to read every detail of the CV, important achievements should be easily identifiable.

It is often tempting to embellish your accomplishments on a CV. This should not be done. Professionalism is key; you should highlight your achievements, but you should not state an untruth. Invariably, such claims will catch up with a person, and the product of years of hard work and sacrifice could be lost in a heartbeat. For example, a faculty member who claimed on his CV to be a Rhodes Scholar was not a Rhodes Scholar at all; apparently, he was nominated for but never awarded the prestigious award. Now, in addition to likely losing his academic position, the faculty member is accused of defrauding the federal government and may face lawsuits, imprisonment, and other civil and criminal penalties.

You should include a focused and accurate cover letter with your CV (Appendix 11-2). The cover letter should be adapted to the job for which you are applying. A single cover letter does not fit all job opportunities. A cover letter for a specific position should emphasize what you find interesting about the position, why you believe you are qualified for the job, and how you can benefit the employer if given the position. The cover letter must be short and limited to one page; otherwise, its impact on the employer is diminished. Both the CV and cover letter should be proofread carefully; you should also ask a knowledgeable friend or faculty member to review them. Make sure that the correct address appears on the cover letter and that the addressee's name is spelled correctly; otherwise, the employer may infer that the applicant is sloppy and does not pay attention to detail.

Personal references may be included with the cover letter and CV. You need not include the most senior faculty member in your program as a reference, but it is probably a good idea to include your program director as a reference. According to an informal survey in an academic medical center, a positive recommendation from a program director is very important, especially for an applicant fresh out of residency or fellowship training. You should also know how many letters of recommendation are requested by the prospective employer. (Usually, two or three letters are requested.) You should not supply more letters than requested and should not supply any letters unless asked to do so.

A letter that may determine whether a person secures a job is too important to casually request in a hallway conversation. Your program director can provide insight into how various faculty members evaluate their trainees. Therefore, you should make an appointment with your program director to discuss the recommendation request and determine who has first-hand knowledge of your strengths, is sympathetic to your plight, and will write an excellent and informative letter. You should allow the letter writer enough time (usually 3 to 4 weeks) to write a thorough and thoughtful letter; gentle, occasional reminders may be necessary. It is probably not in your best interest to ask for a letter of recommendation that is needed immediately; the letter writer may omit important information. It is courteous to send short thank-you cards or letters to those who write letters of recommendation and to update them on the progress of the job search.

Many potential employers contact someone they know at an applicant's institution or program, even if that person is not listed as a reference, to ask specific questions about the applicant. Thus, you should always strive to maintain cordial and collegial relations, even in the face of conflicting personalities.

The Job Interview: How to Prepare

Obtaining an interview is a very positive step toward securing a job because one has been selected as a candidate from a pool of all potential applicants. It is more than likely that more than one "potential hire" has been invited for an interview. A job candidate's performance at the interview could make or break his or her prospects for employment with the company. When invited for a job interview, a candidate should dress neatly and conservatively and arrive on time. The job candidate's goal in the interview is to impress upon the potential employer that he or she is the right person for the position; the interview is the time to exude confidence without coming across as arrogant. Therefore, a job candidate should relax, act naturally, and pay attention to his or her body language.

The format of the interview may vary. Most interviews are relaxed exchanges of information and are typically pleasant. Even in such "relaxed" interviews, you should think about your answers to the interviewer's questions (Appendix 11-3). In some cases, especially in academic institutions, the candidate is expected to make a presentation to the faculty. Such a presentation may reveal much about a job candidate's communication skills and management of stress. Therefore, it is important that the applicant carefully prepare and rehearse the presentation. Having an experienced faculty member review and criticize "the talk" may be crucial to giving a successful presentation at the interview.

You should anticipate that questions to which you do not know the answers will be asked during and/or after the presentation. If this occurs, you should try to retain your composure and answer honestly that you do not know the answer. You are not expected to have all the answers, and some questions may be quite esoteric. In some cases, the interviewer may choose to perform a "stress interview" to see how the applicant behaves under stress or pressure. Constant interruptions during the formal presentation is one commonly used technique to determine whether the candidate has grace under pressure as well as the flexibility and adaptability to finish the presentation on time and without losing his or her mental place. In other cases, to determine the candidate's diagnostic skills and medical knowledge and weed out "weak" applicants, interviewers may show job candidates slides or other clinical materials during a "test interview," or there may be some discussion about relevant clinical topics. In a common (and less "in-your-face") approach, the interviewer may say, "We're having some debate among ourselves about several cases in Drs X and Y's area of expertise, and I know you trained with Drs X and Y. I'd like to show these cases to you and get your opinion." This is perhaps unfair on many levels. For example, you cannot volunteer that you actually did not spend very much time with Drs X and Y, especially after Drs X and Y wrote letters of recommendation to this very interviewer! You cannot control the interviewer's techniques, but you should not panic; instead, you should be aware of, and prepare for, the possibilities.

A job candidate should always prepare for an interview. One should research the position carefully (see "How to Evaluate the Job" in this chapter), anticipate possible questions, and be prepared to provide good answers to such questions (Appendix 11-3). Similarly, the candidate should set aside some time to formulate his or her own questions for the interview. The job candidate should also understand the responsibilities of the position. Are there administrative duties? What about call schedules—does everyone share frozen sections, autopsies, and "call" equally? Does the position entail supervising technical staff? What opportunities will one have for advancement or partnership? One should also ask about the group's organization and governance: Who makes the clinical, business, and financial decisions? Does the group have direct billing? How is the group reimbursed for Part A services? Are there any managed care contracts? Is there a separate fee or salary for administrative duties? Questions concerning compensation and benefits should be withheld until the end of an interview. In many cases, there will be a second interview, and the compensation issues will be discussed at that time. This is almost always the case in academic interviews; usually, only the department chair or other senior administrator actually knows what the compensation package is and has the ability to negotiate compensation.

During an interview, you should not criticize what is done in your current institution. It is also imprudent to criticize any of the interviewing group's practices or customs. The job candidate should understand what is done and, if necessary, mention an alternative way that may work, without being critical of any given practice. If you notice something egregious that may affect patient care or that you personally cannot accept, perhaps you should not join the group. Finally, after the interview, you must remember to send a follow-up thank-you note to the interviewer(s), emphasizing your strong points and what your employment in the position would add to the practice or institution.

A job candidate may wonder about how he or she will be evaluated after the interview. Private or community pathology groups may have a different evaluation process than academic medical centers, which place a heavier priority on research and educational skills. The following items, which are not necessarily listed in order of their importance, provide a general idea of how potential employers evaluate job candidates.

- Is there a fit with the group's or institution's current needs? (You may be a superb surgical pathologist and a splendid person, but if the group needs a pathologist with subspecialty training and experience in transfusion medicine, you may fall short of the group's needs.)
- Interpersonal and communication skills during the interview
- Board certification
- Reputation of the candidate's residency program
- Recommendation of the candidate's program director
- Recommendation from someone known, respected, and trusted
- Other letters of recommendation
- Additional training, qualification, fellowship, and subspecialty certification
- Prior pathology or other experience
- Reputation of the candidate's medical school
- In academic jobs: the number of presentations, abstracts, peer-reviewed publications, grants, etc; the journals in which the candidate has published his or her research; and the candidate's author rank order (first author, middle author, etc) on such publications

Job candidates should remember that the pathology practice universe is small, especially in academic circles. Burning your bridges may make you feel better in the short term, but one phone call damning a candidate to a prospective employer can instantly erase a lifetime of hard work without leaving the slightest trail.

When offered a position, certain elements of the offer should be scrutinized. The offer should describe the work expected and the location of the work. Whether the position's responsibilities include anatomic pathology only, clinical pathology only, or both anatomic pathology and clinical pathology, or whether the work includes subspecialty review, should be clear. If the group covers more than one hospital, travel (eg, circuit riding responsibilities) should be described.

Other questions should be addressed. Will there be after-hour call duty, and how often? Will there be an expectation for research and medical school teaching? In academics, a key question evolves around "protected time" to pursue scholarship. It is critical to know what percentage of the total work time should be spent in academic pursuits, and how that time is structured—by the day, week, or month. In terms of percentages, 2 months may be approximately the same amount of time as 15%, but how the time is provided—in one block or by the week—may have a huge impact on probable success. A job candidate should also ask about how performance will be evaluated. Is there a job description for the position? Are there performance standards? Is there a description of the expectations regarding workload and productivity? Although some of these questions were probably answered during the job interview, it is important for a candidate to make sure that what is put on paper correlates with his or her understanding of the position. It is also especially important to pay particular attention to the terms of the employment contract, as discussed below.

The Contract: Definitions, Assumptions, Prerequisites, and Types

A contract is an agreement or covenant. A position offer is a legal document between an employee and an employer. Contracts are usually written to protect the employer. Therefore, it is in an employee's best interest to read the contract carefully and have it reviewed by a lawyer who is experienced in physician/pathologist contracts. In a large institution, there may be a standard contract (and more often, just a letter of offer). For a pathologist fresh out of residency or a fellowship, it may be almost impossible to initiate any significant changes to such a contract. In governmental institutions (state medical schools, medical examiner offices, National Institutes of Health, etc) contracts are drafted to be in compliance with all mandated rules, regulations, and laws and are constructed to withstand constant legal challenge; there is little flexibility. At the very least, you should understand the agreement you are signing. In small institutions, private pathology groups, or community hospitals, you may be able to negotiate amendments to the contract. You should not have higher expectations than what is included in the contract.

The assumptions in a contract include the following: that the parties involved have a mutual desire to work together and have mutual respect for one another (in this case, among pathologists, other physicians, medical staff, and administration); that there will be equitable compensation; and that there will be professional independence and economic interdependence. There are also certain prerequisites for contract negotiations in addi-

tion to having an attorney with experience in medical/pathology contracts review the contract; these include honing your negotiating skills and being able to negotiate terms of the contract, and familiarizing yourself with the hospital's or group's financial condition, past contracting history or concessions, prior contracting problems, pending litigation, and standard contract (if any).

You can familiarize yourself with contract negotiation by taking a course (the CAP offers several courses on contract negotiation) and by reviewing a text on the subject, such as the CAP *Professional Relations Manual*,[8] which may be purchased at a modest cost or downloaded by CAP members at www.cap.org/cappress. See also Appendix 11-4 for an introduction to negotiation.

In addition, you must understand the federal and state regulations regarding pathology practice. For hospital-based positions, you need to be familiar with the medical staff bylaws. Again, in academic institutions under governmental control, there is very little to negotiate, and you shouldn't take out your frustrations over such matters on the "negotiator." The chair may love to pay twice the offered income, but the dean will only allow a narrow salary range for starting assistant professors who have just completed training.

Pathologists just out of residency or fellowship training should be flexible in contract negotiations. They should determine which items are essential, or "must-haves" (eg, benefits like health insurance and malpractice insurance), which items are important but not essential, and which items are not essential but would be nice to have. Pathologists may be in a better position to negotiate their contracts if they have a specific skill or talent that is desperately needed by the group or institution, have proven how valuable they have been to a group or institution, or have acquired some regional, national, or international reputation. Pathologists should negotiate their contracts with those who have the authority to make changes to their contracts, keep complete notes of such negotiations, and document all promises. It is important that pathologists be calm, think things through, and not rush their decisions; an attorney should be consulted before any commitments are made. Each negotiation session should end on a positive note; you should recap your position and concessions and thank the employer or representative for his or her time and courtesy (Appendix 11-4).

Types of Contracts

The many kinds of contract that pathologists may be party to include contracts with hospitals to provide pathology services and laboratory supervision; employment agreements (also known as professional service agreements) with hospitals, multi-specialty groups, pathology practice groups, or pathology partnerships; partnership agreements (if one joins a group as a partner rather than as an employee); and contracts with managed care organizations. Some of these contracts are discussed in Chapter 10, "Financial Management of the Pathology Group."

The Employment Agreement

The most common contract or agreement that a pathologist is asked to sign when beginning practice is the employment agreement or professional services agreement (Appendix 11-5). This agreement is between an employer, which could be a hospital, a pathology group, or even an individual pathologist who has a contract with a hospital, and the employee, who can be an individual pathologist or a professional corporation. In certain states, professionals such as physicians and attorneys can form a professional corporation, which has certain tax, pension contribution, and liability advantages; for example, certain expenses that are taxable to an individual might be deductible to a corporation. The advantages of professional corporations are offset by the costs of establishing and maintaining a corporation, and an attorney and an accountant should be consulted before forming a professional corporation. The term of the employment agreement may be anywhere from 1 to 5 years, but it might have a cancellation clause that shortens the effective term. Employment agreements rarely stipulate that a partnership will occur after a specific time.

The employment agreement should clearly specify the employee's duties and responsibilities and detail what the employer will provide in terms of space, equipment, and secretarial services. The agreement should also be quite specific regarding the compensation package. If the payment is a salary, then the salary as well as the other components of the package must be detailed, including pension plan contributions and health, life, disability, and malpractice insurance. If the payment is a fee to a professional corporation, that corporation would pay for the usual benefits, and the payment should be proportionally greater. There may be a clause that specifies that the salary

will be increased over the course of a multi-year contract. The agreement should also specify vacation, educational, and sick leave allowances as well as other ancillary benefits such as reimbursement for dues, books, and travel to scientific meetings. Again, if a pathologist is organized as a professional corporation, such ancillary expenses would be the corporation's responsibility. If a pathologist is expected to travel to other sites (eg, in a multihospital situation), the contract should establish a reimbursement mechanism for travel expenses.

Most agreements contain a covenant not to compete, which states that if a pathologist leaves the employer, he or she would not practice pathology within a certain geographic area for a certain period of time. However, covenants not to compete are often unenforceable and/or illegal in certain states and jurisdictions; therefore, pathologists should seek legal advice before they sign the agreement.

All contracts or agreements address termination; most include a "no-cause" termination clause, which states that either party can terminate the agreement within a specified period of time, usually 60 or 90 days. The rationale for such a clause is that most employees do not leave employers because of "for-cause" terminations due to incompetence, insubordination, loss of license, criminal activity, or other accepted "causes," but because personalities or temperaments simply do not match, and people are unable get along—and that, without a no-cause clause, is virtually impossible to defend in a court of law. Most pathology groups' contracts with hospitals have similar no-cause cancellation clauses. In addition, most contracts state that if an employee's contract is terminated, the employee's medical staff membership is also cancelled—another protection against post-termination competition. The majority of professional services agreements do not address partnership; if a pathologist moves from employee to partner, a new partnership agreement has to be executed.

> **There was once a radiology group** in a large community hospital. The group employed a younger radiologist who was particularly skilled at ultrasound imaging and had gained the respect of the clinicians in the hospital. The young radiologist decided to leave the group, rent an office in the medical building across the street from the hospital, and start his own ultrasound practice. Needless to say, he siphoned off a significant part of the hospital radiology group's business. Because there was no covenant not to compete, the group had no recourse.

Malpractice Insurance

Hospital contracts and professional services (employment) agreements both require pathologists to have malpractice insurance. Large academic institutions and professional practice groups may self-insure. In community or private pathology groups, the insurance is obtained from an insurance carrier. If a pathologist is an employee of a pathology practice group, the group may provide the pathologists with malpractice insurance as a benefit. If a pathologist has a professional corporation, the cost of insurance is the responsibility of the corporation, and the pathologist's compensation should be adjusted accordingly. As a general rule, an employee or a contracted professional corporation should obtain malpractice insurance from the same carrier and have the same limits and deductibles as others in the group.

The two kinds of malpractice insurance are occurrence insurance and claims-made insurance. Occurrence insurance covers the insured for any incident that did or did not occur while the policy is or was in force, regardless of when the incident is reported or when the incident becomes a claim. Occurrence insurance is rarely offered today because of the difficulty of projecting long-term claims costs. In claims-made insurance, coverage is limited to liability for claims that arise from incidents or events that occur and are reported to the insurance company while the policy is in force. Claims-made insurance policies do not cover incidents or events that are reported after the policy has expired or after the pathologist leaves the group practice or retires. To be protected from events occurring after a policy has expired, pathologists should obtain tail coverage or extended reporting coverage; this coverage protects the insured against all claims that arise from professional services performed while the claims-made policy was in effect but were reported after the termination of the policy or after the pathologist leaves the hospital or group. Some insurers offer this feature free of charge to retiring doctors who meet certain requirements. Who is responsible for paying the insurance premiums and who is responsible for the tail coverage should be determined during contract negotiation.

Hospital Contract

On rare occasions, usually in smaller hospitals, a new pathologist may be offered the position of pathologist and laboratory director and asked to execute a hospital contract. The components of this type of contract are discussed in Chapter 10, "Financial Management of the Pathology Practice."

Group Structures

There are a number of possible structural arrangements for individual pathologists and pathology groups. The contractual arrangements as well as the legal and tax implications are very different for each arrangement and vary significantly from state to state. Therefore, pathologists must obtain both legal and accounting (tax) advice when considering the structure of either an individual practice or group practice. Individuals may function legally as an independent contractor or as an employee, or they may form a professional corporation. Individual pathologists who have their own hospital contracts may hire other pathologists as employees. Groups of pathologists may form a limited liability corporation or partnership, which may be composed of individual pathologists or professional corporations and employ new or per diem pathologists as well as secretaries or business managers. (See also Chapter 10, "Financial Management of the Pathology Practice.")

Regardless of its structure, the group should have certain attributes.

- There must be a designated director with a written job description (position charter) to which all members of the group agree.
- There should be written job descriptions for all members of the group, including partners, associates, employed pathologists, per diem employees, etc.
- There should be an organizational chart for the pathology group that describes domains, authority, and reporting relationships.
- There should be a formal decision-making process that defines the director's authority as well as individual members' areas of authority, responsibility, and the reporting relationships.
- There should be written policies for the group's governance and operation.
- There should be a written strategic and financial plan for the group. All members of the group must have a sense of participation in the group's decision-making process. All members of the group should agree on the mission statement and the strategic plan for the group and the laboratory.
- There should be written and published duties and call and vacation schedules.

■ It is essential to develop a "one for all and all for one" philosophy. Each member of the group must be an excellent pathologist and have the respect of his or her colleagues.

How to Keep the Job

Policies, Procedures, Rules, and Regulations

Each institution or practice has a defined mission and vision as well as policies and procedures that enable it to realize its goals. The first duty of a new member of a group is to become familiar with these policies and procedures. The transition may be quite challenging for new hires, especially those fresh out of training. There is usually an organizational chart in all institutions. Remember, the larger the institution, the lower one may be on the totem pole. New pathologists must know the chain of command and endeavor not to overstep the perceived boundaries. For example, in an academic institution, there may be section heads, division directors, and departmental chairs. One should not go over the division director to discuss issues that relate to that division with the departmental chair unless there are extenuating circumstances.

Understanding the policies and procedures of an institution leaves no ambiguity as to what is expected of its employees. Newly hired employees who do not understand something should not make assumptions; they should explore the best procedure for their institution. As the saying goes, "Assumption is the mother of all foul-ups." One may also want to ask the following questions: To whom do I report, and how will I be judged or evaluated? What is the policy regarding leave or vacation time? How is the vacation schedule determined? Is there a calendar that fairly distributes assignments, calls, autopsies, committee work, teaching assignments, and other duties? How are differences/conflicts handled? What is the policy regarding turnaround time? How are mistakes handled? Is there a second read of all new cancer cases? Will my reports be periodically reviewed for completeness or accuracy? Are there policies guiding external consultation? Is there a policy regarding internal consultations? What is the policy regarding transfer/hand-off of cases? What is the quality assurance and peer review program? Is there a pathology assistant, and is there a policy guiding his or her work? Will there be after-hours call duties, and what is the policy guiding after-hours calls? Will there be multidisciplinary conferences? Are there outreach activities? Pathologists should be familiar with the answers to some, if not most, of these questions before accepting an offer for employment.

Within the practice, pathologists should understand the expectations and procedures related to clinical activities. New pathologists are responsible for adapting to the way the practice does things—not the other way around. You should actively work on relationships in the group by communicating, being courteous and considerate, and learning and knowing your limitations. If you have an innovative idea on how to improve things, the presentation of this "new idea" is almost as important as the idea itself. You should never say, "In my residency, we did it this way," as if to suggest that the method one used in residency is the only logical way of doing things. Before suggesting changes or showing how things could be improved, you should understand why things are done the way they are, settle into the culture of the new practice, and gain the trust of your new associates.

Working Relationships

Pathologists should establish good working relationships with the medical staff. One cannot establish any relationship if one is invisible, hiding behind the microscope or behind the "paraffin curtain." Pathologists should be visible to the medical staff; they should eat with the clinicians, make "rounds" in the surgeons' lounge, and visit the wards. When speaking with or writing to clinical colleagues, pathologists should use clinical nomenclature and avoid arrogance. Pathologists should also be ready to quickly respond to the clinicians' requests, respectful of senior colleagues, ready to address issues raised by clinicians and surgeons, and enthusiastic about participating in tumor boards, infection control committees, transfusion committees, and other institutional committees. Other things that establish pathologists as supportive members of the medical staff include participating in medical staff oversight functions, such as utilization review, peer review, and outcomes research; volunteering in the medical staff's educational programs (eg, presenting clinical pathological conferences, organ recitals); and, most importantly, participating in medical staff social events, such as dances and golf tournaments. In addition, pathologists need to gain the respect of others in the hospital by making themselves visible to the hospital administration and ancillary staff, including nursing, purchasing, information technology, housekeeping, and engineering staff; pathologists should learn their names and what they do, and thank them for their work.

Pathologists must also gain and keep the respect of the administrative and nonphysician laboratory staff. Pathologists should make daily rounds in the laboratory or section that is their domain or responsibility; learn the names of the employees, their spouses, and children; and acknowledge the employees' contributions in the laboratory—it is important that they feel appreciated. Pathologists should be easy to work with. One may bring occasional treats (like donuts or cake) for the staff and should be careful not to forget the laboratory employees on the evening, graveyard, and weekend shifts. It is important to also recognize that many laboratories have diverse employee populations with varying food preferences and sensitivities.

A pathologist's success in a new position may be summarized by Hausner's three A's: affability, availability, and accuracy.[7]

Affability: Pathologists should be friendly and easy to deal with. Therefore, you should be friendly with your associates (for example, by sending cards on their important anniversaries) and the clinicians (by eating and talking with them) and attend hospital and laboratory social functions. Also, pathologists should not forget the ancillary staff and never gossip or criticize.

Availability: Pathologists should be readily accessible. Therefore, they should have an open-door policy, check their voicemail/answering services regularly and return all calls the same day, and check their emails regularly and reply to them promptly. Pathologists should also be ready to pick up additional responsibility; they should come in early and stay late if needed, and come in on weekends as necessary.

Accuracy: A pathologist is only as good as his or her last diagnosis. Pathologists should know their limitations and consult with their colleagues when necessary. Standard report formats should be used (for example, for surgical pathology cancer reports), and a checklist should be used to ensure that all the mandated elements are included in a report.

References

1. *Trends in Pathologist Workforce. Results from the 2007 Practice Characteristics Survey.* Northfield, IL: College of American Pathologists; 2008. Available at: http://www.cap.org/apps/docs/advocacy/ workforce_survey_07.pdf. Accessed Nov 12, 2010.
2. *2004 Practice Characteristics Survey.* Northfield, IL: College of American Pathologists; 2005.
3. Horowitz RE. Expectations and essentials for the community practice of pathology. *Hum Pathol.* 2006; 37(8):969-973.
4. Kass ME, Crawford JM, Bennett B, et al. Adequacy of pathology resident training for employment: a survey report from the Future of Pathology Task Group. *Arch Pathol Lab Med.* 2007;(131):545-555.
5. Talbert ML, Ashwood ER, Brownlee NA, et al. Resident preparation for practice: a white paper from the College of American Pathologists and Association of Pathology Chairs. *Arch Pathol Lab Med.* 2009;133(7):1139-1147.
6. Horowitz RE. The successful community hospital pathologist: what it takes. *Hum Pathol.* 1998;(29):211-214.
7. Hausner RJ. Insights into Finding, Evaluating, and Keeping a Position in Pathology Practice. Seminar, University of California, Los Angeles, Department of Pathology. Jan 16, 2002.
8. Practice Management Committee. *Professional Relations Manual.* 12th ed. Northfield, IL: College of American Pathologists; 2003.

Bibliography

Goldsmith JD, Siegal GP, Suster S, Wheeler TM, Brown R; for the Surgical Pathology Committee, College of American Pathologists. Reporting guidelines for clinical laboratory reports in surgical pathology. *Arch Pathol Lab Med.* 2008;132:1608-1616.

Hemmer PR, Karon BS, Hernandez JS, et al. Leadership and management training for residents and fellows: a curriculum for future medical directors. *Arch Pathol Lab Med.* 2007;131(4):610-614.

Strauss SE, Straus C, Tzanetos K. Career choice in academic medicine: systematic review. *J Gen Intern Med.* 2006;21(12):1222-1229.

Walk EE. The role of pathologists in the era of personalized medicine. *Arch Pathol Lab Med.* 2009;133(4):605-610.

Challenge Questions

What is the difference between claims-made and occurrence-based malpractice insurance?
Answer: See page 207 and Chapter 10, pages 179 to 182.

Describe the different settings in which a pathologist can work.
Answer: See pages 197 to 199.

What are the essential elements of an employment agreement or contract for a pathologist?
Answer: See pages 205 to 207 and Appendix 11-5.

Appendix 11-1.
Template for a Curriculum Vitae

- Personal information
  - Name (previous name in parentheses if there has been a name change)
  - Date and place of birth
  - Citizenship
  - Marital status
  - Contact address and telephone number
- Professional summary: Quick overview of training and experience; no more than two sentences
- Education: Start with the most recent training
- Board certification
- Medical licensure (do not include the actual license number)
- Honors and awards: Preferably from medical school to the present; it is not important to include honors from elementary school
- Military service
- Previous employment or experience (for example, experience as a laboratory technologist, computer programmer)
- Academic appointments, titles
- Scholarly activities: This may be broken down into teaching responsibilities and research activities
- Research grants, if any
- Presentations: This may be broken down into presentations in an institution and at local, regional, national, and international meetings
- Service to the program, department, institution, etc (for example, committee activities, administrative activities, service responsibility)
- Service to the profession: Include committee membership in local, regional, or national medical societies
- Professional and society memberships
- Publications: This may be broken down to published abstracts, manuscripts, book chapters, or books

Appendix 11-2.
Cover Letter Template

Your Address

Contact Information
[email address and phone number]

Date

Employer's Address
[starting with the name of the physician listed as the contact]

Dear Dr. _____,

I am interested in the surgical pathologist [or any other position] position in your department advertised in the July edition of *Archives of Pathology and Laboratory Medicine* [or however you learned of the position]. I am board certified in anatomic and clinical pathology with subspecialty training and board certification in cytopathology [or any other subspecialty].

The opportunity to participate in research and the exciting variety of cases seen in your institution are of particular interest to me. I believe that my rigorous residency training and my fellowship training in a high-volume cancer center have prepared me well to work as an independent pathologist. I have actively participated in translational research activities and have worked in various committees in my institution. My resume is attached.

I look forward to the opportunity to interview with you. I thank you in advance for your consideration of my application.

Sincerely,

Your Name

Appendix 11-3.
Interview Questions

You need to be prepared for the full spectrum of questions that may be presented, such as the following:

- Tell me about yourself.
- Tell me about your experience in pathology so far.
- What is your most important accomplishment to date?
- How would you describe your ideal job?
- Why did you choose pathology?
- When did you decide on this career?
- What goals do you have in your career?
- How do you plan to achieve these goals?
- How do you personally define success?
- Describe a situation in which you were successful.
- What do you think it takes to be successful in this career?
- What accomplishments have given you the most satisfaction in your life?
- If you had to live your life over again, what one thing would you change?
- Would you rather work with information or with people?
- Are you a team player?
- What motivates you?
- Why should I hire you?
- Are you a goal-oriented person?
- Tell me about some of your recent goals and what you did to achieve them.
- What are your short-term goals?
- What is your long-range objective?
- What do you see yourself doing 5 years from now?
- Where do you want to be 10 years from now?
- Do you handle conflict well?
- Have you ever had a conflict with a boss or professor? How did you resolve it?
- What major problem have you had to deal with recently?
- Do you handle pressure well?
- What is your greatest strength?
- What is your greatest weakness?
- If I were to ask one of your professors to describe you, what would he or she say?

- Why did you choose to attend your residency training program?
- What changes would you make at your program?
- How has your training prepared you for your career?
- What were your favorite rotations? Why?
- Do you enjoy doing independent research?
- Who were your favorite professors? Why?
- How did you do on your board exams?
- Do you have any plans for further education?
- How much training do you think you'll need to become productive?
- What qualities do you feel a successful manager should have?
- Why do you want to work here?
- What do you know about our group?
- Why are you interested in our group?
- Do you have any location preferences?
- How familiar are you with the community that we're located in?
- Are you willing to relocate? In the future?
- Are you willing to travel? How much?
- Is money important to you?
- How much money do you need to make to be happy?
- What kind of compensation are you looking for?

Other Popular Interview Questions

Warm-Up Questions

- What made you apply for this position?
- Could you briefly summarize your work history and education for me?

Work History

- What is important to you in a company or organization?
- Describe one or two of your major accomplishments.

Education

- What special aspects of your education or training have prepared you for this job?
- Why did you choose your subspecialty or area of concentration?
- What job-related skills have you developed?

Self-Assessment

- Which three adjectives would you use to describe yourself?
- How do you cope with conflict?
- Describe a time when you overcame an obstacle.

Motivation

- Where do you see yourself in a perfect future?
- How will this position enable you to reach your goals?
- What will you bring to the company or organization that is unique?

Oral Presentation Skills

- Have you ever done any group presentations?
- How comfortable are you speaking in front of groups?
- What is your experience with making presentations?

Leadership

- How do you facilitate group communication?
- Describe a time when you delegated responsibilities to group members.
- How do you set an example to others?
- How would you describe your basic leadership style?
- Describe a time when you worked in a team.

Stress Tolerance

- How do you cope with pressure?
- Give an example of a time when you worked well under pressure.

Job Performance

- What would you say are some areas that you need to improve on?
- Do you prefer working alone or in groups?
- How do you receive feedback?
- Describe a time when you successfully explained a complex concept or method to a colleague.

Creativity

- Of your creative accomplishments, which gave you the most satisfaction, and why?
- What kind of problems have people recently called on you to solve? Tell me how you solved them.
- What methods do you employ while brainstorming?

Decisiveness

- What did you do the last time you did not know what decision to make?
- What was the last major problem that you were confronted with? What action did you take?
- How do you determine or evaluate success?

Appendix 11-4. Negotiation: A Very Brief Introduction

- Assumption: There have been several interviews and a job offer has been made. Be prepared to participate in several negotiating sessions. Rarely is a contract or agreement finalized in one sitting.
- Prerequisites
  - Take a course (or read a book) on negotiation
  - Read the CAP *Professional Relations Manual*
  - Know federal and local laws and regulations regarding pathology practice as well as medical staff by-laws and regulations regarding hospital based physicians
  - Obtain information about the group and person with whom you will negotiate
    - Consult previous pathologists
    - Consult members of medical staff
    - What is their financial condition
    - Do they have a standard contract
    - Did they make prior concessions
    - Are there prior contracting problems
    - Is there pending litigation
  - Prepare information about your value to hospital or group
    - What specific skills or talents do you bring
    - Do you have a community or national reputation
  - Define your objectives
  - Select negotiating team: attorney and accountant

- Strategy and Tactics
  - Refine your objectives and rank them as follows:
    - Essential
    - Important
    - Nice to have
  - Negotiate only with someone in authority
  - Show you are knowledgeable about them
  - Express your own needs, but show you are aware of their needs and limitations
  - Control the negotiating session (or process)
    - Be assertive and confident; show what value you add to the organization
    - Sell yourself, but do not oversell
    - Begin with and concentrate on points of agreement
    - Don't be intimidated and don't haggle
    - Approach negotiation as a collaboration to achieve agreement
  - Be prepared to trade
    - Try not to compromise or to give anything away first
    - If necessary, give away a "nice to have"
    - Have predetermined fall-back positions
  - Don't rush, be calm, think things over
  - Defer disagreements—"must check with attorney or wife"
  - Keep complete notes, document all promises
  - End each session on a positive note, recapping your position and concessions and thanking them for their time and courtesy

Bibliography

Burrows S. *Win/Win Outcomes. A Physician's Negotiating Guide*. Chicago, IL: Pluribus Press; 1984.

Fuller G. *The Negotiator's Handbook*. Upper Saddle River, NJ: Prentice-Hall; 1991.

Appendix 11-5.
Checklist for a Professional Services Contract

- Types of Contracts
  - Between group (partnership) and individual (professional corporation)
  - Between senior pathologist and associates and assistants
  - For employed and locum tenens pathologists
- Definition of Parties
- Term of Agreement
  - Length of primary agreement
  - Length of time to reach partnership and parity
- Duties
  - Clear definition of duties and responsibilities
  - Position charter or job description
  - Frequency of "call"
  - Teaching, research, and other expectations
  - Equal share of autopsies, surgical pathology call, etc
- Space and Equipment
- Supplies and Utilities
- Secretarial and Technical Personnel
- Compensation
  - Fee to professional corporation
  - Fee related to responsibility and work load
  - Salary
  - Separate income exclusion (consultation)
  - Pension plan contribution
  - How much? Starting pay? Pay after 1 or 2 years?
  - Benefits
  - Locum tenens (per diem without benefits)

- Insurance
  - Malpractice
  - Term life insurance
  - Public liability
  - Health
  - Disability
  - Workers' Compensation
- Time Off
  - Vacation
  - Educational meetings
  - Sick leave and disability
- Other Benefits
  - Professional association dues
  - Books and journals
  - Automobile or travel allowance
  - Credit cards for promotion and entertainment
- Covenant Not to Compete
  - Time
  - Location
- Termination
  - Notice
  - Causes/disqualification
  - Cancellation of hospital staff membership
- Partnership Buy-In
  - Depends on what value or income you add to the partnership, eg, consulting practice, special skills, hospital contract
  - Time to full equity, 0 to 3 years
  - Cost of buy-in
  - Payment method
    - Lump sum
    - Lesser income
- Partnership Buy-Out

CHAPTER 12

Laboratory Laws and Regulations

Elizabeth A. Wagar, MD

Contents

A Landmark Laboratory Law

Although the Clinical Laboratory Improvement Act was actually passed in 1967, the Clinical Laboratory Improvement Amendments of 1988 (CLIA '88) was the landmark legislation that provided for major federal oversight of clinical laboratories. CLIA '88 was fully implemented in 1992 after national input from laboratories, clinicians, and patients. Instigating its passage were reports of numerous "scandalous" cytology Pap mills that operated with poor quality oversight and employed illegal billing practices. The regulations established by CLIA can be found in Section 353 of Chapter 42 of the Code of Federal Regulations.[1] CLIA is administered by the Centers for Medicare and Medicaid Services (CMS) within the US Department of Health and Human Services. A CLIA certificate is required of all operating clinical laboratories regardless of whether the laboratory performs services for Medicare patients.

CLIA '88 introduced the concept of test complexity categories. Tests were classified as waived tests, moderate complexity tests, or high complexity tests. (Waived tests are not subject to some CLIA standards because they are defined as tests that are so easy to perform that the chances of error or harm to a patient are negligible.) In 1993, the provider-performed microscopy (PPM) category was established. The PPM category enabled a typical physician office laboratory to include wet-mount microscopy and other simple microscopy procedures in their waived test menus. A fifth CLIA test category, accurate and precise testing—a hybrid of waived tests and moderate complexity tests—required quality control (QC), proficiency testing (PT), and quality assessment; however, personnel requirements and inspections were relaxed. After the accurate and precise testing category was established, it became clear that CLIA would have to be significantly revised to account for the increased complexity of some point-of-care testing instrumentation and facilitate proper quality assessment. Major CLIA revisions were therefore implemented in 2003 and codified in 2004.[2]

In CLIA '03, moderate complexity tests and high complexity tests were combined and are now referred to as nonwaived tests. These tests are sub-

Moderate Complexity	High Complexity
• Laboratory Director	• Laboratory Director
• Technical Consultant	• Technical Supervisor
• Clinical Consultant	• Clinical Consultant
• Testing Personnel	• General Supervisor
	• Testing Personnel

Figure 12-1. CLIA 2003 Personnel Categories.

ject to CLIA validation and quality requirements; however, the requirements for highly complex tests are slightly more stringent than those for nonwaived tests. CLIA '03 also changed *quality assurance* to *quality assessment* to imply a more active review of quality measures. In addition, the requirement for validating new tests was added, indicating that all new tests should be reviewed for accuracy, precision, reportable range, and reference range, and that documentation of this process should be available for review. CLIA '03 also affirmed that PT would be scored when participants had 80% agreement or better and clarified that no personnel education or training requirements were required for waived testing. However, CLIA '03 segregated the qualifications for individuals performing nonwaived testing into moderate and high complexity personnel training and skills. The existence of moderate and high complexity personnel categories when tests are categorized as waived versus nonwaived has been a point of confusion.

The QC changes in CLIA '03 are also somewhat controversial. According to these changes, QC may be reduced to two levels per day rather than two levels per run. However, QC must still "detect immediate errors" and "monitor over time the accuracy and precision of test performance that may be influenced by changes in test system performance and variance in operator performance." Laboratories accredited by the College of American Pathologists (CAP) and other agencies probably already follow more stringent QC rules, making the new QC definition less of a concern for accredited laboratories.[3] The distribution of CLIA '03 personnel titles is shown in Figure 12-1.

Recent CMS data indicate that more than 19,000 CMS-inspected laboratories have certificates of compliance, 129,000 laboratories have certificates of waiver, 38,000 laboratories have PPM certificates, and 16,000 laboratories have certificates of accreditation from the CAP and others.[4] Since

CLIA '88 was first implemented, the number of CLIA-accredited laboratories has grown considerably, especially among waived testing sites.

Other government statutes and regulations also have impacted the laboratory industry. In 1993, the Occupational Safety and Health Administration (OSHA) implemented new bloodborne pathogen standards, partly in response to the HIV epidemic. The term *universal precautions* was adopted and implied that all types of human specimen contact, regardless of HIV or other infectious disease status, should be regarded as having the potential to transmit infectious disease. Subsequently, the term *standard precautions* was adopted to clarify that all human specimens should be treated as if they were of an infectious origin.[5] Bloodborne pathogen training is required with employment and is one of the competencies for all laboratory employees who handle blood and other body fluids. OSHA also establishes standards and regulations for employee health (eg, rules governing histotechnologists' and residents' exposure to formalin) and, together with the National Institute for Occupational Safety and Health, ergonomic advisories. Many states have separate occupational health agencies with additional rules and regulations (eg, rules governing the disposal of hazardous waste and solvents and employee ergonomics).

Coding is another complex government-regulated activity (see also Chapter 10, "Financial Management of the Pathology Practice"). The Current Procedural Terminology (CPT) code set was derived and is still maintained by the American Medical Association through the CPT Editorial Panel. CPT has been adopted by CMS and is used for Medicare and Medicaid billing. The CPT code set describes all types of medical, surgical, and diagnostic services, including pathology and laboratory services. It is designed to communicate uniform information about medical services and procedures among physicians, coders, patients, accreditation organizations, and payers for administrative, financial, and analytical purposes. The current version is the CPT 2011. An understanding of correct CPT coding for pathology and laboratory services is essential for compliance with federal, state, and local regulations. Also, coding has been adopted by most private insurance carriers and thus applies to most technical and professional work. The American Medical Association website (www.ama-assn.org/ama/pub/physician-resources/) is a resource for CPT code information.[6]

In 1996, CMS issued guidelines requiring medical necessity documentation for pathology and laboratory tests billed to Medicare. The current diagnostic codes are the International Classification of Diseases (ICD)-9 code set, version 3. ICD-9 codes must be provided with CPT codes to obtain reimbursement from Medicare and Medicaid. Diagnostic codes must originate with the clinical provider for any CP laboratory requests. Payment denials occur when the tests ordered are not linked to the diagnostic codes or when no ICD-9 code is provided. A common example is nonreimbursement for thyroid-stimulating hormone testing, because no ICD-9 code for thyroid disorders is provided. Currently, a new set of ICD codes, ICD-10, published by the World Health Organization in 1993, is due to be implemented in the US, effective October 1, 2013. More information regarding ICD codes can be found at www.cms.hhs.gov/ICD9ProviderDiagnosticCodes/.[7] Pathologists should have the most recent ICD codes and CPT codes in their laboratories for reference and review.[8] CMS monitors additional regulations and guidelines for coding and billing compliance (see Chapter 10, "Financial Management of the Pathology Practice").

A number of recent laws have also affected the business aspects of the laboratory industry. For example, the Stark ban, named after Fortney Hillman "Pete" Stark Jr., of the Subcommittee on Health, House Ways and Means Committee, prohibits self-referral of laboratory testing to physician-owned laboratories. Also, the Health Insurance Portability and Accountability Act of 1996 (HIPAA; discussed in Chapter 4, "Personnel Management") has important implications for the secure and confidential management of patients' personal health information. Pathologists can stay informed of recent legal interpretations by frequently reviewing the Office of Inspector General rulings from the Department of Health and Human Services.

A special area of regulation involves the management of hazardous and infectious agents. The Centers for Disease Control and Prevention (CDC) coordinates its public health efforts through each state's department of health. Each state usually has its own public health laboratories that serve the clinical laboratories of a given county, region, or state and accept from them information regarding select microbiological specimens, depending on the state reporting list of infectious agents. The state public health laboratories then report federally tracked agents to the CDC. The Laboratory Response Network for bioterrorism is similarly managed, with individual laboratories (sentinel laboratories) reporting suspected bioterrorism agents to the Laboratory Response Network's reference laboratories (typically state public health laboratories). Bioterrorism agents are subsequently referred to higher-level federal (CDC) and/or armed forces laboratories that have level-4 biosafety capabilities.

The US Department of Transportation, the International Civil Aviation Organization, and the International Air Transport Association all have specific requirements that govern the transport of infectious and hazardous substances. The Department of Transportation regulates the commercial transportation of dangerous goods by both air and ground carriers. For the most part, these regulations are quite effective. In 2003, of the nearly 4,920,000 primary containers shipped, only 106 (0.002%) were reported to have been broken during transit.[9] Secondary or outer containers maintained the breakage in all cases.

Infectious agents are classified as either Category A or Category B agents. A Category A agent is "an infectious substance which is transported in a form that, when exposure to it occurs, is capable of causing permanent disability, or life-threatening or fatal disease to otherwise healthy humans or animals." Category B agents are "infectious substances which do not meet the criteria for inclusion in Category A. In general, they are not in a form capable of causing illness." Clinical, diagnostic, and patient specimens that are shipped for routine culture or other non–Category A infectious microorganisms are often Category B agents. The International Air Transport Association assigns United Nations (UN) numbers to designate Category A and Category B agents. Category A agents are assigned UN2814 (Category A: Infectious Agent, Affecting Humans) or UN2900 (Category A: Infectious Agent, Affecting Animals). Category B agents are assigned UN3373. Categorization is largely based on the pathologist's judgment regarding the medical history and symptoms of the specimen's human or animal source.

Any introduction to laboratory law requires a discussion of institutional review board (IRB) activities. (A more detailed review of IRB activities is described in Chapter 14, "Ethics for Pathology and Laboratory Medicine.") IRBs, which provide oversight of an institution's biomedical and behavioral research programs, are governed in the United States by the Code of Federal Regulations (CFR),

Title 45, Part 46. IRBs determine the appropriate management of all human research to protect the rights and welfare of research participants and ensure that informed consent is obtained from research participants. A laboratory director involved in research programs may be required to formally apply to the IRB for approval of a research program. IRBs interface with many other ethical issues, as described further in Chapter 14 "Ethics for Pathology and Laboratory Medicine."

This chapter briefly reviews the recent history of laws and regulations affecting the laboratory and their widespread impact on the laboratory industry. CLIA is central to all clinical laboratory services. But many other areas of the laboratory, including coding, billing, privacy, safety, and contracting, are impacted daily by numerous statutes, regulations, and interpretations. Pathologists and laboratory directors must remain informed of current regulations. Subscription services, such as Washington G-2 Reports, and advocacy groups, such as the CAP, the American Association for Clinical Chemistry, the American Society for Clinical Pathology (ASCP), and the American Pathology Foundation, provide frequent valuable updates for laboratory leadership.[10]

Regulatory Affairs for the Laboratory Leader

An effective method for internalizing regulatory affairs is to understand each regulatory agency's contributions to an individual laboratory's operations. Described here are the basic requirements that must be considered for CLIA and the US Food and Drug Administration (FDA) and the regulatory aspects of accreditation agencies such as the Joint Commission and the CAP.

Clinical Laboratory Improvement Amendments (CLIA)

As mentioned above, CLIA originally specified categories for waived, moderate complexity, and high complexity testing. Waived tests must meet certain requirements. CLIA defines waived tests as "tests cleared by the FDA for home use" and "tests using such simple and accurate methodologies that the likelihood of erroneous results is negligible." Only eight analytes were listed as waived analytes when the CLIA regulations were first implemented in 1992.[1] That list is now 10-fold longer (see www.accessdata.fda.gov/scripts/cdrh/cfdocs/cfCLIA/analyteswaived.cfm), and it is represent-

ed by hundreds of methodologies.[11] Congress revised the CLIA waiver process in 1997 so that a waiver may be granted to (1) any test listed in the regulation, (2) any test system for which the system's manufacturer or producer requests a waiver and meets the statutory criteria as evidenced by scientifically valid data provided by the manufacturer, and (3) any test system cleared by the FDA for home use (ie, over-the-counter tests). Waived tests have no specifications for personnel requirements or QC requirements other than those listed by the manufacturer. It is only recently that limited inspections of waived testing laboratories have been performed.

Waived tests are not the same as point-of-care tests. The term *point-of-care* testing may be applied to bedside or patient-centric testing sites that perform moderate or higher complexity tests in appropriately CLIA-certified facilities. An example is the testing of blood gases in an operating room: The testing itself is of moderate complexity, but it has oversight in a given hospital or institution by a CLIA laboratory director, ensuring that the testing is performed by appropriately trained and experienced personnel. QC requirements, PT, and competencies are required for all moderate complexity testing in "point-of-care" sites. The CLIA laboratory director is responsible for all quality assessment activities. The CLIA certificate covering such activities may be a central laboratory CLIA certificate (eg, for a hospital core laboratory) or a separate CLIA certificate from the main laboratory, with an appropriate laboratory director designated to perform point-of-care testing. Some institutions prefer the latter arrangement, since it allows for more specific oversight of point-of-care testing for Joint Commission, CAP, and CLIA inspections.

Aside from the scenario described above, moderate and high complexity testing are frequently performed in centrally controlled settings such as clinical, hospital, or reference laboratories. In 2000, the FDA assumed the responsibility of grading seven criteria to determine whether laboratory test systems are of moderate or high complexity (Figure 12-2).[12] Each of the seven criteria are graded as 1, 2, or 3, with 1 being the least complex and 3 being the most complex. Test systems that receive a total score of 12 or lower are categorized as moderate complexity. Test systems with scores above 12 are categorized as high complexity. Approximately half of the available test systems (excluding waived tests) marketed today are of moderate complexity, and half are of high com-

- Knowledge
- Training and experience
- Reagent and material preparation
- Characteristics of operational steps
- Calibration, quality control, and proficiency testing materials
- Test system troubleshooting
- Interpretation and judgment

Figure 12-2. FDA Criteria for Test Complexity.

plexity. Typically, moderate complexity tests are automated and require less judgment, whereas high complexity tests require significant judgment and reagent management. Many microbiology tests, such as biochemical results evaluation, Gram stain morphology, and parasite identification, are examples of high complexity testing.

Proficiency testing is another key element of CLIA legislation. As described in Chapter 7, "Quality Management in Laboratory Medicine," PT is important for examining a laboratory's internal quality of testing as it compares to that of other laboratories using the same technology to perform similar testing. Successful performance of PT is required for maintaining a CLIA certificate. At a minimum, all laboratories must be enrolled for the CLIA-specified federally regulated analytes. Additional analyte testing may be required depending on state requirements and accreditation status of the laboratory. The list of federally regulated analytes can be found at www.cms.hhs.gov/CLIA.[13]

Enrollment in PT is required for each CLIA certificate except the certificate of waiver. PT programs must be approved by CMS, and laboratories cannot randomly change from one approved PT program to another. Laboratories must enroll and participate in one approved program for one calendar year before designating a different program. If a new regulated analyte is added to a laboratory, the laboratory must enroll in PT as soon as possible and complete the PT for the remainder of the year.

Proficiency testing programs typically provide challenge specimens three times per year. The PT specimens are to be treated as much like patient specimens as possible within the framework of CLIA requirements. The results of a PT specimen test at one CLIA-accredited laboratory should never be disclosed to another CLIA-accredited laboratory, even if referral testing typically occurs between the two laboratories. For example, Gram

stains performed in a core laboratory may typically be referred to a separate CLIA laboratory for confirmation; however, PT for Gram stain in the core laboratory cannot be disclosed or discussed with the referral laboratory despite the fact that patient specimens are handled in a different manner. Testing sites that fail the same analyte in two of three consecutive PT events can be sanctioned. Sanctions can range from requiring the laboratory to submit plans for corrective action to suspending testing for the failed analyte in the laboratory. (A laboratory can also fail PT for not submitting results on time, not testing a PT specimen, or making clerical errors in submitting the results.) At least 80% of the participating laboratories must agree with the result to obtain consensus. If the PT does not produce consensus among participating laboratories, the PT result is noted as "ungradable," and an artificial score of 100% may be entered. In some cases, the Clinical and Laboratory Standards Institute (CLSI, formerly NCCLS) provides some direction for the grading of PT challenges; for example, the CLSI Informational Supplement, *Performance Standards for Antimicrobial Susceptibility Testing* (M100-S20-U; June 2010 Update), may be used in PT grading. (A variety of other standards are available from CLSI and are added as references throughout this text.) All laboratory directors should be aware of how CLSI standards impact laboratory operations.

For unregulated analytes, CLIA requires that laboratories take steps to ensure the accuracy of testing in lieu of testing PT samples. CLIA also requires that laboratories verify the accuracy of any test or procedure that is performed, but not listed in Subpart I of the CLIA regulations, at least twice per year. PT for many unregulated analytes is available from approved PT providers; this is the most reliable route for managing unregulated analytes. However, for newer genetic and molecular tests, internal twice-annual PT may have to be developed. Such PT could involve an exchange of blinded specimens with another laboratory that performs the test. Documentation should be maintained for analytes for which no PT provider is available, and documentation of all PT records must be maintained for 2 years from the date of the PT event.

Quality assessment, as defined by CLIA '03, is organized to follow the path of patient specimens through the testing process, ie, through the preanalytical, analytical, and postanalytical steps. Thus, all aspects of testing—patient identification, specimen submission, specimen integrity, analytical

Table 12-1. Elements of a Standard Operating Procedure: CLIA

Patient preparation
Specimen collection
Specimen labeling
Specimen preservation
Specimen transport
Referral
Specimen acceptability or rejection
Step-by-step procedure performance
Instrument calibration and calibration verification
Reportable range
Quality control and corrective actions
Limitations to methodology
Reference intervals
Critical values
Literature reference
Reporting of results
Course of action when testing system is inoperable

specifications, QC, calibration, and timely reporting, among others—are included in quality assessment and continuous quality improvement mandates. The laboratory should demonstrate "ongoing monitoring that identifies, evaluates, and resolves problems."[14]

CLIA also requires that procedures and procedure manuals have high-quality standard operating procedures. Electronic or written procedures for all tests performed in the laboratory must be available to all testing personnel. The necessary elements of the manual are specified in detail in section 493.1251.[2,14] The elements of standard operating procedures as specified by CLIA are shown in Table 12-1.

Manufacturers' product inserts may be used to partially meet procedure requirements, but these inserts cannot be used exclusively as procedures. Initially, procedures must be approved, signed, and dated by the laboratory director, and any subsequent changes to procedures must be reapproved by the laboratory director.

CLIA '03 also details the verification of performance specifications for nonwaived tests. Data that enable a laboratory to decide how to manage the system must be collected. The performance characteristics that need to be established for any new test or test system are accuracy, precision, reportable range, and verification of a manufacturer's reference interval as appropriate for the patient population. Test sites may develop their own reference ranges. If a test site modifies an FDA-approved system, additional testing is necessary to determine sensitivity and specificity, appropriate reference ranges, and any other performance characteristics that may be required.

Quality control is also specifically addressed in federal regulations, section 493.1256.[2,14] For each nonwaived testing system, "the laboratory is responsible for having control procedures that monitor the accuracy and precision of the complete analytical process." The control procedures must detect immediate errors, test system failure, adverse environmental conditions, and operator performance, and they must monitor over time the accuracy and precision of test performance. As mentioned previously, the concept of "equivalent quality" testing is controversial, and CMS is currently rethinking the concept. However, laboratories that are meeting stricter requirements for accreditation agencies for QC are probably already performing appropriate QC review.

Food and Drug Administration

A second federal agency involved in laboratory operations is the FDA. The FDA regulations that most frequently impact laboratories are those related to medical devices and biologics. The FDA defines a medical device as "any instrument, apparatus, or other article that is used to prevent, diagnose, mitigate, or treat a disease or to affect the structure or function of the body, with the exception of drugs."[15] Diagnostic test systems (ie, instruments and reagents) are included in this definition. Computer systems used to manage the collection and distribution of blood and blood products are also included in the definition of medical devices and require corresponding validation before implementation at the test site. FDA-approved tests and test systems do not require a notation on the laboratory report regarding the reagent or test status and are typically billable procedures if they meet other medical necessity and coding requirements. Manufacturers must receive premarket approval from the FDA before selling diagnostic test systems and other medical devices. This premarket approval process is referred to as the 510(k) process. Information about medical device approvals can be found at www.fda.gov. The regulations have requirements for reporting adverse events related to devices. Some accreditation agencies, notably the CAP, require that laboratories have mechanisms for FDA reporting.

In 1997, the FDA defined analyte-specific reagents (ASRs) for tests that were developed using commercially distributed analyte components. (For example, commercially distributed primers and probes can be purchased and incorporated into a laboratory's polymerase chain reaction system.) The definition of ASRs has added a level of complexity to clinical laboratories and in vitro test development. In addition, numerous ASRs have entered the market since 1997. As of 2008, the FDA defines ASRs as "antibodies, both polyclonal and monoclonal, specific receptor proteins, ligands, nucleic acid sequences, and similar reagents which, through specific binding or chemical reactions with substances in a specimen, are intended for use in a diagnostic application for identification and quantification of an individual chemical substance or ligand in biological specimens."[16] ASRs are medical devices that are regulated by the FDA. They are subject to general controls, including current good manufacturing practices as well as the specific provisions of the ASR regulations.[16] A test performed with an ASR includes the following statement in the final laboratory report: "This test was developed and its performance characteristics determined by [Laboratory Name]. It has not been cleared or approved by the US Food and Drug Administration." In 2007, the FDA, indicating that ASRs should not provide laboratories with unfettered control, narrowed the definition of ASRs further by requiring peer-reviewed publications describing given diagnostic procedures and limiting the ASR to a single component rather than multiple components.

Analyte-specific reagents are the "active ingredients" of tests that are purchased to detect a given disease or condition and are not subject to 510(k) approval. ASRs are purchased by manufacturers that use them as components of FDA-cleared or -approved tests and by clinical laboratories that use ASRs to develop assays for their exclusive use. The FDA classifies medical devices including diagnostic devices such as ASRs into Class I, II, or III devices according to the level of regulatory control that is necessary to provide a reasonable assurance of safety and effectiveness. These classifications include consideration of the level of risk associated with the device. The classification of an ASR determines the appropriate premarket approval process.

Class I ASRs are subject to general controls under section 513(a)(1)(A) of the *Federal Register*. The manufacturer's labeling on exempt Class I ASRs must bear the statement: "Analyte Specific Reagent. Analytical and performance characteristics are not established." Class II ASRs are reagents used as components in blood banking tests that have been classified Class II devices (eg, certain cytomegalovirus serological and *Treponema pallidum* nontreponemal test reagents). Class III ASRs are intended as components in tests intended to diagnose a contagious condition that is highly likely to result in a fatal outcome and for which prompt, accurate diagnosis offers the opportunity to mitigate the public health impact (eg, HIV/AIDS or tuberculosis). Class III ASRs are also intended for use in donor screening for conditions for which the FDA has recommended or required testing to safeguard the blood supply or establish the safe use of blood and blood products (eg, tests for hepatitis or for identifying blood groups).

In 2010, as the complexity of laboratory-developed issues increased, the FDA held a public comment session in an effort to more closely define laboratory-developed tests and assays and highlight the trend of commercial entities bringing increasingly complex tests to market, and sometimes directly to consumers, without FDA review. Examples included direct-to-consumer marketing of genetic testing for disease risk factors. The FDA notified these entities that their tests appear to meet the definition of medical devices and are subject to FDA authority.

No language is required for the unmodified use of an FDA-cleared test (eg, FDA-cleared tests for in vitro diagnostic use). However, whether additional oversight and language will be developed and required for the laboratory-modified use of an FDA-cleared test (eg, the laboratory-verified use of an additional sample type or claims of extended stability) remains unclear. By definition, these are laboratory-developed tests and may require the use of new language for their description. More guidance from the FDA regarding this issue is expected in 2011.

Research-use only (RUO) test kits require a separate disclaimer and are subject to language required by the FDA and language specified in a given manufacturer's RUO and material transfer agreements. RUO tests are in vitro products in the research phase of their development. This research may use animal or human tissues. A research device is not intended for human clinical diagnostic or prognostic use; thus, RUO tests are typically not reimbursed by Medicare, Medicaid, and most insurance carriers. Any laboratory results of RUO tests should have the disclaimer: "For research use only–not for use in diagnostic procedures." Such testing should be clearly segregated in billing systems, since CMS does not allow billing for RUO tests. Whether or not this truly applies to RUO tests/reagents used in anatomic pathology is highly contentious, with supporting legal opinions issued on both sides. Some molecular probes used in FISH and similar molecular genetic testing of solid tumors falls into this category. Given that reimbursement has occurred in support of such solid tumor diagnostic tools, it remains a gray area within the definitions of RUO tests.

FDA biologics oversight includes the collection and distribution of blood and blood products, vaccines, and certain other therapeutic agents derived from living organisms. Blood banks and transfusion medicine sections are involved in multiple regulatory agencies, including the CAP and the AABB (formerly the American Association of Blood Banks), an international nonprofit organization that represents individuals and institutions involved in transfusion medicine and cellular therapies. Laboratories' transfusion medicine sections commonly obtain dual accreditation by the CAP and the AABB.

FDA oversight is nonvoluntary. Blood banks that collect and distribute blood and blood products are governed by FDA regulations and inspected annually by FDA inspectors. The FDA is responsible for ensuring the safety of the blood supply in the United States. The FDA blood safety system depends on (1) accurate and complete educational material for donors so they can assess their risk, (2) sensitive communication of the donor screening questions, (3) donor understanding and honesty, (4) quality-controlled infectious-marker testing procedures, and (5) the appropriate handling and distribution of blood and blood products for patient use. The use of new testing methodologies (notably, nucleic-acid–based testing for infectious agents) in the last few years has considerably improved the safety of blood products. It is now estimated that the risk of HIV transmission in a blood transfusion is less than one in one million. However, it is not possible to ensure zero risk of transmitting an infectious disease.

The FDA status of a given transfusion medicine service depends on whether an institution has a blood donation program or only distributes blood to patients. Also, FDA status is linked to the institution's sharing of blood products. A transfusion medicine donor site that distributes blood across state lines requires an FDA license. A blood bank donor site that restricts blood distribution to intrastate sites requires FDA registration. Compared to CLIA regulations, in which the laboratory director is often considered the first responsible leader, FDA regulations focus more directly on the "owner." In many cases, the FDA allows the chief executive officer or chief operating officer of a hospital or other institution to represent the owner as the "responsible head." Within the FDA, the Center for Biologics Evaluation and Research has primary oversight over blood banks. Regional investigational oversight is administered through the Office of Regulatory Affairs. The two organizational units jointly develop good manufacturing practices regulations (legislated in 1996), inspection guides, procedural manuals, and training programs.

The FDA has performed annual blood bank inspections since 1988. The results of the blood bank inspection, including observations, deficiencies, and violations, are given to the individual responsible for the facility—usually the "responsible head." The inspection report lists the observations that are significant enough to require a response or corrective action. If the observations are of sufficient magnitude, or if they continue after substantial notice has been given, the FDA may issue a warning specifying the violations and threatening additional legal action if the problems are not addressed within a short time, usually 30 days. A full discussion of the FDA's role in blood banking is beyond the scope of this book; however, pathologists and laboratory directors should be aware of the FDA's impact on laboratory operations.

Research Administration

Since the end of the Second World War, research administration has geometrically expanded in this country in parallel with research productivity. Research encompassing basic, translational, and clinical arms has, in turn, been driven in large part by the need to document one being a good steward of funds received from mostly the National Institutes of Health, an arm of the Department of Health and Human Services, but also from the many dozens of federal agencies awarding funds (eg, Department of Defense, National Science Foundation, NASA) as well as state, local, and philanthropic organizations. This has resulted in the creation of a corps of professional grants administrators at either end of the financial pipeline. In 1993, the Research Administrators Certification Council was formed; their role, according to their website, is "...to certify that an individual, through experience and testing, has the fundamental knowledge necessary to be a professional research or sponsored programs administrator" (http://www.cra-cert.org/). To that end, that organization partnered with the Professional Testing Corporation to define the critical base of knowledge and tasks used in the certifying examination to define the field.

This corpus of knowledge could be defined by four broad categories, ie, project development and administration, legal requirements, and sponsor interface, along with financial and general management. Each of these, in turn, was further subdivided—in the first example, into collection and dissemination of information, proposal development, administration of awards, ethics and professionalism, intellectual property, and electronic research administration. Each of these could be still further subdivided into, for example, resource documents, application materials and information, dissemination of information/publications, proposal writing, negotiation techniques, and contracting basics (http://www.cra-cert.org/bodyof-knowledge.html). Thus, the depth and complexity of this field now parallels that of administrating the laboratory, has its own literature,[17] and requires the laboratory director to reach out for appropriate assistance and support.

Regulatory Context of Accreditation Programs

The CAP interfaces with regulatory activities at two levels: (1) through its Laboratory Accreditation Program and (2) proficiency testing. Other accreditation agencies also provide laboratory accreditation and/or PT.

What role does laboratory accreditation have in the regulatory arena? Laboratory accreditation began with a formal accreditation program offered by the CAP in 1961. At that time, laboratory accreditation was largely an educational and voluntary activity. Laboratories participated to improve their quality and achieve a standard of excellence in the laboratory industry. Central to this laboratory accreditation process was peer review by inspection by CAP-accredited institutions of similar size and service. In 1994, the federal government recognized the CAP Laboratory Accreditation Program as fulfilling CLIA's requirements for a certificate of accreditation. Once CMS deemed it

an accreditation provider, the program took on additional regulatory requirements since a CLIA certificate could, in some states, be issued after passing a CAP inspection and without a CMS inspection. In 2008, approximately 16,000 laboratories received CLIA certificates of accreditation, 5,700 of which were provided by the CAP. (The specific types of CLIA certificates are described later in this chapter.) In 2009, the CAP was again deemed a laboratory accreditation provider by CMS.

Another recognized accreditation system is the International Organization for Standardization (ISO) system. ISO is an internationally recognized system for managing quality and is especially prominent in the industrial sector worldwide. ISO has assigned a working group for analyzing the specific standards for clinical laboratories—essentially a merger of two other ISO standards (ISO/International Electrotechnical Commission 17025 and ISO 9001)—that better account for the medical care and patient safety environment of clinical laboratories. The working group has made available this set of standards, referred to as ISO 15189 standards, and collaborates with the CAP to provide dual accreditation.

Similarly, the Joint Commission uses its own standards for clinical laboratories to provide laboratory accreditation. The Joint Commission's laboratory accreditation is separate from its hospital or health care institution accreditation. Laboratories that are CAP accredited can elect to not undergo Joint Commission accreditation inspections as part of the Joint Commission's review of their institutions. Even with CAP accreditation, however, the Joint Commission is interested in the processes used to track specimens and patients through patient specimen testing. This tracking process requires the cooperation of the laboratory director and other laboratory staff at an institutional Joint Commission review.

A special category of regulation is drug-testing management. The US Department of Health and Human Services maintains a certification program for testing current and potential employees for drug use, coordinated by the Substance Abuse and Mental Health Services Administration. A listing of certified laboratories is published in the *Federal Register* the first week of each month. These laboratories may provide employment and pre-employment drug testing for private-sector and state government employers. The World Anti-Doping Agency (WADA) also accredits laboratory testing, primarily for athletes engaged in organized sport-

Table 12-2. Responsibilities of the Laboratory Director

Ensures that testing systems provide quality services during the preanalytic, analytic, and postanalytic phases of testing
Ensures that the physical and environmental conditions are adequate and appropriate for the testing performed
Ensures that the employees' environment is safe from physical, chemical, and biological hazards
Ensures that a general supervisor (if high complexity testing is performed) is available to provide day-to-day supervision of all testing personnel, report test results, and provide on-site supervision of minimally qualified testing personnel when they perform high complexity testing
Ensures that the laboratory employs a sufficient number of appropriately educated, experienced, and/or trained personnel who provide appropriate consultations, properly supervise tests, accurately perform tests, and report test results in accordance with the written duties and responsibilities specified by the laboratory director
Ensures that new test procedures are reviewed, included in the procedure manual, and followed by personnel
Ensures that each employee's responsibilities and duties are specified in writing

ing events, including the Olympics. WADA publishes two sets of statistics per year. The first set of statistics is a summary of WADA's laboratory results and findings. The second set of statistics is a summary of laboratory results and findings from WADA-accredited laboratories. There were approximately 35 WADA-accredited laboratories worldwide in 2009.

Pathologists must be aware that certain regulations overlap with some accreditation activities. This is the overlap that occurs most frequently in PT and laboratory accreditation. In recent years, this overlap has received increased attention as laboratory errors have been identified and questions about the quality of CMS-deemed services have arisen. In response, laboratory accreditation agencies and PT providers have realigned their activities to more explicitly meet federal regulations and guidelines.

Responsibilities

Laboratory Director

The CLIA laboratory director has many important responsibilities related to maintaining proper CLIA compliance. Some of these responsibilities cannot be delegated to others and must be maintained by direct oversight (Table 12-2). An excel-

lent brochure provided by CMS and the CDC that describes the responsibilities that can be delegated to specific CLIA personnel categories can be obtained at www.cms.hhs.gov/CLIA/downloads/brochure7.pdf.[18]

CLIA laboratory directors can direct a maximum of five laboratories, including laboratories that perform nonwaived testing. For each certificate type, there are three exceptions that allow one laboratory director to direct multiple locations:

- Laboratories that are not at a fixed location, eg, mobile units, health screening fairs, or other temporary testing locations, may be covered under the certificate of the designated primary site.

- Not-for-profit or federal, state, or local government laboratories that engage in limited public health testing (not more than a combination of 15 moderately complex or waived tests per certificate) may file for a single application.

- Laboratories that are within a hospital or that are located at contiguous buildings on the same campus and under common direction may file a single application or multiple applications for the laboratory sites within the same physical location or at the same street address.

The CLIA authorities within a given jurisdiction should be notified of a change in laboratory director within 30 days. The state health department and any accrediting agencies should also be notified of this change to ensure a smooth transition.

How should pathologists and laboratory directors ensure that delegated responsibilities are performed appropriately? Above all, there should be a clear mechanism in place for ensuring effective communication among management and laboratory personnel. Regular reviews and meetings can enhance some types of communication. For example, quality assessment activities and problems can be part of a quality committee review. Similarly, the quality committee can identify performance improvement projects. All complaints should have a resolution process. Any PT outliers as well as the procedure for performing PT should be investigated; an audit of PT and PT processes may be of value. A review of personnel competencies and performance evaluations may help determine whether personnel are sufficiently trained. Also, a regular review of analytical test performance, laboratory reports, and preanalytical processes can identify early problems in all phases of testing.

Every laboratory director should have a clear understanding of the descriptions and requirements for each of the CLIA laboratory personnel categories. Knowing the competencies of the laboratory staff is key to appropriate delegation and compliance.

Technical Consultant

The technical consultant is qualified by education and either training or experience to provide technical advise and direction for each of the specialties and subspecialties of service in which the laboratory performs moderate complexity tests or procedures. The technical consultant is responsible for the technical and scientific oversight of the laboratory (subpart M, section 493.1413).[19] If moderate complexity testing is performed, a laboratory director who is appropriately trained in all areas of testing provided can serve as the technical consultant.

Clinical Consultant

The clinical consultant provides consultation regarding the appropriateness of the testing ordered and the interpretation of test results. The clinical consultant is the laboratory's clinical representative for evaluating test results. The clinical consultant's duties include the following:

- Providing clinical consultation to the laboratory's clients
- Assisting the laboratory's clients to ensure that the appropriate tests are ordered to meet clinical expectations
- Ensuring that reports of test results include pertinent information required for specific patient interpretation
- Ensuring that consultation is available and communicated to the laboratory's clients for matters related to the quality of the test results reported and their interpretation concerning specific patient conditions (subpart M, section 493.1419)[19]

Technical Supervisor

The technical supervisor is responsible for the technical and scientific oversight of the laboratory. The technical supervisor is not required to be on-site whenever testing is performed; however, he or she must be available on an as-needed basis to provide supervision in the laboratory. The technical supervisor is also responsible for assessing the competency of testing personnel, identifying training needs, determining testing technology, determining instrumentation, establishing a quality program, enrolling in PT, and verifying test results (subpart M, section 493.1451).[19]

General Supervisor

The laboratory must have at least one general supervisor who, under the direction of the laboratory director and supervision of the technical supervisor, provides day-to-day supervision of testing personnel and test results reporting. In the absence of the director and technical supervisor, the general supervisor is responsible for the proper performance of all laboratory procedures and test results reporting (subpart M, section 493.1461).[19]

Testing Personnel

The testing personnel are responsible for processing specimens, performing tests, and reporting test results. Each individual performs only those moderate or high complexity tests that are authorized by the laboratory director and require a degree of skill commensurate with the individual's education, training, experience, and technical abilities (subpart M, section 493.1425).[19]

As discussed in Chapter 4, "Personnel Management," most personnel categories in human resources departments do not exactly match the titles and descriptions of the CLIA personnel categories. Therefore, the laboratory director should work closely with human resources to cross-reference titles and match the CLIA categories so that sufficient personnel are available to test human specimens. Also, human resources may have additional titles and categories, such as a manager title, that oversees multiple supervisors. Some types of specialist titles match the technical supervisor title found in CLIA. A special quality manager title is an important resource for every laboratory director to ensure uniformity of quality approaches and sufficient oversight of all laboratory quality activities.

Where laboratory technologists are trained depends somewhat on the specific requirements of the state and the federal government. Technologist schools can be affiliated with colleges or universities. Often, the internship year is spent in local health care institutions and independent reference laboratories. The National Accrediting Agency for Clinical Laboratory Scientists accredits training programs and technologist schools and has recently aligned with the ASCP Board of Certification, which provides examinations and credentialing of laboratory technologists. Some states accept the Board of Certification examination in lieu of their own state examinations or requirements. Other states (eg, New York) may require their own examination or a passing rate higher than that typical of the ASCP Board examination.

Some states require individual licensure of personnel and/or state licensure of individual laboratories in addition to CLIA certification. A thorough knowledge of the local legal requirements is essential to managing a clinical laboratory. A few states (eg, New York and Washington) have deemed status with CLIA, meaning that their regulations and/or licensure do not require separate CLIA oversight. However, most states collaborate with CMS and CLIA to provide some level of oversight through the state health departments.

Application Procedures

CLIA Certification

There are six types of CLIA applications. All types of applications must be renewed every 2 years. A pathologist who is only performing waived tests and setting up a waived testing laboratory—the common type of laboratory in physician offices— should apply for a CLIA Certificate of Waiver. A basic fee is applied. In 2008, there were over 129,000 Certificates of Waiver in the US, the largest number of CLIA certificates in any one category.

A laboratory that performs simple types of microscopy can apply for a PPM CLIA certificate. Section 493.19 of CLIA provides the following specifications for PPM[20]:

> (1) The examination must be personally performed by one of the following practitioners:
>
> (i) A physician during the patient's visit on a specimen obtained from his or her own patient or from a patient of a group medical practice of which the physician is a member or an employee.
>
> (ii) A midlevel practitioner, under the supervision of a physician or in independent practice only if authorized by the State, during the patient's visit on a specimen obtained from his or her own patient or from a patient of a clinic, group medical practice, or other health care provider of which the midlevel practitioner is a member or an employee.
>
> (iii) A dentist during the patient's visit on a specimen obtained from his or her own patient or from a patient of a group dental practice of which the dentist is a member or an employee.
>
> (2) The procedure must be categorized as moderately complex (not high complexity).

> (3) The primary instrument for performing the test is the microscope, limited to bright-field or phase-contrast microscopy.
>
> (4) The specimen is labile or delay in performing the test could compromise the accuracy of the test result.
>
> (5) Control materials are not available to monitor the entire testing process.
>
> (6) Limited specimen handling or processing is required.

More than 38,000 laboratories maintain a PPM CLIA certificate. It is particularly applicable to physician office laboratories, eg, dermatology clinic laboratories that perform potassium hydroxide preparations or obstetrics and gynecology practice laboratories that perform wet mounts from the vaginal tract.

Higher levels of CLIA certificates are required if even one moderate or high complexity test is performed in a given laboratory. When opening a new clinical laboratory, before actual patient testing has begun, pathologists must submit a CLIA application and receive a CLIA certificate. The cost of CLIA certificates varies according to test volumes. The first CLIA certificate a new laboratory receives is a CLIA Certificate of Registration, which includes a newly assigned CLIA identification number and indicates that the laboratory has registered and can begin testing. This certificate is held until a CMS CLIA inspection occurs or until a successful primary accreditation inspection (such as a CAP inspection) has been completed.

At one point I proposed that we discontinue CAP inspections and just use the Joint Commission and state inspections, which were mandatory. I almost had a revolution among my medical technologists. They wanted—no demanded—that we continue with the CAP inspections, because it always demonstrated how good they were and how flawlessly their laboratory sections operated. The sections competed with one another to see who had the fewest deficiencies. Of course they were right; it was a great morale builder, and on occasion we also learned something.

A major use of an inspection is to support a request for space or equipment. For years I had a crummy autopsy suite, and administration was not forthcoming with the funds needed to update it—until one year I showed the CAP Inspector how awful our morgue was, and convinced him to give us a couple of deficiencies. With these in hand, I was able to convince administration to make the needed changes.

It is very important for pathologists and, particularly, Laboratory Directors to become inspectors. Not only do you learn how to prepare your own laboratory for inspections, but whenever I inspected another laboratory, I always learned something that I could take home that was new or useful for my own laboratory.

Certificate of Waiver: Waived testing only

Certificate of PPM: Office-based microscopy

Certificate of Registration: New laboratory CLIA not yet inspected

Certificate of Compliance: Inspected by CLIA/CMS inspectors

Certificate of Accreditation: Inspected by a laboratory accreditation agency (CAP, COLA)

Figure 12-3. CLIA Certificates.

A laboratory that chooses to be CLIA inspected receives a CLIA Certificate of Compliance after a successful inspection and is inspected by a CLIA inspector every 2 years thereafter. A laboratory that chooses to be inspected by a deemed laboratory accreditation agency receives a CLIA Certificate of Accreditation after a successful inspection. In some states, the accreditation inspection that occurs every 2 years will serve as the CLIA inspection. In other states, separate CLIA or state inspectors, along with inspectors from accreditation agencies, may inspect every 2 years. The types of CLIA certificates are summarized in Figure 12-3.

Laboratory Inspections

If there is one pervading activity in clinical laboratories, it is the inspection cycle. This section focuses on regulatory-related inspections by CLIA and by the CAP in its deemed CMS capacity. Inspection processes could be discussed at length; however, a few essentials can help laboratory directors develop a perspective of "continuous readiness."

Both CLIA and CAP inspections occur on a 2-year cycle unless a complaint or problem initiates an inspection. CAP inspections are unannounced inspections that occur within a 3-month window of the anniversary date of the laboratory's first CAP inspection. (A laboratory's first, or primary, inspection can be an announced inspection.) In 2009, the CAP was again reviewed and approved as an accreditation provider by CMS. CAP inspections are checklist based. The checklist model contains specific items that must be addressed as "yes," "no," or "not applicable." Each checklist item or standard is assigned a designation of Phase I or Phase II. Phase II inspection citations are the more serious citations, requiring corrective action, documentation supporting the corrective action, and a follow-up report to the CAP within 30 days. Although Phase I citations do not require that documentation of corrective action and a re-

port be submitted to the CAP within 30 days, they do stipulate that corrective action must be taken by the next internal (interim) inspection. Phase 0 checklist questions are posed for developmental and information purposes and are not citations that require corrective action. CAP checklists are customized according to the laboratory's test menu and services provided.

The CAP *Laboratory General Checklist* comprehensively addresses most regulatory and compliance topics such as quality management plans, performance improvement, personnel, facilities, and safety. The CAP also now provides a laboratory director checklist to assess the credentials and performance of the laboratory director. Until the recent CMS renewal of the CAP Laboratory Accreditation Program, CAP checklists were available online to the public. With the 2009 renewal of deemed status, checklists are only available to participants in the accreditation process.

CMS inspectors or their agents (ie, state inspectors) approach inspections using a tracer methodology that involves tracing specific patients and patient specimens and investigating compliance with specific CLIA regulations. Thus, CMS inspectors examine all three phases of testing, review the quality assessment program, examine personnel training and competencies, review the facilities and safety required for the work environment, and examine the credentials of the laboratory director and other categories of CLIA personnel. CMS inspections are currently announced inspections, but this may change in the future.

A CMS inspection may include reviewing an out-of-range QC and examining corrective actions. To determine whether the results were released, an inspector may ask how patient specimens were handled on a given date when the QC was out of range. The laboratory reports from that date would be retrieved to confirm that the results were not released without QC corrective action(s). The procedure for the test and for the QC would be reviewed to determine whether the procedures were followed and whether the laboratory director had signed off on the procedures. Each of these steps helps determine whether quality assessment is in place and whether patient specimens are being managed appropriately.

Above all, every laboratory should operate in a constant state of readiness for inspection. If a laboratory has a well-developed quality management plan with widespread participation, and if a laboratory has a defined document control system, a

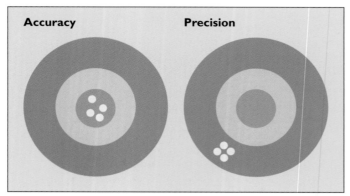

Figure 12-4. Accuracy versus Precision. A figurative demonstration of accuracy versus precision using a bull's eye target.

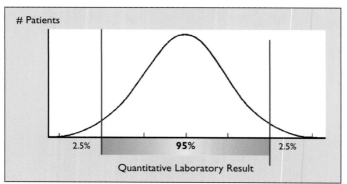

Figure 12-5. Reference Range Statistics. A bell-shaped curve demonstrating development of a reference range using a continuous quantitative analyte.

laboratory can readily respond to inspectors' questions regardless of whether the quality leadership or laboratory director is present. The keys to quality are also the keys to continuous readiness.

Metrics Applicable to CLIA Regulations

Test Validation

Test validation refers to the establishment of documented evidence that provides a high degree of assurance that a test or test system consistently functions as expected. According to CLIA '03, full test validation includes assessing a test's accuracy, precision, linearity, and reference and reportable ranges. Depending on the test analyte and targeted detection ranges, other types of metrics may also be applicable (eg, dilutions).

Accuracy and Precision

Accuracy is the degree of correctness or true value (ie, the comparison of value to true value) of a given laboratory result. Accuracy also implies

freedom from error. Many of the quality assessment processes (QC, PT) described in Chapter 7, "Quality Management in Laboratory Medicine," exist to ensure the accuracy of testing or freedom from error. Precision is the degree to which a test provides the same measurement over time. The best statistical tool for measuring precision is the coefficient of variation. A comparison of accuracy versus precision is shown in Figure 12-4.

Accuracy implies that the test results are close to the true value of an analyte, whereas precision simply implies that a result is close to the same result over time with repeated measurements. In some cases, good precision is a valuable tool; for example, if therapeutic drug levels provide high precision useful for the clinician's monitoring of therapy but do not actually reflect the whole blood level, the result is still valuable if the clinician knows how to use the results clinically. Precision analysis of new instrumentation should be a part of every test validation.

Reference Ranges

CLIA also requires that test results be reported with reference ranges, or intervals, which are sometimes incorrectly referred to as normal ranges. The reference range is defined as the range of laboratory test results expected for a given condition, usually health. The range for continuous analyte quantitative results (such as electrolyte levels), as compared to positive versus negative results, is typically established as the central 95% of a population of interest. This range is demonstrated in a bell-shaped curve (Figure 12-5).

To have adequate power to accurately assign the upper and lower limits of the reference range, a full reference interval study of an analyte requires a large number of subjects. The CLSI recommends 120 subjects in each group.[21] The central 95% of the data represents the reference range. However, conformance to a Gaussian distribution may be incomplete. A natural logarithm transformation produces a nearly Gaussian distribution. In such a distribution, of all presumed "healthy" individuals tested, 2.5% will be outside the reference range on the low side, and 2.5% will be outside the reference range on the high side. In all discussions regarding individual patient results, it is important to recognize that if 20 tests are ordered for one patient, statistically, there is a 1 in 20 chance that a laboratory result will be "abnormal" but may not reflect illness in the patient. Clinicians should be aware that large panels can create unnecessary secondary over-utilization of testing

		Sensitivity and Specificity		
		Target Disorder		
		Present	Absent	
Diagnostic Test Result	+	A	B	A+B
	–	C	D	C+D
		A+C	B+D	A+B+C+D

Sensitivity = A / (A + C)

Specificity = D / (B + D)

Figure 12-6. Bayes' Theorem in the Laboratory: Calculation of Sensitivity and Specificity.

services if an evaluation of "abnormal" results is not a thoughtful part of any clinical evaluation. Pathologists or laboratory directors may be responsible for educating clinicians in this regard.

Recently, a multilaboratory CAP Q-Probes quality study investigated the origin of reference intervals.[17] In the study, individual laboratories were surveyed about their methods for determining reference intervals, and variations in the intervals for selected analytes were examined. Less than half of the reporting laboratories conducted an internal study of healthy individuals in developing their reference ranges; most laboratories relied on external sources to establish their reference intervals. There was slight variation in intervals used by the central 80% of laboratories. Thus, many laboratories may adopt reference intervals from manufacturers without conducting on-site testing of healthy individuals. However, the reference intervals used by facilities that forgo on-site testing are not statistically different from the reference intervals validated with on-site studies. Therefore, reference ranges established with vendor support may not significantly differ from those of fully developed internal studies. All laboratory directors and pathologists should be aware that adopting vendor reference ranges requires good faith and a thorough evaluation of the methods the vendor used to develop specific reference ranges.[22]

Sensitivity, Specificity, and Predictive Values for Positive and Negative Results

Sensitivity, specificity, and the predictive values for positive and negative results are important tools clinicians use to determine the value of a test result for their patients within the context of specific patient populations. Sensitivity is the likelihood of a positive or abnormal result when the patient has the disease of interest. Specificity is the likelihood of a negative (normal) test result when the patient does not have the disease of interest.[23] In other words, sensitivity represents the proportion of persons who truly have a disease in a screened population who are identified by the test as having that disease; it is a measure of the probability of correctly diagnosing a condition. Specificity is the proportion of persons who truly do not have a disease and are so identified by a screening test; specificity is a measure of the probability of correctly identifying a person who does not have a particular disease. For a given test, a sensitivity of 95% and a specificity of 92% implies that 5% of the tests are false-negatives and 8% of

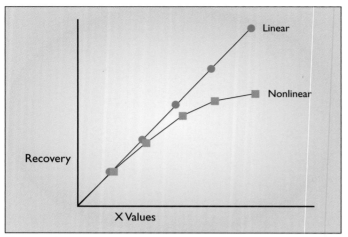

Figure 12-7. Linearity. An example of linear versus nonlinear data points.

the tests are false-positive. A four-square diagram based on Bayesian statistics can be used to determine sensitivity and specificity (Figure 12-6).

Predictive values are based on the prevalence of a disease in a given patient population. A predictive positive value in a population in which the disease is rare enhances the likelihood that a positive result represents a false-positive result. If a disease is common in a particular patient population, the likelihood that a positive result represents true disease increases. Predictive values can be calculated as follows:

Positive Predictive Value =
True-Positives / (True-Positives + False-Positives)

Negative Predictive Value =
True-Negatives / (True-Negatives + False-Negatives)

Linearity and Reportable Range

Linearity is the ability of a test to obtain results that vary in a manner directly proportional to changes in the concentration (amount) of the analyte in the sample or by a well-defined mathematical transformation. According to CLSI evaluation protocol 6A, a quantitative analytical method is said to be linear if the analyte recovery from a series of sample solutions (the measured value) is linearly proportional to the actual concentration or content of the analyte (the true value) in the sample solutions.[24] Linearity studies require five different concentrations, equally spaced, spanning the analytical range. Spiking known amounts of an analyte, performing serial dilutions, and creating mixtures of different ratios of a high and low standard are acceptable approaches to creating a linearity study. At least two replicate samples should be performed for each point (Figure 12-7).

Statistical regression analysis is the statistical method most frequently used to analyze linearity. When the solutions have known values, the ideal value of the slope of the regression line is 1.0. Deviation from the slope is used as an estimate of proportional systematic error. The G test is a statistical challenge to determine whether a fit is linear enough to use regression analysis. A polynomial method also can challenge data for nonlinearity and is employed by the CAP Instrumentation Resource Committee to challenge for linearity. It is also used as a means by which laboratories can assess the linearity for test systems and compare their performance to that of other laboratories. For details for the statistical evaluation of linearity, other references are available.[24,25]

The reportable range evaluation is a linearity check of new instrumentation or test systems, compared to the reportable range as provided by a manufacturer. The reportable range is defined as the highest and lowest results that can be reliably given in a laboratory report. Two pools, one from near the lowest detectable limit and one from near the highest detectable limit, can be diluted to achieve an equally spaced set of five challenges. Linearity can be examined visually or with statistical analysis as described above to verify the reportable range indicated by the manufacturer.

Discussion and Controversies: Proficiency Testing

A recent emphasis in CMS compliance is the appropriate management of PT in the clinical laboratory. PT is not required for waived testing under CLIA. However, accreditation agencies such as the CAP may require PT. Regardless, enrolling in PT for waived testing improves the quality of the testing one can provide to patients.

The more complex problems surrounding PT occur when larger laboratories perform nonwaived testing. PT is required for regulated analytes (Table 12-3.) The laboratory director is responsible for choosing a vendor from an approved PT provider listed on the CLIA website. The laboratory must enroll for all testing related to the regulated analyte list. For example, for bacteriology, the laboratory must enroll in multiple PT samples per testing event, including Gram stain, direct antigen, organism identification, and/or susceptibility testing.

Proficiency testing must be performed in the same manner as patient specimen testing. That is, PT samples must be tested the same number of times as patient specimens, at the same time as pa-

Table 12-3. Federally Regulated Analytes

Chemistry

Routine Chemistry
Alanine aminotransferase
Albumin
Alkaline phosphatase
Amylase
Aspartate aminotransferase
Bilirubin, total
Blood gases (pH, pO_2, pCO_2)
Calcium, total
Chloride
Cholesterol, total
Cholesterol, HDL
Creatine kinase
Creatine kinase isoenzymes (CK-MB)
Creatinine
Glucose (excluding waived testing)
Iron, total
Lactate dehydrogenase (LDH)
LDH isoenzymes (LDH1 / LDH2)
Magnesium
Potassium
Sodium
Total protein
Triglycerides
Urea nitrogen
Uric acid

Endocrinology
Cortisol
Free thyroxine
Human chorionic gonadotropin (excluding waived testing)
T3 uptake
Triiodothyronine
Thyroid stimulating hormone
Thyroxine

Toxicology
Blood alcohol
Blood lead
Carbamazepine
Digoxin
Ethosuximide
Gentamicin
Lithium
Phenobarbital
Phenytoin
Primidone
Procainamide (and metabolites)
Quinidine
Theophylline
Tobramycin
Valproic acid

Hematology

Cell identification or white blood cell differential
Erythrocyte count
Hematocrit (excluding spun microhematocrit)
Hemoglobin (excluding waived test hemoglobin)
Leukocyte count
Platelet count
Fibrinogen
Partial thromboplastin time
Prothrombin time

Diagnostic Immunology

General Immunology
Alpha-1-antitrypsin
Alpha-fetoprotein (tumor marker)
Antinuclear antibody
Antistreptolysin O, quantitative
Anti-human immunodeficiency virus
Complement C3
Complement C4
Hepatitis markers (HBsAg, anti-HBc, HBeAg)
Immunoglobulin (Ig) A
IgG
IgE
IgM
Infectious mononucleosis
Rheumatoid factor
Rubella

Syphilis Serology
Qualitative and quantitative

Immunohematology

ABO group (excluding subgroups)
D (Rh) typing
Unexpected antibody detection
Compatibility testing
Antibody identification

Microbiology

Bacteriology

Mycobacteriology

Mycology

Parasitology

Virology

Source: Clinical Laboratory Improvement Amendments (CLIA). Proficiency Testing Dos and Don'ts.[13]

tient specimens, by the same personnel who routinely test patient specimens, and with the same test system that is routinely used for patient specimens. PT samples should be rotated among the testing personnel in the laboratory. Because of PT sample stability issues, some PT samples require special handling (eg, reconstitution). However, PT samples should never be sent out of the laboratory for any reason, including sending patient specimens for referral, confirmation, or reflex testing, even if one would do so as part of standard operating procedure. Likewise, if a laboratory receives PT samples from another laboratory, it should not test the samples.

Case Example: Proficiency Testing and Human Resources

The biannual CLIA inspector makes an appointment to inspect a laboratory in 7 days. Since the laboratory director is continuously prepared, the only preparation she performs is ensuring that all records are readily available for the inspector when he arrives at 8:00 AM. When the inspector reviews the records of PT testing on a date last August, he notes that the "instrument tape" for total bilirubin does not match the PT result reported to the CAP for the proficiency survey. When the inspector asks the technologist who performed the testing about this result, the technologist replies that he had performed three replicates on the PT sample for total bilirubin, and he had reported the mean of those three results. When the inspector asks if three replicates are performed on every patient specimen, the technologist replies, "No, I only perform three replicates on PT samples." The inspector then asks for all PT records for the chemistry section and informs the laboratory director that she is about to receive a serious citation. Very concerned, the laboratory director asks about the citation, and the inspector confirms that the PT sample was being handled differently from the patient specimens. What should the laboratory director do?

A full review of the technologist's quality performance record is in order. In this case, a second example of the technologist performing inappropriate replicate testing is identified in the PT records, and it is noted in the employee's personnel file that he received a warning letter for reporting test results on a day when the QC was out of range. Thus, the technologist has received three documented performance citations in the past year. The human resources department indicates that the third infraction makes the employee eligible for suspension or termination. The laboratory director decides that, given the severity of the technologist's most recent infraction, which could result in the laboratory having to cease testing, termination is the appropriate action and recommends this to the human resources representative.

Serious infractions of PT of regulated analytes are reported to CMS and can result in CMS ordering the laboratory to cease testing. Although CMS makes every effort to view PT as an educational activity, gross violation of PT could be an event sufficient to justify CMS action. CMS is increasingly examining all details of PT on a national basis.

Laboratory personnel who work in two different CLIA-certified laboratories should not test the same PT sample at both sites; if possible, they should be advised not to test the same PT sample in both laboratories or share the results between the two laboratories. Care should be taken in any communication regarding PT samples or PT results between CLIA-certified laboratories until the official results for the PT challenge have been published.

These pitfalls can cause significant problems for a laboratory, including a 6-month suspension of testing. Such pitfalls are best avoided by maintaining an excellent PT standard operating procedure, maintaining records for each PT challenge and result, taking the appropriate corrective actions when any deviance occurs in results or procedures, and educating testing personnel about the differences and limitations of PT sample testing versus patient specimen testing.

References

1. US Department of Health and Human Services. Medicare, Medicaid and CLIA programs: regulations implementing the Clinical Laboratory Improvement Amendments of 1988 (CLIA). Final rule. *Fed Reg.* 1992;(57):7002-7186.

2. US Department of Health and Human Services. Medicare, Medicaid and CLIA programs: regulations for the Clinical Laboratory Improvement Amendments of 2003: Code of Federal Regulations. *Fed Reg.* 2004;(68):967-1087.

3. Lusky K. With '03 regulation, CLIA '88 closes QC loop. *CAP Today.* March 2003:1-5.

4. US Department of Health and Human Services. Clinical Laboratory Improvement Amendments (CLIA): Overview. Available at: www.cms.hhs.gov/ CLIA. Accessed Jan 21, 2011.

5. US Department of Labor. Occupational Safety and Health Standards: Part 1910.1030 (a-i), Subpt. Z, Toxic and Hazardous Substances, Blood Borne Pathogens. *Fed Reg.* 1996;(71):5507.

6. American Medical Association. Physician Resources. Available at: http://www.ama-assn. org/ama/pub/physician-resources.shtml. Accessed Jan 5, 2011.

Challenge Questions

The laboratory director of a new laboratory performing nonwaived testing wants to apply for CLIA and CAP accreditation. Which of the following apply?

A. The director will apply for a CLIA Certificate of Compliance
B. The inspection will be an announced inspection by the CAP
C. An inspection will be performed by CMS CLIA inspector
D. The director will first apply for a CLIA Certificate of Registration
E. B and D
F. B, C, and D

Answer: F; see pages 226 to 227.

A common statistical tool for the evaluation of the reportable range is:

A. Student's t-test
B. Coefficient of variation
C. Regression analysis
D. Bayesian test
E. Standard deviation

Answer: C; see page 230.

What is the relationship between ICD and CPT codes and medical necessity?

Answer: See pages 216 to 217 and Chapter 10, pages 175 to 179.

7. US Department of Health and Human Services. Centers for Medicare and Medicaid Services. ICD-9 Provider and Diagnostic Codes. Available at: www.cms.hhs.gov/ICD9ProviderDiagnosticCodes/. Accessed Nov 17, 2010.

8. *PMIC's ICD-9-CM 2011 Hospital/Payer Edition.* Vols 1-3. Los Angeles, CA: Practice Management Information Corp; 2010.

9. World Health Organization. Guidance on Regulations for the Transport of Infectious Substances. Geneva, Switzerland: World Health Organization; 2005:1-30.

10. Washington G-2 Reports. Available at: www.g2reports.com. Accessed Jan 5, 2011.

11. Wagar EA, Yasin B, Yuan S, Point-of-care testing: twenty years' experience. *Lab Med.* 2008; 39:560-563.

12. US Department of Health and Human Services. CLIA Complexity Process. Available at: http://www.fda.gov/AboutFDA/CentersOffices/CDRH/CDRHOffices/ucm124269.htm. Accessed Nov 17, 2010.

13. US Department of Health and Human Services. Clinical Laboratory Improvement Amendments (CLIA). Proficiency Testing: Dos and Don'ts [brochure]. Published September 2008. Available at: www.cms.hhs.gov/clia/downloads/CLIAbrochure 8.pdf. Accessed Jan 20, 2011.

14. US Department of Health and Human Services. Subpart K—Quality Systems for Nonwaived Testing, 493.1200(b). Available at: http://www.cdc.gov/clia/regs/subpart_k.aspx. Published 2003. Accessed Jan 20, 2011.

15. The Library of Congress. H.R. 3095. Safe Medical Devices Act of 1990. Available at: http://thomas.loc.gov/cgi-bin/bdquery/z?d101:HR03095:@@@D&summ2=1&|TOM:/bss/d101query.html. Accessed Jan 20, 2011.

16. US Department of Health and Human Services. Food and Drug Administration. CFR Title 21 Database. 21 CFR 809.10(e), 809.30, 820, 864.4020. Available at: http://www.accessdata.fda.gov/scripts/cdrh/cfdocs/cfcfr/cfrsearch.cfm. Accessed Jan 20, 2011.

17. Centers for Medicare and Medicaid Services. Centers for Disease Control and Prevention. Clinical Laboratory Improvement Amendments (CLIA): Laboratory Director Responsibilities, What Are My Responsibilities As A Laboratory Director [brochure]. Published August 2006. Available at: www.cms.hhs.gov/CLIA/downloads/brochure7.pdf. Accessed Feb 3, 2011.

18. US Department of Health and Human Services. Centers for Disease Control and Prevention. Current CLIA Regulations; Subpart M, Sec. 493.1413-1461. Available at: http://www.cdc.gov/clia/regs/ subpart_m.aspx#493.1413. Accessed Jan 20, 2011.

19. US Department of Health and Human Services. Centers for Disease Control and Prevention. CLIA provider-performed microscopy (PPM) procedures. Available at: www.cdc.gov/clia/ppm.aspx. Accessed Jan 20, 2011.

20. *Defining, Establishing, and Verifying Reference Intervals in the Clinical Laboratory. Approved Guideline.* 3rd ed. Wayne, PA: Clinical and Laboratory Standards Institute; 2008. Document C28-A3.

21. Friedberg RC, Souers R, Wagar EA, Stankovic AK, Valenstein P. The origin of reference intervals: a College of American Pathologists Q-Probes study of "normal ranges" used in 163 clinical laboratories. *Arch Pathol Lab Med.* 2007;131:348-357.

22. Tetrault GA. Laboratory statistics. In: Henry BD. *Clinical Diagnosis and Management by Laboratory Methods.* New York, NY: WB Saunders Co; 2001:138-147.

23. Tholen DW, Kroll M, Astles JR, et al. *Evaluation of the Linearity of Quantitative Measurement Procedures: A Statistical Approach. Approved Guideline.* Wayne, PA: NCCLS; 2003. Document EP6-A.

24. Jhang JS, Chang CC, Fink DJ, Kroll MH. Evaluation of linearity in the clinical laboratory. *Arch Pathol Lab Med.* 2004;128:44–48.

25. Kroll MH, Praestgaard J, Michaliszyn E, Styer PE. Evaluation of the extent of nonlinearity in reportable range studies. *Arch Pathol Lab Med.* 2000;124:1331-1338.

CHAPTER 13

Legal Affairs for Pathologists

Elizabeth A. Wagar, MD

Contents

The Lawyer and the Doctor: A Contrast in Philosophies

The histories of law and medicine describe the history of civilization. Societies have always used some semblance of law to mitigate disputes and manage the rights of the individual within the rights of a society. Even the best-known set of early laws, Hammurabi's Code, created in Babylon in the eighteenth century BCE, appears to be a compilation of even earlier laws and standards. Unlike law, which arose because of people's intrinsic sense of fairness, medicine arose from the human need to explain birth, death, and disease. The Lascaux cave paintings, which are among the earliest expressions of human society, show the administration of herbal treatment. Ancient Egypt had a highly advanced public health system in which physicians specialized in different types of diseases; this system was overlaid with heavy religious significance and influence. In Babylonia, Esagil-kin-apli of Borsippa (1069–1046 BCE) wrote one of the earliest medical diagnostic handbooks, which contained express instructions to "examine and inspect" for disease findings. The philosophies of medicine and law come to some confluence in the Hippocratic Oath, which was written by Hippocrates of Kos (460–437 BCE) in Greece. The Hippocratic Oath includes instructions to do no harm and respect individuals' right to privacy—implicit elements of the laws of many early societies.

Today, the ways in which information is collected and evaluated in law and medicine diverge significantly. In many legal systems, evidence regarding an individual case is gathered and compared to that of earlier similar cases; this is referred to as precedent. Thus, rulings—the knowledge base of law—consist of single cases to which judges apply previous single-case rulings, which may in turn be based on a statute. On the other hand, the knowledge base of modern medicine is accumulated through the scientific method, a test of truth described in earlier times by Ibn al-Haytham (965–1039) and advanced during the Renaissance. The four steps of the scientific method are observing a phenomenon, forming a hypothesis to explain the phenomenon, using deductive reasoning to predict an explanation for the phenomenon, and testing, or experimenting, to verify the explanation.

In some respects, intrinsic conflicts exist between modern law and modern medicine. Each

Figure 13-1. Medical Versus Legal Knowledge. A comparison of the mechanisms by which knowledge is accumulated in the medical and legal professions.

area's definitions for evidence and knowledge are remarkably different, and the conclusions drawn from such evidence reflect these philosophical differences. Scientific medical knowledge is an accumulation of the tested observations of natural phenomena, whereas legal knowledge is the accumulated rulings of a given jurisdiction. The mass of scientific knowledge can spread concentrically from a central hypothesis to additional ancillary knowledge. This differs from the linear knowledge base of the legal system, which is accumulated as successive examples based on precedent (Figure 13-1). An overview of the relationship between law and medicine can be found in the discussions of Spicker et al.[1]

Regardless of these differences, lawyers and physicians frequently encounter each other in the course of their professional activities, and they must learn to work together. For example, pathologists, who gather information about the causes of disease or injury to individual patients, provide the foundational evidence for many court cases. Pathologists can also find themselves on trial for directly or indirectly harming patients, for example, by failing to provide accurate reports or performing unnecessary procedures. Therefore, pathologists and laboratory professionals must have a basic knowledge of how the legal system operates and the many ways in which the laboratory can interface with legal activities.

Pathologists' Effect on Their Liability

Pathologists can harm patients in one of two ways: (1) by causing direct injuries to patients or (2) by causing indirect injuries to patients. Direct injury can occur when pathologists perform procedures such as fine-needle aspirations or bone marrow biopsies. Direct injuries (eg, infection, nerve damage) that result from performing such procedures pose significant malpractice challenges. Indirect injury is patient injury caused by the use of inappropriate or incorrect laboratory data or pathology reports. A common cause of indirect injury is a mislabeled specimen, which can result, for example, in a missed diagnosis of cancer.

Professional conduct that results in injury, loss, damage, or death to the patient is considered malpractice. Under such circumstances, the "standard of care" and/or local minimal practice standards are used to determine whether a malpractice case is likely to be successfully litigated. Direct-harm malpractice cases might be more effectively referred to as professional negligence cases and typically reflect professional performance below the standard of care. When a physician is accused of malpractice, these cases are litigated as part of civil law.

Civil Law and Torts

Civil law concerns private issues between individuals or between an individual and the government. Criminal law, on the other hand, refers to legal actions taken on behalf of and to protect the public; such actions are typically initiated through police investigations and indictments. Civil law is composed of contract law and tort law. Contract law involves reviewing and enforcing promises and agreements established in a verbal or written contract. Tort law is the legal management of a civil injury and/or wrongful act committed against another person that results in harm; in tort law cases, victims are usually awarded monetary compensation. Tort law is the basis of most malpractice cases. Unless harm occurs, there is no tort (ie, legal action). Most civil law cases are managed outside the courtroom. An event may be litigated by both civil and criminal law; for example, a pathologist who willfully misinterprets test results, leading to the death of a patient, may be prosecuted for homicide in a criminal court and sued for monetary compensation in a civil court. The basic principles of the law as they relate to medicine can be found in overview textbooks by Edge and Groves[2] and Fremgen.[3]

Intentional torts occur when someone intentionally harms another person. Intentional torts include assault (threat of bodily harm), battery (actual bodily harm), false imprisonment, defamation of character, fraud (deceitful action that deprives individuals or the government of their rights), embezzlement (illegal appropriation of the others' property), and invasion of privacy (unauthorized release of personal information). Most pathologists do not typically encounter intentional torts.

However, unintentional torts are common in malpractice cases. Unintentional torts such as negligence occur when a physician (pathologist) causes injury to a patient as a result of not exercising an ordinary standard of care.

Malpractice Ruling Requirements

The requirements for a malpractice ruling, sometimes referred to as the four D's, include the following[4,5]:

- **Duty:** the duty or responsibility that exists between a physician/laboratory professional and the patient. For pathologists, duty is often implied with a patient's admission to the hospital or presentation at a phlebotomy station and the pathologist's acceptance of a specimen. Pathologists do have the right to refuse services (eg, phlebotomy) to patients; for example, a pathologist could refuse to create a patient "contract" because of a patient's failure to pay his bill, fraudulent use of another patient's name, or disruptive behavior at the draw station.
- **Dereliction of duty** is the failure of a pathologist or laboratory professional to provide a standard of care to a service provided to the patient, such as drawing blood, managing a specimen, or reporting laboratory results.
- In cases of **direct cause,** the injury occurs or is closely related to a pathologist's negligence.

Negligence on the part of a pathologist may not be the most proximate cause of the injury. In fact, the negligence may be attributable to a laboratory technician under the supervision of the pathologist; however, there must be no proven intervening cause.

- **Damages** refer to any injury to the patient caused by the defendant. Damages may range from physical or mental disability to medical expenses and past and future loss of earnings. Damages may include pain and suffering. (In some states, a cap is placed on pain and suffering awards for malpractice.)

If a wrongful death occurs, the deceased patient's heirs may also sue for damages to compensate for the loss of future earnings to the estate. Evidence in the case has to demonstrate a financial loss, and the defendant's actions have to be a direct cause of death or proximate to the cause of death.[3,6]

Direct Injury

Direct injuries can occur, for example, when a pathologist performs a fine-needle aspiration and an infection occurs at the site of entry. Negligence can occur through omission or commission. An omission to perform professional duties implies that someone has failed to do something that should have been done (eg, failing to scrub the site of a fine-needle aspiration with an antibacterial solution). Commission implies active negligent performance (eg, performing a poorly directed fine-needle aspiration procedure that results in contamination and infection).

Indirect Injury

Pathologists are much more likely to be liable for indirectly injuring patients.[7,8] Some examples of indirect injuries are shown in Table 13-1. Each of these examples results in incorrect information regarding the patient being reported to the patient's physician.

Pathologists are not knowingly negligent and make every attempt to avoid indirectly harming patients. Malpractice can result from a pathologist lacking anatomic pathology skills, incorrectly performing phlebotomy after being momentarily distracted, misplacing a specimen on a busy day in the grossing room, or forgetting to dictate a comment regarding the margins of a carcinoma, among other causes. Data from insurers show that the most frequent malpractice actions involve breast specimens, dermatopathology specimens

Table 13-1. Examples of Indirect Injury Caused by Pathologists

Indirect Injury	Example
Misinterpretation of a specimen	A melanoma is misinterpreted as an atypical nevus.
Failure to disclose the limitations of a specimen	A sputum Gram stain is reported as negative; only squamous cells are seen on the smear. This is not noted in the report.
Failure to disclose divided opinions	One member of the pathology group disagrees with the other group members regarding an osteosarcoma, and the disagreement is not noted.
Lost specimens	A colon biopsy is received in the grossing room; however, no histology is performed, and the biopsy cannot be located.
Mislabeled specimens	A laboratory phlebotomist mislabels a patient's blood specimen. After type and cross are performed, the patient is given the wrong blood.
Critical values	A patient potassium's level is 6.5 mmol/L. The laboratory fails to call this critical value, and the patient expires.

(especially melanoma specimens), hematopathology specimens, and gynecologic and fine-needle aspiration cytopathology. Common allegations include failure to diagnose, failure to solicit consultation, failure to perform special studies, misdiagnosis of frozen section, loss of specimens, and mistakes in reporting.[7,8]

Since pathologists are often responsible for numerous laboratory employees (phlebotomists, technicians, laboratory technologists, pathology assistants, etc), it is important that pathologists also be aware of the term *respondeat superior* when discussing the indirect harm for which they may be responsible. *Respondeat superior* is a Latin phrase that means "let the master answer." That is, according to the Clinical Laboratory Improvement Amendments and most state and local statutes, the employer and the laboratory director are liable for the negligence of their employees. Although the physician is ultimately responsible for correct procedure performance, both the employer and the laboratory director may be held liable according to numerous precedents. For example, if a laboratory phlebotomist fails to remove a tourniquet after drawing a patient's blood in the middle of the night, and the patient suffers nerve damage as a result, the patient can sue both the hospital and the laboratory director for damages.

Malpractice Prevention

Malpractice prevention is actually a component of quality management. In effect, many quality metrics (described in Chapter 7, "Quality Management in Laboratory Medicine"; Chapter 8, "Quality Assurance in Anatomic Pathology"; and Chapter 9, "Financial Management of the Lab-

oratory") serve as good malpractice prevention mechanisms. Quality metrics that directly impact malpractice prevention include correct specimen identification, timely reporting, and critical value notification. A number of textbooks review the quality metrics for both laboratory medicine and anatomic pathology.[9,10] However, some general comments are provided here to emphasize the importance of documentation and communication in avoiding malpractice litigation.

Documentation

Documentation is the most important aspect of recording events related to patient care. Documentation is many things, but it is not a "blame game" in which individual fault or responsibility is assigned. The central document is the patient's medical record. If a pathologist performs a procedure or consultation, he or she must accurately document the action in the medical record. Signed consent forms should be obtained before any procedure. Above all, items already entered into the medical record should not be deleted or altered, and no space should be left for entering comments at a later date.

Gross and microscopic anatomic pathology findings should be described accurately, and the results should not be changed without a formal addendum that has been properly dated and signed. Similarly, a pathologist must highlight any errors in laboratory reports, taking care to note who corrected the error, when the error was corrected, and in what manner the error was corrected so the report can be easily distinguished from prior reports. Should a case be litigated, any alterations to the documentation—regardless of their harmlessness or helpful intent—could provide the court with sufficient cause to side for the plaintiff.

Incident Reports

Another important document is the incident or event report. All institutions have mechanisms by which incidents (errors) are reported, either internally (within the laboratory) or externally (for the institution). One of the maxims of the patient safety movement encourages events and incidents to be reported so that root causes can be determined and corrective actions taken to help prevent future scenarios subject to malpractice litigation (see Chapter 7, "Quality Management in Laboratory Medicine," Appendix 7-2, for an example of an incident report). Event reporting should include patient or employee identification, an accurate timing of the event, a category, and a severity ranking. Severity ranking promotes the reporting of events and allows the identification of precursor events that may contribute to more severe outcomes.

Some physicians have concerns regarding incident reporting because they feel it exposes them to more liability. Plaintiffs may demand evidence from pathologists and institutions, and recorded errors or incidents may be provided depending on the rules of evidence and the civil procedures in a given state. Discoverability is the right of a plaintiff to gain access to information in the possession of others. Such information must be relevant to the case at hand; however, relevance can be broadly applied. The legal protections that can block the discovery of data include general rules of evidence for a given jurisdiction, the medical peer review privilege, and special statutory privileges for particular reporting systems. The medical peer review process may have statutory protections or regulations under the medical board for a given state. Similarly, many states have statutory protections for incident or event reporting. Unlike documentation and records, such as appointment records, medical records, and personal journals, incident reports may not be discoverable. The goal of such protection is to encourage institutions to frequently review errors and improve their systems. Pathologists should be aware of any statutory privileges for incident or event documentation in their state of practice.[11]

Communication of Protected Health Information

One of the best means of avoiding malpractice litigation is to understand the role communication plays in patient complaints. A key aspect of communication is maintaining patient confidentiality. In 1996, Congress passed the Health Insurance Portability and Accountability Act (HIPAA), which has had a major impact on more uniformly defining patient privacy. The HIPPA Privacy Rule, a regulation developed from the original legislation and enacted in 2001, is designed to ensure the following:

- Standardization of electronic patient health records
- Provision of unique identifying codes for providers, health care plans, employers, and individuals
- Provision of secure electronic health information with standards protecting the confidentiality and integrity of protected health information (PHI)

Protected health information refers to individually identifiable information that relates to a patient's past, present, and future physical or mental conditions and the health care provided to him or her. HIPAA requires that covered entities (ie, those entities managing PHI, including health care providers, insurers, billing agencies, and coding units) limit their disclosure of patient information to only the information necessary to carry out medical treatment. A notice of privacy practices must be distributed to every patient. The patient's information cannot be released beyond the covered entities without the patient's written authorization. In academic medical centers, special rules for research-related confidentiality are usually managed under an institutional review board. Not only is ensuring the confidentiality of PHI a good idea from a malpractice prevention standpoint, it is the law.

Direct Communication to Patients

Directly communicating with patients regarding their health outcomes has recently been shown to reduce malpractice liability. In one study that investigated the reasons patients sue, 37% of the survey respondents claimed that an explanation of the error and an apology would have made the difference in their decision to litigate.[12] Another study indicated that 24% of the patients surveyed filed suit when they found that "the physician had failed to be completely honest with them about what happened, allowed them to believe things that were not true, or intentionally misled them."[13] Most recently, an examination of the practices regarding apologies at the University of Michigan showed that the university hospital was able to reduce claims 50% between 2001 and 2006 by implementing a procedure for apologizing for errors; the study also revealed that the average time for processing a claim dropped from 20 months to 8 months in the same period.[14,15]

Pathologists usually have fewer opportunities to directly communicate with patients. Patients who contact pathologists for reports and test interpretations are typically referred to the physician who ordered the diagnostic tests or procedure. While this is the most appropriate response for most instances of patient interaction, if a patient expresses displeasure with a result, a test reporting interval, or other services directly related to the laboratory (eg, phlebotomy), a pathologist should employ his or her best listening skills and identify the next best steps for addressing the patient's concerns. Patient complaints may also require that the pathologist speak with the clinician caring for the patient to identify the point at which displeasure developed. All patient complaints should be taken seriously and investigated appropriately, and any inquiries should be provided the appropriate follow-up. Any special communication for patients (eg, instruction sheets for 24-hour urine collection, glucose tolerance testing, or fasting blood collection) should be carefully drafted with the pathologist or laboratory director's input.

One area that is unique to pathologists and laboratory directors is patient complaints regarding billing for pathology procedures and laboratory tests. Because pathologists do not typically see patients, many patients do not understand the additional professional charges for pathology procedures. This lack of understanding can create ill feeling towards pathologists and can contribute to malpractice issues. Anesthesiologists used to encounter similar problems for billing related to anesthesia in the operating room. More than 20 years ago, the anesthesiology professional society generated an active effort towards creating opportunities to meet patients before their procedures. In addition, the American Society of Anesthesiologists created the Anesthesia Patient Safety Foundation and subsequently implemented many important items to enhance communication between anesthesiologists and patients.[16] Such actions have reduced complaints against anesthesiologists and provided a quality communication environment. Pathologists may wish to consider opportunities to work more closely with their service chiefs in medicine and surgery. Direct patient interaction opportunities may also exist. For

example, many institutions have surgical education sessions for patients anticipating surgery for cancer. Discussing the biopsy procedure and the generation of the pathology report at these educational sessions helps clarify the pathologist's role in the diagnosis.

Pathologists' Effect on the Liability of Others

Pathologists frequently affect the liability of others in the health care system. Pathology and laboratory reports provide large amounts of information, which in turn is used by clinicians for direct patient care. Other ways that a pathologist can provide information that affects the liability of others include performing autopsies, analyzing the timing of nonfatal lesions, staging cancer, and expressing opinions about adverse outcomes by commission or omission.

Autopsies

Autopsies provide the most important and detailed account of the circumstances surrounding a person's death. As such, they provide a unique description of value in any dispute regarding the cause and timing of death. According to Don Harper Mills, a pathologist and lawyer, "A case is always better when litigated with an autopsy than when litigated without an autopsy."[17] Unfortunately, even though the Joint Commission requires an examination of autopsy rates for quality assurance, autopsies are becoming increasingly rare in the practice of pathology. For example, a recent survey revealed that the autopsy rate in Chicago hospitals decreased from a high of 55% in 1955 to 11% in 1995.[18] Several physicians have suggested that the causes of this decrease included the use of other technologies to determine the cause of death, the lack of reimbursement for autopsies, and the absence of a specified autopsy percentage in Joint Commission recommendations. A recent investigation of pathology residency program directors from 18 states reported an average autopsy rate of 16% (range, 1% to 70%); this report also noted that medical students observed only one autopsy on average, and that 20% of medical students did not observe an autopsy unless they took a pathology elective.[19]

This is an unfortunate trend given that important information can be derived from well-performed autopsies. Autopsies provide a starting point for retrospection. For example, they can be used to determine when a fatal lesion was diagnosed and whether it was diagnosable. An autopsy can determine the component parts and timing of the fatal lesion. An autopsy can also reveal the effect of treatment and whether the condition was treatable. Also, there are significant limitations to death by exclusion if the entire systems review is not performed at autopsy. The well-performed autopsy provides important clinical information regarding the factors that contributed to death, and this valuable information is transmitted to clinicians through autopsy clinical-pathological correlation conferences, which are held at many institutions.[20,21]

There is one important caveat pathologists must remember when creating clinical summaries for an autopsy report: It is best to not create conflict for oneself or others by drawing conclusions regarding the clinical course or selectively biasing the description by indicating certain components of the clinical record and not other parts of it. A disagreement between an autopsy clinical summary and other medical records and physician testimony can create significant problems for the pathologist involved in a given case. A clinical-pathological summary, or epicrisis, that correlates the clinical course and the autopsy findings is a valuable teaching tool in training programs but often is not included in the autopsy report in the community hospital setting.

Nonfatal Lesions

Timing nonfatal lesions and staging cancer are two areas in which pathologists frequently provide evidence regarding medical-legal cases. When providing evidence concerning nonfatal lesions and cancer stage, a pathologist may review reports and slides along with any supportive immunohistochemistry, molecular pathology, laboratory, or cytogenetics results. In court, a pathologist may be called as an expert witness or as an institutional representative as part of case review. Pathologists must be aware of how a physician's diagnosis and treatment may affect a patient's adverse outcome because commission and/or omission may be part of the analysis of the evidence.

Subpoenas, Depositions, Court Appearances, and Other Legal Activities

The United States legal system is an adversarial trial system. This system is derived from common law in Great Britain and governs civil and criminal law in all 50 states except Louisiana, whose civil law is based on that of France. In an adversarial trial system, each side in a dispute presents evidence publicly. The evidence, which must be submitted in the presence of the accused, is subject to challenge. The purpose of the court is to settle a dispute in a civilized manner, thus avoiding vendettas and providing a fair review of the dispute.

Ronald Dworkin expresses the role of the adversarial trial system, as follows[22]:

> The bulk of the law—that part which defines and implements social, economic, and foreign policy—cannot be neutral. It must state, in its greatest part, the majority's view of the common good. The institution of rights is therefore crucial, because it represents the majority's promise to the minorities that their dignity and equality will be respected. When the divisions among the groups are most violent, then this gesture, if law is to work, must be most sincere… [Taking individual rights seriously is] the one feature that distinguishes law from ordered brutality.

Court Systems

Courts are described in terms of their jurisdiction, or power to hear a case. The federal court system hears disputes related to federal law or the United States Constitution. In federal court, the US government is one of the parties in the dispute. Typically, a dispute must involve citizens of different states, or a US citizen and a foreign national, and a minimum of $75,000 in damages to be heard in a federal court. Federal courts also cover disputes that occur in international waters. The levels of the federal court system are district (or municipal) court, court of appeals (circuit courts), and the US Supreme Court. Cases are first tried at the lowest level; challenges to a lower court's ruling, or appeals, are tried at the next higher level.

Like the federal court system, state court systems typically consist of lower courts (district or municipal trial courts), the state court of appeals, and the state's highest court of appeals, usually a state supreme court. Lower state courts may also designate small claims courts for low-value claims and traffic courts for driving violations. Specialized state courts also may include probate (estate) courts, which handle the affairs of the deceased.

Witnesses

Witnesses are the source of information for cases proceeding within the legal system. In a civil pro-

Table 13-2. Types of Witnesses

Witness Type	Description
Percipient	An individual directly involved in the incident being investigated. This may be an eyewitness or someone who has direct, firsthand knowledge of the matter.
Fact	A person who possesses information that relates to or explains the circumstances leading up to and including the issue in question.
Predicate	An individual who has no knowledge of the facts of the case but is necessary to establish the legal predicate or foundation for the admissibility of evidence.
Character	A person who has direct knowledge of the past action of one or more of the parties in given situations or circumstances.
Expert	An individual who has education, training, skill, or experience and is believed to be more knowledgeable than the average person in a particular subject matter. The level of knowledge should be deemed sufficient to rely on his or her opinion about evidence or a fact issue within the scope of his or her expertise.

ceeding, witnesses may represent the plaintiff's or the defendant's position; in a criminal proceeding, witnesses may represent the prosecution or the defense. There are several types of witnesses (Table 13-2).[23] The types of witnesses include percipient, fact, predicate, character, and expert witnesses. Pathologists must understand the witness role they are asked to play in a given legal scenario.

Trials

The grand jury is one mechanism by which an indictment can be created. It applies to federal courts and is used in some states. Grand juries consist of 12 to 23 individuals drawn from the jury pool to determine whether a case has enough merit to be heard in court. In criminal cases, the district attorney is responsible for providing evidence sufficient for an indictment. The grand jury has some privileges not typical of other juries in that it can request documents and evidence and speak with witnesses. Alternatively, and more commonly, a judge can generate an indictment. The judge hears the evidence provided by both parties and decides whether such evidence is sufficient for an indictment or hearing.

In criminal cases, prosecutors bring forward cases on behalf of the people. In civil cases, the plaintiff brings forward an action, and the defendant is the person or entity from whom recompense for injury is sought. In civil cases, if the parties cannot come to an agreement or settlement, the case proceeds with or without a jury of the defendant's peers. A jury typically consists of 6 to 12 individuals drawn from a pool of registered voters. The jurors select a leader, or foreman, for a case and hear the evidence and decide the verdict.

The plaintiff and defendant can both waive their right to a jury trial.

The US trial system is based on the premise that all individuals are innocent until proven guilty. The burden of proof (also known as the standard of proof) is the alignment of evidence with the case that is sufficient to prove guilt. In civil cases, the burden of proof is the preponderance of evidence as represented by a majority (51%) of the presented evidence. In criminal cases, the burden of proof is "beyond a reasonable doubt."

Before trial, attorneys representing both sides undergo a process of discovery, or identifying the evidence relevant to the case. As part of the discovery process, a request for the provision of evidence or the appearance of an individual may be received as a subpoena. A subpoena is a written command from the court for an individual to appear before the court or for documents to be provided to the court. In some cases, a deposition can be taken, in which case a statement is presented as sworn testimony to both parties in the presence of a court recorder. An individual who has provided a deposition may not be required to appear in court. However, a deposition does not preclude a court appearance. If an individual gives a deposition and appears in court as a witness, the evidence he or she provides should be consistent in every respect.

Pathologists may encounter the term *subpoena duces tecum*, a Latin phrase that means "under penalty, take with you." The court can levy a penalty for one's failure to appear or present documents. However, documents can also be provided voluntarily to the court, which does not require the subpoena process. A subpoena must be hand-delivered (served) or delivered by registered mail to the person being requested to appear in court. An assistant or colleague cannot accept a subpoena on behalf of the pathologist; under these circumstances, the subpoena is considered "not served." A failure to appear in court or produce materials can be considered contempt of court, which may have severe penalties.

If a medical record or pathology report is being subpoenaed, only the report or record relevant to the case should be provided to the requesting attorney. Pathologists should avoid submitting original documents; if necessary, a photocopy of the original records should be made and inserted into the original file. Notice of subpoenaed records should be sent to the patient by certified mail. In most institutions, the medical records department manages the release of subpoenaed records. Pathologists who are in charge of many records (eg, laboratory reports, pathology reports) should defer all requests for reports to the medical records department as the official repository of this information. Printing out laboratory reports or pathology reports and providing these records as subpoenaed documents without consulting institutional risk management attorneys or personal legal representation is inadvisable.[3]

The process of a civil trial, the type of case pathologists most frequently encounter, is summarized in Figure 13-2.[3] The elements of a malpractice case, as they apply to this diagram, include the following:

- Party (plaintiff and defendant)
- Elements of the case (the four elements of malpractice, as previously described)
- Trial (including jurisdiction, discovery [interviews, document review, depositions], trial procedure)
- Expert testimony based on a Daubert hearing[24]
- Damages
- Statute of limitations

A Daubert hearing is an examination of the application of an expert witness to a case. It confirms (1) that a theory or technique can be tested, (2) that the theory or technique has been subjected to peer review and publication, (3) the known potential for rate of error, and (4) the availability of standard controls. The court must qualify expert witnesses before the case can proceed.

The types of medical malpractice cases vary across the spectrum of the medical profession and include:

- Misdiagnosis, failure to diagnose, delayed diagnosis
- Surgical errors
- Anesthesia errors
- Medication errors
- Adverse reactions to procedures, drugs, or drug interactions
- Wrong treatments
- Medical procedure errors

The majority of malpractice cases involves misdiagnoses, diagnostic errors, or delayed diagnoses.[25] It is estimated that 50% to 65% of all physicians will be sued at least once during their careers and that 25% of all practicing physicians are sued annually.[25-27] In 2001, nearly 50% and 33% of malpractice trials were brought against surgeons and nonsurgeons, respectively, in 75 of the largest counties in the US; plaintiffs won 27% of these medical malpractice cases. [28] According to a US Department of Health and Human Services National Practitioner Data Bank summary report, there were 191,804 reports of medical malpractice in the US between 1990 and 2004. One survey indicated that only a small fraction of these claims lacked documented injuries; claims without evidence of injury or error accounted for only 13% of total litigation costs.[29] More recent data from the

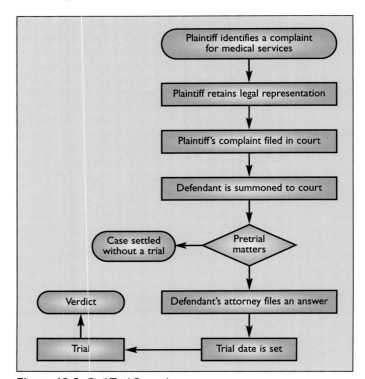

Figure 13-2. Civil Trial Procedure.

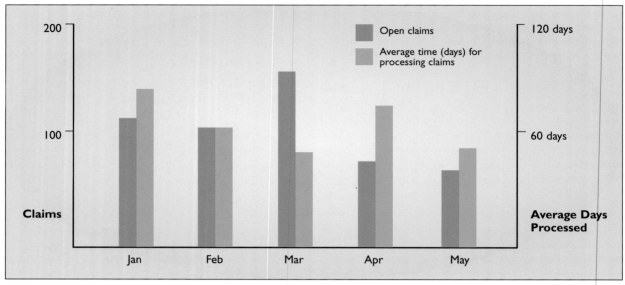

Figure 13-3. Open Claims and Average Processing Time Data.

American Medical Association physician practice information survey (2007–2008) confirmed the continuation of this trend.[30] In this survey, the median indemnity payments among paid claims were $200,000 for settled claims and $375,000 for tried claims. Pathologists, as the keepers of much of the "evidence of injury or error," are obviously not only subject to cases regarding their own performance, they also frequently serve as witnesses in the cases that involve other nonpathologist physicians.

Working with Risk Management

Risk management involves the development of tools and metrics to control or minimize the incidence of problems that result in injury or harm to patients and employees. Risk management departments have become widespread not only in health care but also in many other industries. The factors that risk management measures can range from basic facilities services that impact patient safety (for example, the prevention of patient falls on wet floors) to record keeping and documentation (for example, establishing and maintaining informed consent procedures). In addition, risk management provides an important interface between the medical staff organization and institutional administrative leadership. Internal legal representation is often based in the risk management department.

Some of the metrics used in risk management include documenting the number of open (unsettled) and closed (settled) claims each month as well as a metric that shows the time required for processing a claim. An example of how these metrics might look when presented to the medical staff committee is shown in Figure 13-3.

Recently, risk management practice has extended beyond these basic metrics to develop a proactive program for reducing risk. Failure mode and effects analysis is one tool for analyzing such measures (see Chapter 7, "Quality Management in Laboratory Medicine"). Failure mode and effects analysis attempts to incorporate an estimate of risk category (catastrophic to insignificant), frequency of occurrence, and visibility into a score that helps predict which activities will have the highest impact on improving patient safety.[1]

Pathologists and laboratory directors can interact with risk management departments in numerous ways.[4] Pathology departments are information rich; they maintain huge amounts of data that are useful for risk management activities. Pathologists provide much of the data that are eventually analyzed by risk management personnel. Pathologists also have an intrinsic interest in maintaining low-risk processes for specimen and patient identification. Phlebotomists and specimen processing or grossing areas must have standardized processes for maintaining high-quality identification techniques.

Pathologists and laboratory directors who observe problems within their laboratories should consult regularly with the institution's risk management personnel and legal representatives. Early consultation allows the risk management department to begin an investigation whose re-

Case Example: How to Handle the First Subpoena

Dr. Red has recently been hired into a practice of 12 pathologists in a large urban tertiary care medical center. He primarily signs out hematopathology, with additional support to the lymphoma and solid tumor service. He also is the director of the hematology laboratory for the hospital.

Nine months after starting his new job, Dr. Red encounters an unusual dual-infection case of malaria with *Plasmodium falciparum* and *Plasmodium malariae* in a patient who recently travelled to Asia and Africa. The patient, who has central nervous system findings and disseminated intravascular coagulation, is in the intensive care unit (ICU). The ICU physician does not immediately see the blood smear results, and an infectious disease consultation does not occur for 24 hours. After the infectious disease consultation, however, appropriate anti-malarial interventions are given, and the patient recovers. The patient's family is upset at the delay in therapy and consults with a lawyer, requesting the medical records for the ICU admission. The pathologist receives a subpoena (the pathologist's first!) for the laboratory reports on the patient during the ICU admission. What should the pathologist do?

After receiving a subpoena, a human reaction is to question one's interpretation and wonder whether any mistakes were made. Instead, the subpoena should be perceived as a routine request, and the pathologist should acknowledge,

without confrontation, the server as an innocent bystander of the legal process. First, the pathologist should gather all materials pertinent to the case, such as laboratory reports, laboratory work sheets, slides, blocks, and wet tissue, and sequester them in a safe, locked place. Next, the pathologist should contact his or her malpractice insurance carrier and request that an attorney be assigned to assist in responding to the subpoena. Even if the pathologist is only an evidentiary witness, the malpractice insurance carrier will assist him or her. The pathologist should consult with an attorney before responding to any requests to appear or to provide reports, slides, or other materials. The pathologist should not discuss the case with family and friends or try to determine whether any harm was done to the patient as a result of the admission. However, the pathologist can discuss the subpoena with the pathology service chief and inform the risk management department of the subpoena so they can create a file for the occurrence.

Since the laboratory report on this patient is officially part of the medical record, the pathologist may wish to contact or have risk management personnel contact the lawyer who requested the subpoena and indicate that the pathologist does not have access to the pertinent records. The pathologist or risk management department can kindly inform the lawyer of the proper route for communicating with the medical records department and ask that the subpoena be dismissed on the basis of this information.

sults are more likely to be productive. It also allows for various types of early interventions that reduce the likelihood of a claim. Preventative interventions may include ensuring appropriate patient and physician contact and preventing inappropriate billing. A friendly relationship between pathology and laboratory medicine personnel and the risk management team is a natural tendency; both organizations have the goals of maintaining quality and assuring patient safety.[31,32]

How to Be an Expert Witness

A pathologist or laboratory director may be asked to testify as a plaintiff, primary defendant, evidentiary (fact) witness, or expert witness. A pathologist who chooses to perform services as an expert witness provides expert advice beyond the general knowledge of the population. An expert witness should assist the judge and jury in deciding a case by providing expert testimony. Expert witnesses in malpractice cases are physicians or scientists with extensive knowledge in a given area of medicine. Expert witnesses may use charts and graphs to help explain their testimony. Typically, expert witnesses do not testify to the actual facts of the case but instead assist in the interpretation of facts; for example, an expert witness may be called to interpret DNA evidence. The opinion of an expert witness has legal worth.

Expert witnesses are typically paid a fee for their services. Those who provide expert witness testimony should be aware that their history, credentials, and experience will be reviewed and their fee discussed publicly in any deposition or court appearance. An expert witness should also respect and be sensitive to the needs of the jury. Most juries are inclined to be respectful of a physician, so it is a lost opportunity when a physician does not speak or dress respectfully in court. The jury's time is valuable. The same teaching skills that a pathologist uses in his or her institution should be applied when serving as an expert witness, especially in front of a jury. Before giving testimony, expert witnesses should have in mind the points they want to make and prepare ways of stringing their thoughts together. During the testimony, expert witnesses should make eye contact, speak slowly, and assemble their thoughts in an effective order. A shy and retiring person may wish to avoid opportunities to serve as an expert witness.

Attorneys may use several tactics when cross-examining an expert witness. Expert witnesses who are challenged with questions regarding how much they are being paid for their testimony should reply slowly and thoughtfully that they are not being paid for their testimony, but rather for their time, professional experience, and expertise and for studying the medical facts of the case. If an expert witness is challenged regarding a perceived disagreement between his or her opinion and the opinion of another expert witness, a good reply is to state that it is a complicated medical matter open to interpretation, and that in this case the two interpretations disagree. It is acceptable for expert witnesses to ask to refer to their notes. It is also acceptable and expected that expert witnesses say that they have consulted with the attorneys who sought their services if asked whether they have discussed the case with others. If asked a question beyond the scope of one's expertise, it is always acceptable to respond that you do not know the answer. The CAP publication, *The Pathologist in Court*, discusses how physicians who serve as expert witnesses should prepare for testifying, gather evidence needed for opinions, handle fees for their services, address trick questions, respond to abusive attorneys, and effectively address conflicting medical reports and opinions.[33]

Challenge Questions

Which of the following is true of an expert witness?
A. Is required to go to court as a defendant
B. Provides medical expertise for determining a malpractice case
C. Must be a licensed physician
D. Should be paid
E. B and D
F. B and C
Answer: E; see pages 245 to 246.

A pathologist who receives a subpoena should do what?
A. Immediately review and change any related medical records or reports to meet the case requirements
B. Discuss the case with his or her family
C. Contact the plaintiff
D. Contact his or her attorney
E. Change his or her court date to accommodate a scheduled vacation
Answer: D; see pages 244 to 245.

You receive a request from another hospital to review slides of a skin biopsy done at your hospital several years earlier. It was signed out as an atypical juvenile nevus. The patient now has metastatic melanoma. The pathologist who signed out the case no longer works in your group. Now what?
Answer: See pages 244 to 245.

References

1. Spicker SF, Healey JM, Engelhardt HT, eds. *The Law-Medicine Relation. A Philosophical Exploration.* Dordrecht, Holland: D. Reidel Publishing Co; 1981.
2. Edge RS, Groves JR. *Ethics of Health Care. A Guide for Clinical Practice.* 3rd ed. Clifton Park, NY: Thomson Delmar Learning; 2006.
3. Fremgen BF. *Medical Law and Ethics.* 3rd ed. Upper Saddle River, NJ: Pearson Prentice Hall; 2009.
4. Teare EL, Masterton RG. Risk management in pathology. *J Clin Pathol.* 2003;56:161-163.

5. Harvard Medical Practice Study. Patients, doctors and lawyers: medical injury, malpractice litigation, and patient compensation in New York. Report of the Harvard Medical Practice Study to the State of New York. Cambridge, MA: President and Fellows of Harvard College; 1990.

6. Institute of Medicine. Committee on Quality of Health Care in America. *Crossing the Quality Chasm. A New Health System for the 21st Century.* Washington, DC: The National Academies Press; 2001:218-219.

7. Troxel DB. Error in surgical pathology. *Am J Surg Pathol.* 2004;28(8):1092-1095.

8. Troxel DB. Medicolegal aspects of error in pathology. *Arch Pathol Lab Med.* 2006;130(5):617-619.

9. Valenstein P. *Quality Management in Clinical Laboratories. Promoting Patient Safety Through Risk Reduction and Continuous Improvement.* Northfield, IL: College of American Pathologists; 2005:38-40.

10. Nakhleh RE, Fitzgibbons PL. *Quality Management in Anatomic Pathology. Promoting Patient Safety Through Systems Improvement and Error Reduction.* Northfield, IL: College of American Pathologists; 2005.

11. Protecting voluntary reporting systems from legal discovery. In: Institute of Medicine. *To Err is Human. Building a Safer Health System.* Washington, DC: The National Academies Press; 2000:109-131.

12. Vincent C, Phillips A, Young M. Why do people sue doctors: a study of patients and relatives taking legal action. *Lancet.* 1994;343:1609-1613.

13. Hickson GB, Clayton EW, Githens PB, Sloan FA. Factors that prompted families to file medical malpractice claims following prenatal injuries. *JAMA.* 1992; 267:1359-1361.

14. Boothman RC, Blackwell AC, Campbell DA, Commiskey E, Anderson S. A better approach to medical malpractice claims: the University of Michigan experience. *J Health Life Sci Law.* 2009; 2:127-159.

15. Kraman SS, Hamm G. Risk management: extreme honesty may be the best policy. *Ann Intern Med.* 1999;131:963-967.

16. American Society of Anesthesiologists. *Syllabus on Ethics 1999. Introduction to Informed Consent.* Park Ridge, IL: American Society of Anesthesiologists; 1999.

17. Personal communication. Don Harper Mills, MD, JD, Medical Director of the County of Los Angeles Medical Malpractice Program. 2008.

18. Hastings MM, Andes S, Hsu A. Institute of Medicine's Association for Health Services Research Meeting. *Abstr Book Assoc Health Serv Res Meet.* 1997;14:181.

19. Horowitz RE, Naritoku WY. The autopsy as a performance measure and teaching tool. *Hum Pathol.* 2007;38:688-695. Epub 2007 Mar 21.

20. Collins KA, Hutchins GM, eds. *Autopsy Performance and Reporting.* 2nd ed. Northfield, IL: College of American Pathologists; 2003.

21. Hanzlick R. *Cause of Death and the Death Certificate. Important Information for Physicians, Coroners, Medical Examiners, and the Public.* Northfield, IL: College of American Pathologists; 2006.

22. Dworkin R. *Taking Rights Seriously.* Cambridge, MA: Harvard University Press; 1978:205.

23. Muller M. *The Manager's Guide to HR.* New York, NY: AMACOM; 2009:182-183.

24. Daubert v Merrell Dow Pharmaceuticals. 509 US 579 (1993).

25. Dodge AM, Fitzer SB. *When Good Doctors Get Sued.* Gig Harbor, WA: BookPartners, Inc; 2011.

26. Studdert DM, Mello MM, Brennan TA. Medical malpractice. *N Engl J Med.* 2004;350:282-292.

27. Mello MM, Studdert DM, Brennan TA. The new medical malpractice crisis. *N Engl J Med.* 2003;348: 2281-2284.

28. Office of Justice Programs. Bureau of Justice Statistics (BJS). Available at: http://bjs.ojp.usdoj.gov/. Accessed Jan 24, 2011.

29. Studdert DM, Mello MM, Gawande AA, et al. Claims, errors and compensation payments in medical malpractice litigation. *New Engl J Med.* 2006; 354: 2024-2033.

30. Kane CK. *Medical Liability Claim Frequency. A 2007-2008 Snapshot of Physicians. Policy Research Perspectives.* Chicago, IL: American Medical Association; 2010.

31. Brigham CR, Babitsky S. How to be an Effective Medical Witness [VHS]. Chicago, IL: SEAK Publishers; 1994.

32. Hookman P. *Medical Expert Testimony. Advanced Syllabus for Healthcare Professionals.* Sterling, VA: Potomac Press; 2008.

33. Forensic Pathology Committee. *The Pathologist in Court.* Northfield, IL: College of American Pathologists; 2003.

Chapter 14

Ethics for Pathology and Laboratory Medicine

Elizabeth A. Wagar, MD

Contents

The Philosophical Framework for Values and Ethics

Since ancient times, philosophers have strived to explain the human tendency to create systems of moral principles. Morals are individual principles that address right or wrong conduct. Ethics, on the other hand, are a system of moral principles or rules of conduct that are recognized within a particular category of activity, eg, medical ethics.[1] Ethics, which reside in an area of thought that is sometimes uncomfortable for scientists and physicians to breach, is ultimately based on a sense of values that can be shaped by one's cultural mores, morals, personal beliefs, and faith.

In the course of examining and analyzing human behavior, philosophers have devised several approaches humans use to assess values and needs. Humans can approach the question of whether they should behave in a particular fashion in several ways. People's values direct them to look at the anticipated consequences of a given action. This is sometimes referred to as consequence-oriented judgments, or utilitarianism, for a right or wrong course. During the eighteenth and nineteenth centuries, philosophers such as Jeremy Bentham, an advocate of utilitarianism, and John Stuart Mill developed the concept of consequence-oriented reasoning.[2,3] Under the concept of utilitarianism, an individual makes a decision based on the sense that good is the net increase of pleasure over pain as anticipated in the course of the action and the final result; the pleasure and pain of others is balanced against the pleasure and pain of the individual. In some ways, this theory mirrors the approaches that pathologists take in solving problems in the laboratory, since pathologists describe the problem with an investigation, list the solutions in terms of patient care and the laboratory, and then compare the possible solutions with the "utility" of what can actually be done to improve the situation. For example, if a laboratory director notes that the number of unsuccessful phlebotomy attempts on the graveyard shift has increased, an investigation may reveal that a poorly trained phlebotomist is responsible. Educating and/or having a highly skilled phlebotomist proctor the poorly trained phlebotomist should improve his or her performance and thus decrease the number of unsuccessful phlebotomy attempts. Utilitarianism is therefore based on consequence-oriented or teleological ("end") reasoning, because the value system looks to the consequences for guidance.

Another approach to a value system is the duty-oriented theory, also referred to as the deontological ("study of duty") system. Immanuel Kant (1724–1804) was one of the primary proponents of this type of values construct.[4] As in many major ethical and religious systems, in the duty-oriented worldview, the consequences of an action are perceived as essentially irrelevant.[5] Experience plays little role in values-based decision making; rather, decisions are made according to a rule to satisfy a principle. All decisions are based on principles that are unconditionally bound to every individual and demand an action. In this theory, the solutions devised are compared to principles or rules. The duty-oriented theory is a more rigid philosophy and presents problems for many modern societies, which have intermingling cultures, morals, and ethnic diversity. If an institution's human resources department has a rule that all employees who have three or more unexcused absences will receive a counseling memo in their personnel file, this action may represent the principles reflected in a deontological system.

A third approach to values determination is virtue ethics. Aristotle first proposed the idea that the action taken is not the core of the philosophy. Rather, the right action begins in the heart of the person performing an action. That is, if an individual retains virtues such as honesty, compassion, wisdom, justice, and temperance, these qualities define that person's actions. Thus, having the right character and motivation drives people to perform in a moral and ethical manner. More recent philosophers, such as MacIntyre, Anscome, May, and Taylor, have also argued for a virtues-based ethic.[6] An individual's character thus becomes the defining attribute of values determination. An individual's moral character ensures that the right values determine an appropriate action. In other words, virtuous acts are chosen for their own sake, and choice is derived from a firm and unchangeable character. Under this system, solutions and comparisons occur, but the comparisons are to the morals embedded in the character of the individual. For example, if a laboratory technologist accidentally enters patient A's results into patient B's report, the laboratory technologist's honesty as a health care professional may drive him or her to generate a corrected report.

A fourth approach to values is divine command ethics. This model may be represented by a formal religion with a divine leader or a founder who is perceived as a morally exemplary individual (eg, Buddhism).[7] The leader sets down a set of rules that followers claim provide guidance and to which adherence is required. The morals and prohibited behaviors of various religions are similar. However, following the rule or law is the most important element of an individual's achieving success and garnering rewards within the religion (whether salvation or enlightenment). The consequences of compared actions are less important. Whether Buddha's Four Nobel Truths or the Judeo-Christian Ten Commandments, the rules or laws are fairly explicit.

From a practical standpoint, most people, including pathologists and laboratory directors, use combinations of these four philosophies in their day-to-day lives. On some occasions, it is most appropriate for a pathologist to take a solutions-oriented approach that examines all consequences. On other occasions, a laboratory director may be asked to determine whether a rule applies to a specific set of circumstances. A laboratory director or pathologist may also be confronted with a situation in which the ethical and legal arenas overlap, such as a laboratory employee's inappropriate release of protected health information as described under the Health Insurance Portability and Accountability Act (HIPAA). An awareness of various philosophies challenges pathologists to think more broadly about their decisions and makes them better pathologists in the eyes of their peers and patients.

The Seven Principles of Medical Ethics

Medical ethics is an example of professional ethics. Professional ethics are those that have evolved as master guidelines for a given profession and recognize the important characteristics of ethics as they are practiced within a given profession. Seven principles recognized for medicine are shown in Figure 14-1.[8]

- Autonomy
- Veracity
- Beneficence
- Nonmaleficence
- Confidentiality
- Justice
- Role fidelity

Figure 14-1. Seven Principles of Medical Ethics.

Autonomy

Autonomy can be defined as "self-governance." The independence of individuals to manage their affairs in a knowledgeable, honest, and open atmosphere is the core to autonomy. The concept of autonomy also implies that others treat the individual with respect for his or her presence as an individual. In health care, patients need to know about the risks and benefits of proposed therapies and have the autonomy to decide whether to pursue the proposed clinical plan. The informed consent process ensures a patient's autonomy in the course of his or her clinical care. Problems in autonomy and ethics occur when minor children's and their parents' rights conflict with health care management. Also, as the elderly population increases, more patients may not be able to decide the course of their health care; in such circumstances, durable power of attorney, living wills, and advanced directives ensure that someone else is legally representing the autonomy of the patient.

Veracity

Veracity is the assurance that the patient–physician relationship is based on truth. Autonomy is only effective when physicians provide their patients with truthful information. Providing the truth about some health conditions can be a sensitive issue depending on one's culture and/or historical perspective. For example, in some cultures it may be inappropriate to tell a patient about a serious cancer diagnosis. However, in the United States, it is now generally accepted that providing truthful information is the preferred action and best represents the exchange of information required for the special contract between a patient and a physician.

The presumption of veracity changes when considering health care professionals who are not physicians. In most circumstances, a laboratory technologist or a phlebotomist should not provide information when a patient asks why or for what condition a test is performed. In such a situation, the best reply is to refer the patient to the physician for further information. The laboratory director may also receive inquiries from patients. Although a fiduciary relationship is established if tests are ordered on a patient, a laboratory director should refer the patient to the ordering physician for consultation regarding test results. On occasion, it may be appropriate for the laboratory director to alert the patient's physician to the patient's questions.

Beneficence

Beneficence is the application of physician skills for the benefit of the patient. It parallels the Hippocratic Oath, which stipulates that the physician "benefit the sick."[9] Health care professionals have an obligation or duty to provide services that are known to provide beneficial results. Before the 1940s, the chance that a physician could provide physiological benefit to a patient through knowledge or treatment was minimal. However, the "country doctor" model surely provided some psychological benefit because the same doctor followed a patient through the course of a disease. (There are probably good reasons that many people look back fondly at that model.) Ethical questions regarding beneficence arise when resuscitation or life support is considered for a patient who may not receive much benefit because of a chronic vegetative state or comatose condition.

In modern scenarios, beneficence may impact pathologists' involvement in decedent affairs and autopsies. Nonforensic autopsies can provide benefit to the decedent's family in the form of information that explains an inherited disorder related to morbidity and mortality. A nonforensic autopsy can also provide closure by confirming the appropriateness of the efforts made in attempting to save a family member's life. Typically, nonforensic autopsies require an autopsy permit signed by the decedent's next-of-kin. Autopsy permission usually includes options for the extent of the autopsy, including "complete," "complete, return all organs," "omit head," and "limited" (eg, heart and lungs only, head only, abdomen only). Contrary to common perception, funeral rites do not affect the rate of autopsy permission. However, religious views can affect the likelihood of receiving permission to perform an autopsy. The Baha'i faith and nonfundamentalist Protestantism, Catholicism, Buddhism, and Sikhism permit autopsies. The Jewish faith permits autopsies, but approval varies according the orthodoxy of the family members and may require the autopsy be completed to allow burial within 48 hours. Some faiths, including Islam, Shintoism, and Greek Orthodox Christianity, do not permit autopsies. As part of the benefit of autopsies, pathologists should be vigilant in providing timely preliminary and final autopsy reports to the clinician and family.

Nonmaleficence

Nonmaleficence applies as a principle in the Hippocratic Oath, as "first do no harm" and "I will never use treatment to injure or wrong the sick."[9] Nonmaleficence is a well-known principle. Medical procedures should never cause intentional harm to a patient. However, the issue has become more problematic because of the many side effects of the multitude of therapies and diagnostics now applied in modern medicine. The choice of therapy and diagnostic tests should be good or at least morally neutral, and the good must outweigh the harm. An example is the use of chemotherapy for treating cancer. Clearly, the side effects are significant and often harmful; however, carefully developed clinical studies have shown significant positive effects in reducing recurrence, reducing tumor mass, and/or improving survival rates. Nonmaleficence also applies to human subject research (discussed below).

Confidentiality

Confidentiality is the assurance to patients that their personal information is protected and their right to privacy is respected. Patients' right to privacy is also included in the Hippocratic Oath: "What I may see or hear in the course of the treatment or even outside the treatment…which on no account one must noise abroad."[9] Health care practitioners have a duty and obligation to respect the privacy of their patients' personal information. Ensuring such privacy allows patients to speak freely about their health concerns so that these concerns may be more effectively addressed. With the widespread use of computer information systems, it has become more difficult to protect a patient's personal information. HIPAA (described in Chapter 13, "Legal Affairs for Pathologists") was devised partially in response to the inappropriate release of patient information from computer records. Patients expect their privacy to be respected, and medical students and house staff should be trained to be highly respectful of private patient information. Phlebotomists, laboratory personnel, and pathologists should avoid discussing their patients' conditions in public areas.

Another area where pathology and confidentiality intersect is the institutional review board (IRB), a committee that is formally designated to approve, monitor, and review biomedical and behavioral research involving humans to protect the rights and welfare of research participants. The Food and Drug Administration and Office for Human Research Protection in the Department of Health and Human Services direct IRBs to approve research, approve research proposals pending modifications, or disapprove research. The IRB must ensure that research conducted on humans meets scientific, ethical, and regulatory requirements. IRBs are governed by the Title 45 Code of Federal Regulations, Part 46, from the National Research Act of 1974. Much of the impetus for this legislation was multiple occurrences of patient abuse. For example, the Tuskegee syphilis study, a project conducted between 1932 and 1972 on black men in rural Alabama, left patients untreated for a treatable infectious disease for a generation. Outrage surrounding this and other such "treatment" of patients led to federal legislation. Specific IRB requirements are defined in the federal regulations as follows:

- The IRB must have at least five members.
- The members must have the experience, expertise, and diversity to make informed decisions regarding the research from an ethical standpoint, ascertain that informed consent is sufficient, and ensure that appropriate safeguards are in place.
- For vulnerable populations, the IRB should have members who are familiar with these groups.
- The IRB should include both men and women.
- The members of the IRB must not all be of the same profession.
- The IRB must include at least one scientist and one nonscientist.
- The IRB must include at least one person who is not affiliated with the institution (ie, community members).
- The IRB members may not vote on their own projects.
- The IRB may include consultants in their discussion to meet requirements for expertise or diversity, but only IRB members may vote.

Why such specific and lengthy requirements? Because the safety and welfare of human subjects is paramount to the management of research trials. Confidentiality is an important component. Pathologists who are involved in research projects are required to file an IRB application for review. In research involving laboratory specimens, the patients from whom the specimens were taken should remain anonymous. To maintain patient confidentiality, no specimens collected for research purposes should be collected without informed consent. As a general rule, confidentiality for research is governed by IRBs; confidentiality for general clinical care is governed by HIPAA.

Pathologists involved in either or both activities should review and understand this divide.

Justice

Justice is a seemingly familiar ethical position. However, when applied to health care, it can become more complex. Health care in the United States is driven by scarce or unequally distributed health care resources. How to provide these resources in a complex society is the focus of modern decision-making policy. Part of the justice principle is recompense for harm or injury. As described in Chapter 13, "Legal Affairs for Pathologists," this is a major activity for risk management, in which laboratories and pathologists are often primary sources of detailed clinical information. Justice as an ethical principle should be provided evenly and fairly within the constraints of the medical care system. An example of "legislated" justice is the federal Emergency Medical Treatment and Active Labor Act, which was passed to ensure emergency room care to all patients with an emergent medical situation. The law provides for when and how a patient may be refused at an emergency room and how a patient may be transferred. Refusing care to a patient in an emergency medical situation based on their ability to pay for services is illegal.

Role Fidelity

Role fidelity is the identification of a practitioner with a specified professional role. Most modern health care is provided by teams of physicians, nurses, social workers, pharmacists, laboratory professionals, and others. Pathologists' roles as health care professionals have become more discreetly defined. Ultimately, physicians have the primary responsibility, using the patient–physician contract, for providing advice and insight regarding their patients' medical findings and treatment. Typically, the roles assigned to other health care professionals are more selective. A social worker may help find assisted living arrangements for an elderly patient who is being discharged from the hospital. Laboratory technologists are responsible for verifying patients' test results to make sure the results meet required quality standards before they are released. Pharmacists are responsible for distributing drugs and accurate information about their side effects and administration. The nature of medical specialties creates specific roles. Pathologists, for example, provide detailed reports that conform to the knowledge physicians require to provide patient care; pathologists also have special relationships with various medical specialties, depending on the services provided.[10] Conforming to the health care role is an obligation and duty, regardless of one's profession. It is not appropriate, for example, for a laboratory technologist to discuss therapy for a disease with a patient. Patients have the right to expect appropriate role behaviors from their assorted health care team members. The College of American Pathologists (CAP) *Professional Relations Manual* provides guidelines for pathologists and laboratorians.[11]

Bioethics

Bioethics is a special field relating to the ethics of modern medical advances and research. Current examples of bioethics include genetic counseling and organ and tissue donation and transplantation. Bioethics also includes practices not currently available, such as procedures that could be derived from stem cell research. Many newsworthy topics that are discussed in the lay press are bioethical issues. They include in vitro fertilization, surrogate parenthood, quality of life issues, and euthanasia. Bioethics provides a platform from which ethicists, religious leaders, scientists, politicians, physicians, and laypeople can have a voice in the development of modern medical technology and its effects on patient care.

Individual Professional Responsibility

Two aspects govern an individual's personal ethical responsibility: (1) personal guidelines for ethical behavior and (2) state regulations and statutes regarding professional responsibility. The first aspect is the internal thought process that guides people's decisions when they encounter ethical questions. The second aspect is governed by individual state regulations and licensure laws related to laboratory directors and physicians.

Personal Guidelines for Ethical Behavior

The internal thought processes pathologists begin with are in many ways those internally inculcated as they developed into adults. The next step in development is to bring those thought processes forward to a direct awareness of their "rightness" for a given situation and their value as tools in the day-to-day world of pathologists and laboratory

Respect: To honor another person's beliefs.

Honesty: The quality of truthfulness.

Integrity: Unwavering adherence to one's principles.

Fairness: Unbiased impartiality toward others.

Empathy: The ability to experience others' feelings without experiencing their pain/distress.

Compassion: Gentle, caring attitude.

Loyalty: Faithfulness or commitment to employee/employer.

Privacy: Confidentiality toward patients and fellow employees.

Figure 14-2. Interpersonal Ethics.
Source: Fremgen BF. *Medical Law and Ethics.* 3rd ed. Upper Saddle River, NJ: Pearson Prentice-Hall; 2009:12-13.

directors. Interpersonal ethics is a term used for this type of thinking. The qualities generally recognized in interpersonal ethics are shown in Figure 14-2; these include respect, honesty, integrity, fairness, empathy, compassion, loyalty, and privacy.

The work environment creates some explicit recommendations for each of these qualities. To become trustworthy members of the health care community, pathologists must exhibit professional integrity and honesty at all times. Pathologists should also respect people of all backgrounds and ethnicity. Compared to empathy, sympathy is sometimes considered the "lesser" value of empathy, since to be sympathetic is to show an understanding for another person's problems without the inner awareness of that person's feelings. Empathy is the greater goal when a patient is in pain or is suffering. Compassion is the first expression of a caring attitude and can also guide an individual into an empathetic role as he or she listens to a patient's or co-worker's concerns. Privacy—always a goal of health care—is now governed by explicit federal legislation in HIPAA. Finally, loyalty, or a sense of faithfulness, is indeed an important attribute; however, loyalty should not be granted to employers who are involved in unethical or illegal activities.

Norman Vincent Peal and Kenneth Blanchard espoused a three-step ethics model for interpersonal ethics.[12] The three steps are defined by three questions:

- Is it legal?
- Is it balanced?
- How does it make me feel?

In most situations, the first question is probably the easiest to answer. Laboratory directors and pathologists should be aware of the details of lab-

oratory law. Laboratory directors are required to inform many state licensure boards of any address changes or malpractice claims. Even if a pathologist is licensed as a physician and surgeon in a state, the ethics of his or her scope of practice should also be the prime component of his or her professional activities.

"Is it balanced?" is an excellent question to ask in ethical situations. One should not jump to conclusions regarding an ethical question but should logically investigate all sides of the issue. An example is one laboratory employee's claim that he is being harassed by another employee. Thoughtful, considerate, and balanced investigation usually reveals the right approach. Depending on this balanced discovery process, human resources may or may not be involved.

The answer to the third question—"How does it make me feel?"—ultimately rests on one's values, whether it is the virtue model of Aristotle, the rule-based model, or the utilitarian model. When outcomes do not produce the satisfaction that all sides have been heard and the outcome is legal, a more probing review of the circumstances may be required. For example, a young female technician accusing the male chief resident of harassment may seem to be a situation that could be resolved according to human resources policies and harassment law. However, after educating the residents, consulting with the institutional Title IX attorney, and transferring the employee, the resolution does not feel complete. In interviewing the employee, her flat affect and disconnected thoughts indicate that perhaps she should make an appointment with an occupational health provider. It is then discovered that the employee is already in psychiatric care for a psychotic break, and the best resolution is temporary medical leave. Asking the final question—"How does it make me feel?"—caused more questions to be asked and resulted in a better outcome for all concerned.

Medical Practice Rules and Regulations

In the United States, each state has statutes and rules that govern the practice of medicine in that state. These statutes, sometimes called medical practice acts, were devised to protect the health and safety of the public. During the 1800s and early 1900s, the US was beset by many health care practitioners who were poorly trained and had unverifiable medical backgrounds. It was an era of quackery. As modern medical training evolved,

5. Ingram D, Parks J. *Understanding Ethics.* Indianapolis, IN: Alpha Books; 2002.

6. Edge RS, Groves, JR. *Ethics of Health Care. A Guide for Clinical Practice.* 3rd ed. Clinton Park, NY: Thomson Delmar; 2007.

7. Harvey P. *Introduction to Buddhism.* New York, NY: Cambridge University Press; 2006.

8. Edge RS. Groves, JR. *Ethics of Health Care. A Guide for Clinical Practice.* 3rd ed. Clinton Park, NY: Thomson Delmar; 2007:56-76.

9. Temkin O, Temkin C, eds. *Hippocratic Oath, Ancient Medicine. Selected Papers of Ludwig Edelstein.* Boston, MA: Johns Hopkins University Press; 1967:6.

10. Wagner LR. The College of American Pathologists, 1946-1996: ethics and professional relations. *Arch Pathol Lab Med.* 1997;121(9):1009-1014.

11. Practice Management Committee. *Professional Relations Manual.* 12th ed. Northfield, IL: College of American Pathologists; 2003:Section I.

12. Blanchard K, Peale N. *The Power of Ethical Management.* New York, NY: William Morrow; 1988.

13. Council on Ethical and Judicial Affairs. *Code of Medical Ethics of the American Medical Association.* 2008-2009 ed. Chicago, IL: American Medical Association; 2008.

14. American Hospital Association. *Understanding Expectations, Rights and Responsibilities.* 2003. Available at: www.aha.org. Accessed Jan 20, 2011.

15. American Society for Clinical Laboratory Science website: www.ascls.org. Accessed Jan 20, 2011.

16. Wagner LR. The College of American Pathologists, 1946-1996: laboratory standards. *Arch Pathol Lab Med.* 1997;121:536-541.

17. Fremgen BF. *Medical Law and Ethics.* 3rd ed. Upper Saddle River, NJ: Pearson Prentice-Hall; 2009.

18. Simon TL, Dzik WH, Snyder EL, Stowell CP, Strauss RG. *Rossi's Principles of Transfusion Medicine.* 3rd ed. Philadelphia, PA: Lippincott Williams & Wilkins; 2002.

19. Sazama, K, Dechristopher PJ, Dodd R, et al. Practice parameters for the recognition, management, and prevention of adverse consequences of blood transfusion. *Arch Pathol Lab Med.* 2000;124:61-70.

20. Hughes DB, Ullery BW, Barie PS. The contemporary approach to the care of Jehovah's witnesses. *J Trauma.* 2008;65:237-247.

21. Dubovsky SL, Kaye DL, Pristach CA, DeRegno P, Pessar L, Stiles K. Can academic departments maintain industry relationships while promoting physician professionalism? *Acad Med.* 2010;85:68-73.

Appendix 14-1.
Principles of Medical Ethics

The following principles adopted by the American Medical Association are not laws, but standards of conduct that define the essentials of honorable behavior for physicians.

I.   A physician shall be dedicated to providing competent medical care, with compassion and respect for human dignity and rights.

II. A physician shall uphold the standards of professionalism, be honest in all professional interactions, and strive to report physicians deficient in character or competence, or engaging in fraud or deception, to appropriate entities.

III. A physician shall respect the law and also recognize a responsibility to seek changes in those requirements which are contrary to the best interests of the patient.

IV. A physician shall respect the rights of patients, colleagues, and other health professionals, and shall safeguard patient confidences and privacy within the constraints of the law.

V.   A physician shall continue to study, apply, and advance scientific knowledge, maintain a commitment to medical education, make relevant information available to patients, colleagues, and the public, obtain consultation, and use the talents of other health professionals when indicated.

VI. A physician shall, in the provision of appropriate patient care, except in emergencies, be free to choose whom to serve, with whom to associate, and the environment in which to provide medical care.

VII. A physician shall recognize a responsibility to participate in activities contributing to the improvement of the community and the betterment of public health.

VIII. A physician shall, while caring for a patient, regard responsibility to the patient as paramount.

IX. A physician shall support access to medical care for all people.

List of Acronyms

AABB. American Association of Blood Banks (name retired; now AABB)

AACC. American Association for Clinical Chemistry

ABMS. American Board of Medical Specialties

ABN. Advance Beneficiary Notice

ABP. American Board of Pathology

ACCME. Accreditation Council for Continuing Medical Education

ACGME. Accreditation Council for Graduate Medical Education

ACLA. American Clinical Laboratory Association

ACLPS. Academy of Clinical Laboratory Physicians and Scientists

ACO. Accountable Care Organization

ACS. American College of Surgeons

ADA. Americans with Disabilities Act

ADASP. Association of Directors of Anatomic and Surgical Pathology

ADEA. Age Discrimination in Employment Act

AICCCA. Association of Independent Consumer Credit Counseling Agencies

AMA. American Medical Association

AMP. Association for Molecular Pathology

AP. Anatomic pathology

APF. American Pathology Foundation

APLIS. Anatomic pathology laboratory information system

ASCII. American Standard Code for Information Interchange

ASCLS. American Society for Clinical Laboratory Science

ASCO. American Society of Clinical Oncology

ASCP. American Society for Clinical Pathology

ASH. American Society of Hematology

ASHI. American Society for Histocompatibility and Immunogenetics

ASIP. American Society for Investigative Pathology

ASM. American Society for Microbiology

ASP. Application service provider

ASR. Analyte-specific reagent

ASTM. American Society for Testing and Materials (name retired; now ASTM International)

BOC. Board of Certification [ASCP]

CV. Coefficient of variation

CAO. Chief administrative officer

CAP. College of American Pathologists

CBC. Complete blood count

CCI. Correct Coding Initiative

CD. Cluster determinant

CDC. Centers for Disease Control and Prevention

CF. Conversion factor

CFO. Chief financial officer

CFR. Code of Federal Regulations

cGMPs. Current Good Manufacturing Practices

CHAMPUS. Civilian Health and Medical Program of the Uniformed Services

CLFS. Clinical laboratory fee schedule

CLIA. Clinical Laboratory Improvement Act/Amendments

CLIA '67. Clinical Laboratory Improvement Act of 1967

CLIA '88. Clinical Laboratory Improvement Amendments of 1988

CLMA. Clinical Laboratory Management Association

CLSI. Clinical and Laboratory Standards Institute

CME. Continuing medical education

CMO. Chief medical officer

CMP. Certification Maintenance Program [of the ASCP BOC]

CMS. Centers for Medicare and Medicaid Services

CNO. Chief nursing officer

CoC. Commission on Cancer [of the American College of Surgeons]

COO. Chief operating officer

CP. Clinical pathology

CPC. Clinical pathological conference

CPI. Consumer Price Index

CPT. Current Procedural Terminology

CQI. Continuous quality improvement

CRVU. California Relative Value Units

DBMS. Database management system

DICOM. Digital Imaging and Communications in Medicine

DOJ. Department of Justice

DOT. Department of Transportation

DPMOs. Defects per million opportunities

DRG. Diagnosis-related group

DSL. Digital subscriber line

EBITDA. Earnings below interest payments, taxes, depreciation and amortization

EEOC. Equal Employment Opportunity Commission

EHR. Electronic health record

EOQ. Economic order quantity

EPA. Equal Pay Act

EQC. Equivalent quality control

FDA. Food and Drug Administration

FISH. Fluorescence in situ hybridization

FLSA. Fair Labor Standards Act

FMEA. Failure mode and effects analysis

FMLA. Family and Medical Leave Act

FPPE. Focused professional practice evaluation

FTE. Full-time equivalent

GAAP. Generally accepted accounting principles

GDP. Gross domestic product

GFR. Glomerular filtration rate

GPCI. Geographic practice cost index

GPO. Group purchasing organization

GUI. Graphical user interface

HCPCS. Healthcare Common Procedure Coding System

HER2. Human epidermal growth factor receptor 2

HHS. Department of Health and Human Services

HIPAA. Health Insurance Portability and Accountability Act of 1996

HIS. Hospital information system

HIV. Human immunodeficiency virus

HL7. Health Level Seven International

HL7 CCD. HL7 Continuity of Care Document

HL7 CDA. HL7 Clinical Document Architecture

HL7 RIM. HL7 Reference Information Model

HMO. Health maintenance organization

HPV. Human papillomavirus

HSIL. High-grade squamous intraepithelial lesion

IATA. International Air Transport Association

ICAO. International Civil Aviation Organization

ICD. International Classification of Diseases

ICD-9. International Classification of Diseases, 9th revision

ICD-9-CM. International Classification of Diseases, 9th revision – Clinical Modification

ICD-10-PCS. International Classification of Diseases, 10th revision – Procedure Coding System

IEC. International Electrotechnical Commission

IHC. Immunohistochemistry

IHTSDO. International Health Terminology Standards Development Organization

IOM. Institute of Medicine [of the National Academies]

IPA. Independent practice associations

IRA. Individual retirement account

IRB. Institutional review board

IRCA. Immigration Reform and Control Act

ISH. In situ hybridization

ISO. International Organization for Standardization

IT. Information technology

IVD. In vitro diagnostics

JIT. Just in time

JPEG. Joint Photographic Experts Group

LAP. Laboratory Accreditation Program [of the CAP]

LDA. Laboratory developed assay

LDT. Laboratory developed test

LIS. Laboratory information system

LOINC. Logical Observation Identifiers Names and Codes

LOS. Length of stay

LRN. Laboratory Response Network

MBA. Master of Business Administration

MCO. Managed care organization

MLS. Medical Laboratory Scientist

MOC. Maintenance of Certification

MSO. Medical Service Organization

MT. Medical technologist

MUE. Medically unlikely edit

MUMPS. Massachusetts General Hospital Utility Multi-Programming System

NAACLS. National Accrediting Agency for Clinical Laboratory Sciences

NACB. National Academy of Clinical Biochemistry

NCCI. National Correct Coding Initiative

NIC. Network interface card

NIOSH. National Institute for Occupational Safety and Health

NIST. National Institute of Standards and Technology

NLA. National Limitation Amount

NLRA. National Labor Relations Act

NPDB. National Practitioner Data Bank

NPP. Notice of Privacy Practices

NTIS. National Technical Information Service

OIG. Office of Inspector General

OPPE. Ongoing professional practice evaluation

OR. Operating room

OSHA. Occupational Safety and Health Administration

PC. Professional component

PCR. Polymerase chain reaction

PDCA. Plan-Do-Check-Act

PDSA. Plan-Do-Study-Act

PFD. Personal, Fatigue, and Delay [Allowance]

PFS. Physician fee schedule

PHI. Protected health information

PLOC. Plan, lead, organize, control

PNG. Portable Network Graphics

POC. Point-of-care

POSDCORB. Planning, Organizing, Staffing, Directing, Co-Ordinating, Reporting, and Budgeting

PPM. Provider-performed microscopy

PPO. Preferred provider organization

PR. Public relations

PT. Proficiency testing

QA. Quality assurance

QC. Quality control

QM. Quality management

RAM. Random access memory

RBRVS. Resource-based relative value ccale

RCA. Root cause analysis

RCE. Reasonable Compensation Equivalent

RFI. Request for information

RFID. Radio frequency identification

RFP. Request for proposal

ROI. Return on investment

ROR. Rate of return

RUO. Research use only

RVS. Relative value scale

RVU. Relative value unit

RVU-PE. Relative value unit – practice expense

RVU-PLI. Relative value unit – professional liability insurance

RVU-W. Relative value unit – physician work

SD. Standard deviation

SAM. Self-assessment module

SAMHSA. Substance Abuse and Mental Health Services Administration

SCHIP. State Children's Health Insurance Program

SEC. Securities and Exchange Commission

SNOMED CT. Systematized Nomenclature of Medicine Clinical Terms

SOP. Standard operating procedure

SQL. Structured Query Language

SSL. Secure Sockets Layer

SWOT. Strengths, weaknesses, opportunities, threats

TAT. Turnaround time

TCP/IP. Transmission Control Protocol/Internet Protocol

TLS. Transport Layer Security

TQM. Total quality management

UML. Unified Modeling Language

UPI. Unique patient identifier

USCAP. United States and Canadian Academy of Pathology

USMLE. United States Medical Licensing Examination

VPN. Virtual private network

WADA. World Anti-Doping Agency

WHO. World Health Organization

XML. Extensible Markup Language

Index

Also from CAP Press...

Quality Management in Anatomic Pathology: Promoting Patient Safety Through Systems Improvement and Error Reduction is the only comprehensive manual designed to improve patient care while ensuring your laboratory achieves its accreditation standards. The manual provides pathologists and laboratory directors with the tools necessary to develop, implement, and maintain a comprehensive quality improvement program. It emphasizes regulatory compliance, with cross-references to the CAP Laboratory Accreditation Program (LAP) checklist items and CLIA regulations.

Quality Management in Anatomic Pathology contains comprehensive coverage of all segments of the anatomic pathology test cycle (preanalytic, analytic, and postanalytic), detailed benchmark data with extensive references, and information on diagnostic discrepancies and suggested actions. Helpful examples of forms to document quality assurance activity as well as a comprehensive glossary also are included.

Contents include:
- Designing a quality improvement plan
- Regulatory compliance
- Strategies for error reduction and prevention in surgical pathology
- Defining and handling errors
- Quality improvement plan components and monitors
- Quality management in histology, immunohistochemistry, cytology, and autopsy

Item number: PUB118
Price: $95
CAP member price: $65

Quality Management In Clinical Laboratories: Promoting Patient Safety Through Risk Reduction and Continuous Improvement is a practical "how-to" manual written for the laboratory director, supervisor, and practicing pathologist. Sponsored by the College of American Pathologists Quality Practices Committee and Patient Safety and Performance Measures Committee, the manual is designed to help readers manage quality and patient safety in clinical laboratories; comply with quality and patient safety regulations and accreditation requirements; and develop and administer a quality management plan.

Quality Management In Clinical Laboratories covers the most important standards and areas that have proven to be particularly problematic in the management of clinical laboratories. Patient safety issues—an essential and inseparable component of laboratory quality—are discussed throughout the text.

Contents include:
- Case studies based on knowledge of actual events
- Approaches to managing quality and patient safety
- Regulation and accreditation
- Specific quality and patient safety risks and control measures for preanalytic, analytic, postanalytic, and general laboratory operations
- The laboratory quality management plan, with sample plans

Item number: PUB214
Price: $95
CAP member price: $65

Also from CAP Press...

So You're Going to Collect a Blood Specimen: An Introduction to Phlebotomy has served as a basic text and functional reference guide for phlebotomy for more than 35 years. The latest edition emphasizes safety considerations for phlebotomists, other health care professionals, and patients—especially needlestick safety and prevention.

So You're Going to Collect a Blood Specimen provides step-by-step instructions for obtaining blood by venipuncture along with techniques for skin puncture and blood culture. The latest standards and regulations from the Joint Commission, OSHA, CDC, CLSI, and CAP are incorporated.

Contents include:
- Fundamental techniques of phlebotomy
- Proper laboratory practice, safety, and professionalism
- Patient identification and specimen labeling
- Representative blood collection tubes, additives, and applications
- Recommended order of draw and volume limits for a single blood draw
- Timed specimens
- Drawing blood from patients on IV fluids
- Blood collection equipment and materials disposal
- Collecting blood from babies
- Special techniques for difficult venipunctures and what to do in case of a reaction
- Collecting blood in special patient areas

Item number: PUB212
Price: $25
CAP member price: $15

The Best of CAP TODAY Q&A is a compilation of experts' answers to readers' questions as published in the popular "Q&A" section of *CAP TODAY*. Spanning a decade, the columns are aimed at helping practicing pathologists by providing relevant, to-the-point information and references for further reading. Topics will appeal to both anatomic and clinical pathologists as well as cytopathologists, medical technologists, and laboratory directors.

Contents include:
- Body fluids
- Hematology
- Coagulation
- Chemistry
- Microbiology
- Cytology
- Molecular diagnosis
- Point-of-care testing
- Phlebotomy
- Specimen processing
- Critical values
- Stat tests
- Transfusion medicine
- Toxicology
- Therapeutic drug monitoring
- Surgical pathology
- Autopsy
- Laboratory management
- Subject and author indexes

Item number: PUB311
Price: $45
CAP member price: $40